What Our Patients Have Taught Us

What Our Patients Have Taught Us

Physicians Reflect on Lessons Learned about Life Themselves, and Their Profession

WRITTEN AND EDITED BY RICHARD D. FELDMAN, MD

Indiana Historical Society Press | Indianapolis | 2023

Printed in the United States of America

This book is a publication of the
Indiana Historical Society Press
Eugene and Marilyn Glick Indiana History Center
450 West Ohio Street
Indianapolis, Indiana 46202-3269 USA
www.indianahistory.org
Telephone orders 1-317-234-0020
Online orders http://shop.indianahistory.org

The paper in this publication meets the minimum requirements of American National
Standard for Information Sciences—Permanence of Paper for Printed Library Materials,
ANSI Z39. 48–1984

Library of Congress Cataloging-in-Publication Data

Names: Feldman, Richard D., author.
Title: What our patients have taught us : physicians reflect on lessons
    learned about life, themselves, and their profession / written and
    edited by Richard D. Feldman, MD.
Description: Indianapolis : Indiana Historical Society Press, 2023.
Identifiers: LCCN 2022054783 (print) | LCCN 2022054784 (ebook) | ISBN
    9780871954732 (hardback) | ISBN 9780871954749 (ebook)
Subjects: LCSH: Physicians--Indiana--Anecdotes. | Medical
    personnel--Indiana--Anecdotes. | Physician and
    patient--Indiana--Anecdotes. | Medical personnel and
    patient--Indiana--Anecdotes.
Classification: LCC R690 .F44 2023 (print) | LCC R690 (ebook) | DDC
    610.73/706909772--dc23/eng/20230420
LC record available at https://lccn.loc.gov/2022054783
LC ebook record available at https://lccn.loc.gov/2022054784

To my loving and giving wife, Becky

Contents

Foreword

Every year in January roughly fifteen fourth-year medical students join me in the History of Medicine Room at the Indiana University School of Medicine Medical Library for a monthlong intensive Narrative Medicine course. For four weeks we spend nearly fifteen hours a week reading great literature, conversing, sometimes debating, and always writing. The goal of the course is for students to become more aware of the importance of stories in medicine through the practice of close reading, analysis, and reflection. Students become familiar with the Narrative Medicine literature and engage with stories written by well-known authors, as well as those written by patients, practitioners, and family members. We examine case studies and fiction—novels, films, short stories—as well as memoirs and poetry for a deeper understanding of the relationship between narrative and identity, self and other, and literature and medicine. As a result, students become more familiar with the practice of Narrative Medicine as they become more in tune with their interactions with patients as unfolding stories.

Medical Humanities is a growing interdisciplinary field that relies on the humanities to enrich and to inform our understanding of health, disease, and healing. Narrative Medicine contributes to the overall goals of Medical Humanities as it provides medical students the opportunity to study in-depth the concept and experience of illness from a narrative perspective. Students, especially by January of their fourth year, have nearly mastered (we hope) the scientific underpinnings of medicine. What they often lack and subsequently crave is the humanist perspective that is crucial to becoming an empathetic, compassionate physician able to relate to those who are suffering. In Narrative Medicine students view past, present, and future problems associated with our conception of illness from multiple and varied standpoints and work to resolve them using narrative, visual, and artistic methods. Throughout the course of the month my students gain greater insight into the personal experience of illness, the human condition in general, the value of human life, the nature of suffering, and efforts to alleviate it. Most important, they begin to understand how they, as future doctors, fit within the context of patient lives. All happens with and through stories.

Initially, students tend to be excited about the reading but concerned about the writing. At the end of each week we spend two hours writing in class sharing what we have written and reflecting on the writings and the overall experience. Students respond to a specific prompt that varies from week to week, and the eloquence with which students record their experiences is remarkable. They are honest, straightforward, sometimes heartbreaking, and often incredibly clever. And by the end of the month the writing piece of the course is a favorite and students regularly ask for more.

In addition to these weekly reflective writing sessions, students are required to prepare and submit a longer piece of writing for a preselected humanities publication. Last year, it worked out beautifully for students to contribute their final piece of writing for Doctor Richard D. Feldman's book, which was in the early stages of development. Students were excited about the prospect of a published chapter in an edited collection, especially one written by such a notable Indiana physician! Over the course of the month, students recalled memorable patients who had impacted them in some way during their training. They worked on and polished drafts, communicated with Feldman and finally read their essays aloud among their peers on the last day of class. It was such a meaningful experience for all involved. Therefore, it is with great excitement and a bit of pride that I invite you to read this book, which includes stories written by some of the most extraordinary students I have ever known.

I have never written the foreword to a book before, and I am honored to have been asked to write this one. This collection is special not only because it provides us with interesting and meaningful examples of how doctors have been touched by their patients but also because each of these stories invites us into the lives of strangers, which is really a remarkable thing. I invite you, as you begin to read these pages, to recognize the value of the invitation, to immerse yourself in the story, and to carefully consider the experience of the *other*. Stretch your moral imagination and consider carefully what it might be like to be someone else. And in so doing, develop your capacity for empathy so that you better understand the experience of health, disease, and healing specifically, and ultimately, the complex but extraordinary experience of being human.

Emily Beckman, DMH

Director and Assistant Professor, Medical Humanities and Health Studies Program Indiana University, Indianapolis, School of Liberal Arts

Acknowledgments

With pleasure, the author recognizes the more than sixty contributing authors who very generously and thoughtfully submitted essays for this book. Without their valuable contributions, this book would not have been possible. This book was truly a collaboration. The author offers his heartfelt appreciation to Emily Beckman, director and assistant professor, Medical Humanities and Health Studies Program, Indiana University, Indianapolis, School of Liberal Arts, for writing the foreword and for encouraging medical students in her class to write stories for this book. My gratitude also extends to the following individuals and organizations who aided in the book's development: Sarah Halter and the Indiana Medical History Museum, the Indiana Academy of Family Physicians Foundation, and the Indiana Historical Society Press for providing the support necessary to make this publication a reality. Also, Missy Lewis and Chris Berry at the Indiana Academy of Family Physicians; Tabitha Arnett and the Indiana Osteopathic Association; Christopher Parr and the Marian University College of Osteopathic Medicine; Scott Renshaw, MD, and the Department of Family Medicine at the IU School of Medicine; Morgan Perrill at the Indianapolis Medical Society; and Cheryl Wolverton, PhD, RN, Annette Fulton and Christopher Doehring, MD at Franciscan Health Indianapolis for their assistance in solicitation of potential contributing authors. My wife, Becky, continually offered editing advice; Marina Brown Weatherly reviewed the essay on her father and offered several editing suggestions; Tom Mueller, MD, assisted in photo restoration; and Amy Bova for helping with the final submission copy to the IHS Press. My gratitude also to Ray E. Boomhower and Kathy Breen, editors with the IHS Press, for their guidance and for their belief in the value of this work.

Editor's Note

The essays were edited only to correct grammar, to add clarity and conciseness, and to improve flow, understandability, and readability. Edits were also made to remove some medical terminology and replace it with descriptions more understandable to the general public. In some instances, edits were also made to disguise the exact locations, dates, and circumstances for the purpose of protecting patient confidentially. Unless otherwise indicated, all patient names were also changed to protect patient identity.

The reader will also note that the contributing physician authors come from two different educational traditions. Allopathic physicians earn a MD degree and osteopathic physicians earn a DO degree. Today, these physicians may train together in residency programs and practice side by side in their communities.

Finally, the editor took the liberty to place the title of "Doctor" before the names of essayists who were medical students at the time of writing their stories. It was anticipated that students would either earn their medical degrees before the book's publication date or a relatively short time thereafter.

Introduction

*"Let us go forth, the tellers of tales, and seize whatever prey
the heart long for."*
WILLIAM BUTLER YEATS

This is a book I could not write alone. Although I contributed several accounts of my own to this collection of essays, this work could not be solely from my own professional experience. I needed the contributions of friends and colleagues in the medical profession for it to be more inclusive and compelling. I believed this book would have to come from a broad cross-section of physicians and other health-care professionals, capturing the breadth and depth of perspectives and experiences that come from our relationships with patients. My colleagues became contributing authors in this endeavor to bring forward their personal stories regarding the ways a patient touched their lives or what they learned from that patient about life, career, or themselves.

I chose only to accept stories regarding experiences with an individual patient rather than narratives about what was learned from relationships with patients collectively during a career. I anticipated that stories about a specific patient would be more personal and powerful. I think the reader will find these stories true to my intent.

Collecting stories from colleagues was not an easy task; physicians and others in the health professions do not generally consider themselves writers, and some even loath authorship. Most focused their educations on the sciences rather than on the humanities and are not inclined to imaginative or reflective writing. Writing is a chore rather than something enjoyable in which to engage. Perhaps they have written scientific articles along the way. But a thoughtful essay about life experiences? For many, unfortunately not.

As a residency director in family medicine, I recall that at one time I required my residents to semiannually journal a few of their experiences—their moments of brilliance and frustration. In my judgment, it was a splendid exercise in writing and self-expression, but more important in self-reflection. Many of these journal entries, episodes in their formative years of medical experience, were truly thoughtful and touching or self-effacing and honestly told. They were triumphs or lessons learned from their patient encounters, and journaling further reinforced and internalized what they had learned.

For some, it was an affirming experience. But, alas, the residents as a group disliked the task, and I eventually dropped the journaling initiative because of the resistance I encountered. It was not perceived as the positive experience that I had intended.

So, collecting stories was a challenge, but the book eventually came together well. I found there were physicians and other medical professionals who love (or are at least willing) to write and were eager to contribute after all! I gathered essays from practicing doctors and resident physicians, and to my surprise, I received an outpouring of contributions from medical students. I think that occurred because medical students are the newest to the profession, and possibly their earliest experiences are the most formidable and memorable to them personally.

Naturally, most of the stories are from my Indiana colleagues. Since I am a family physician, most are from family doctors, but some are from other specialists. In addition, I invited physician friends and colleagues from across the country who I thought might have a good story to tell. I also sought contributions from other health professionals, including psychologists, nurses, physician assistants, and advanced-practice registered nurses, but unfortunately received very few responses. I gratefully include these other professionals in this book. Since most of the contributing authors are physicians, in the paragraphs that follow in this introduction I may refer solely to physicians; please know that I respectfully believe these discussions are relevant to other healthcare providers as well.

What Our Patients Have Taught Us was a natural extension of one of my previous books. In 2013 I authored and edited *Family Practice Stories: Memories, Reflections, and Stories of Hoosier Family Doctors of the Mid-Twentieth Century,* also published by the Indiana Historical Society Press. Primarily an oral history, the book celebrates and preserves America's Golden Age of Generalism in medicine through storytelling. It is about a time gone by when the doctor-patient relationship, professionalism, the art of medicine, and the art of healing were at a zenith. It captures stories told by and about the grassroots founding fathers of family medicine before they were lost forever. They were truly that Greatest Generation of family physicians who practiced during a crucial time in the history and development of the specialty's philosophical underpinnings. These doctors possessed the character and core values from which the contemporary specialty of family medicine grew, and which it still emulates today.

These elder statesmen of family medicine practiced personalized patient care. They were sensitive to their patient's needs, becoming trusted advisers, navigators of care in the health-care system, and compassionate counselors. They took the time to listen and knew their patients well. And they were there for their patients and committed to their communities. From those stories, just as from the stories in this book, there are lessons to be learned for all of us in medicine. And for the public, it is an opportunity to better appreciate the richness of the doctor-patient relationship.

If anything best defines the essence of family medicine, it is the warm relationships formed with patients. Physicians are drawn to family medicine as a career in large measure for these experiences. With relationship naturally comes knowing the patient's story. This is what family doctors delight in and look forward to everyday. My father, Max Feldman, was a family physician in South Bend, Indiana, for nearly forty years. I recall that he would frequently recount stories at the dinner table about patients he had seen that day. The anecdotes did not concern their medical issues but something interesting about the patients' personal lives that they had shared. My father knew his patients, not just their diseases.

It is important to recognize that the narratives in *Family Practice Stories* are largely about how these physicians helped and enhanced the lives of the patients they served. And that is the direction that these kinds of narratives usually flow: Doctors positively influencing the health and wellbeing of patients.

So, it occurred to me that there is another perspective that needed to be told, one which has not been emphasized enough in the medical humanities literature: How patients influence and positively affect the physicians with whom they entrust their lives. This is a book purely about ways patients have enriched the lives of their physicians (and in a few stories, other health-care professionals). It is not a one-way street.

Doctors certainly learn from their interactions with patients about how to better recognize disease and best treat patients medically. This aspect was minimized in the book. Rather, I was after what physicians learn about life and the human condition, as well as learning about themselves, even their flaws and shortcomings exposed through their interactions with patients.

There is a closeness that grows as the physician comes to know a patient as more than an illness to treat or a person who requires preventative care. Doctors understand their patients as the human beings that they truly are. Personal professional relationships develop. This is especially true, but unquestionably not exclusive, for primary-care physicians who treat patients over time and get to know their patients so well. These are physicians who earn the privilege to be invited into the lives of the people they serve.

Physicians are primarily trained in medical school and residency to diagnose and treat disease. Appropriately so. But they also need to be trained to interact with patients as people, effectively attending to the human dimension, the human exchange. Many excellent clinicians fall short in this regard. This is where the medical humanities, utilizing the narrative, can be so important in a physician's education and on-going development. It can be the path to more empathetic, sensitive, and engaged medical practice with enhancement of the doctor-patient relationship. It invites doctors and other medical providers to encounter insightful discoveries about the finest humanistic aspects of the profession and ultimately to learn from their patients. The door opens not only to becoming a better physician, but also to being a better human being.

There are unfortunately so many barriers that have developed in our contemporary healthcare system to forming rewarding relationships with patients. There has been a corporatization of medicine and a business ethic has increasingly developed. Physician productivity, especially in primary-care specialties, is the primary measure of a physician's worth and performance. Physicians have very limited time with each patient during a busy day. Telemedicine, work-site clinics, urgent care, and retail clinics in grocery stores and pharmacies serve to fragment care and subvert the continuity role of the traditional personal physician. Physicians now often operate in large healthcare teams, especially in corporately owned practices and hospital environments with care managers, social workers, hospitalists, utilization and case management personnel, physician assistants, pharmacists, advanced practice registered nurses, and psychologists.

Family physicians and other primary-care providers, because of system and financial reasons, have largely given up seeing their patients in the hospital. Although this healthcare team approach is widely accepted and certainly in many respects improves quality and efficiency of medical care, it may allow less opportunity for physicians to be truly present with patients over time. There is less occasion to know the patient and their life stories, and to learn from them. How many healthcare professionals can be involved in a patient's care without diluting the doctor-patient relationship? It is the price paid.

Indeed, I believe that relationship along with mindfulness of presence with patients are the essential components necessary for physicians to learn from their patients. The mindfulness of which I refer is when physicians absorb themselves in the patient and in the patient's story, blocking everything else in the world out even if only for a few moments. Physicians have a relationship with each patient, but they certainly are not touched, inspired, or humbled by every patient. From my own experience, most of the time it was from a special relationship that developed.

These relationships were very different with each patient and based on various aspects of our interactions. Some patients shared with me their life experiences or the wisdom they gained throughout their lives; sometimes we shared an interest in national and world events or political perspectives. Others were inspiring through their religious beliefs, their military service, or the love and devotion they displayed for spouse and family. It may have been founded on the way in which they conducted their lives, their dignity and character, their courage and determination through adversity, or sharing with me the historical events and times they lived through. Others simply shared with me a sense of humor or a love to banter during the office visit. Each patient in some way became someone special to me, someone I greatly respected, I felt close to, or someone I just always enjoyed seeing in the office. There was a bond. We enjoyed our interactions with one another on a very human, personal level.

This book is written during a time when doctors are looking for meaning in their careers. We hear a lot about the growing problem of "physician burnout" from the complexities of our contemporary healthcare system with its new pressures including government and insurance company oversight and regulations, administrative and paperwork burdens, frustrations with the electronic medical record, employed-practice situations, and loss of autonomy and control.

We are told physician burnout is reaching epidemic proportions. It is a syndrome of loss of enthusiasm for work and career, emotional exhaustion, cynicism, loss of professional investment, feeling ineffectual in improving the health of their patients, and experiencing a low sense of personal accomplishment. It can be manifested by a "I just don't care anymore" or a "I'm just putting in my time" attitude. Burnout can lead to a loss of professionalism, callousness toward patients, and a lack of prudent medical judgement that may jeopardize quality and safe patient care.

Being a physician can be enormously stressful. Think about it. Physicians are responsible for people's lives and trained with the unrealistic expectation that doctors must never make a mistake. Burnout can be associated with more pervasive problems such as depression and substance abuse. No wonder physicians have a high suicide rate.

Doctors are increasingly losing sight of the rewards and gratification that comes with a medical career. They may simply lose the joy of seeing patients. The causes of physician burnout are complex and multifactorial; there is not one easy answer to this affliction. But if anything will help soothe the pain, it will come with renewed investment every day in the warmth of their patient relationships.

It is my belief that this book will resonate with the public as well as professionally with physicians and other healthcare providers by celebrating the richness of what patients bring to the doctor-patient relationship. This is possible when physicians open their hearts and ponder the wisdom and life experiences of their patients. Physicians are in a unique and privileged position. Patients come to us and share the most personal aspects of their lives. They share their loves, their joys, and their passions, but also disappointments, fears, tribulations, and even their secrets. Patients expose not only their physical wounds but their emotional wounds and scars as well. Pains that they may not share with another living soul. Every patient has a story. And if doctors will only take the time to listen, patients may become their teachers of life's lessons. Establishing meaningful connections with patients adds purpose and meaning to physicians' careers and ultimately their lives. This is what this book intends to convey.

I am fascinated by the power of the narrative in medicine. And what better and enjoyable way to accomplish the goals of this book than by storytelling? After all, everyone loves a good story. I hope you will enjoy reading this book, and I trust that the stories contained within will inspire you and lead you to reflect on your own similar life experiences. For physicians and other healthcare professionals, may this book remind you of the true rewards of your profession and why you entered it. For patients, I hope these stories will strengthen your confidence in the humanity of physicians and others in the healthcare professions.

Richard D. Feldman, MD
Indianapolis
March 2023

"Patients are often surprised when, years later, I still remember who they are. After all, I was their only surgeon, but they were one of thousands of patients I treated. Patients rarely realize how much we value the lessons they teach us. And what we learn remains embedded forever, not only in our memories but also deep in our hearts and minds. Gratitude and compassion are two of the most important lessons I have learned, and ones I strive to imbue in the residents I teach."

Robert Pearl, MD

Stanford University professor, *Forbes* contributor, author, and former CEO of The Permanente Medical Group.

Prologue

Unlike the subsequent stories included in this volume, the first two essays are not stories examining how physicians and other healthcare providers were touched by or what lessons were learned from a specific patient. These two introductory narratives are from different perspectives that complete the understanding of the elements necessary, much of which are inherent or acquired qualities of the physician, for development of a desirable and meaningful doctor-patient relationship. They relate important aspects of these interactions that are essential for the healthcare provider to be receptive to receiving life's gifts from patients.

This first story is not written by a physician or other healthcare provider. Rather, it is the perspective of a patient's family about how they were touched by the humanity, compassion, and sensitivity of their physician. It speaks to the power of tender relationships that can develop between doctor, patient, and family.

The second essay is primarily the story of what a young medical student learned from her physician grandfather about the importance of humanism in medicine and the value of really listening to her patients beyond the clinical information they provide.

These narratives balance the doctor-patient-relationship equation and lay the foundation for the appreciation of the stories that follow.

Shared Moments

SAVANNA FOX, MBA

My little sister, Kristen, has battled Acute Myeloid Leukemia for three years. She went into remission for six months after intensive inpatient and outpatient chemotherapy treatments that lasted about six months. Almost exactly a year after she was diagnosed, she was found to be sick again; the leukemia had come back. At this point, a bone-marrow transplant was the only hope that she would potentially have for a cure. We were fortunate to find a match for her transplant in a fairly short time. Kristen was admitted for her induction chemotherapy before her procedure. This is the weeklong inpatient chemo treatment that prepares the body for the transplant. At this point, Kristen's physician care team consisted of her hematologist, bone-marrow transplant physician, bone-marrow transplant fellow, and the internal-medicine resident. Little did we know we would be spending the next two months in the hospital.

On a day known as her "re-birthday," or "Day Zero" in the transplant world, Kristen received her bone-marrow transplant. The transplant went as planned and Kristen was displaying the normal side effects of the previous week's chemotherapy—nausea, constipation, extreme fatigue, and other unpleasant symptoms. Kristen's care team was pretty much the same at this point, minus the hematologist, who stopped rounding after the chemotherapy was completed without complication.

From day zero to day fourteen posttransplant, Kristen was super tired and in a lot of pain. She mostly slept and the physicians kept her comfortable with a pain pump.

On day fifteen posttransplant, Kristen began to display complications seemingly unrelated to the leukemia, the bone-marrow transplant, or the chemotherapy. While she was more awake and conscious, she was also making very little sense. She was losing track of her thoughts and having some trouble completing sentences. For the first couple of days, the physician team indicated that this was potentially from the heavy use of pain medicines and set a lower limit on the amount she could receive in a day.

By day eighteen posttransplant, Kristen was experiencing some minor hallucinations and a decrease in the use of her hands and feet. The physicians

Kristen Jeffries

suspected drug interactions and looked at her medication list to begin removing anything that could potentially be causing these issues.

On day nineteen posttransplant, I got a text from my sister that let me know something was seriously wrong. Kristen texted me and asked if she could disguise herself and leave the hospital. She wrote me that she did not remember signing in and wanted to take her pillows outside. About two hours later, I got the call from my mom indicating that my sister was found wandering the hospital unit naked and was now considered a flight risk. This was a major turning point in our story and my sister's care; Kristen, who was twenty-four at the time, was experiencing an extreme decline in her mental state and tremors throughout her body.

This is when the physician team changed dramatically. Kristen was not responding to changes in the medication list and every day she got a little worse. Neurology was brought in to assess her. At first, they thought she could be experiencing a drug-induced syndrome or a hospital-induced delirium. This is when we met the new neurologist on her case, Doctor Peterson, who immediately had a different presence with our family. He did not leave the room until he asked everyone individually if they had any other questions. He made eye contact with each person and asked them directly; he made sure we were all heard. That gesture alone made a world of difference.

After five more days of pulling Kristen off several medications, including most of her pain meds and changing medications around, there was still no improvement in her condition. In fact, at this point, she was almost completely nonverbal. She was only able to lie in bed and follow you with her eyes. Her breathing began to become labored in addition to the untimely peak of her chemo-induced mouth inflammation.

As one can imagine, our family stress was at an all-time high. No one could figure out what was going on, and Kristen was getting worse every day. Unfortunately, this situation began to create a "Us vs Them" mentality. I think in times of trauma like this, people just experience so many emotions. My family was experiencing anger with the physicians that truly represented the fear and anxiety we were experiencing at the time.

On day twenty-five posttransplant, Doctor Peterson got an MRI that showed nothing significant going on with her brain and came to the room to tell us in person. He sat down with my mom and me beside my sister's bed. He indicated that he was going to keep exploring every avenue, even though this one did not show anything.

In that moment, I watched my mom's attitude and demeanor shift. Doctor Peterson put his hand on her shoulder and told her that he could not possibly understand how hard this must be for her to watch her daughter in a nonverbal state. In that moment, he was more than the neurologist, he was a human being. He felt just what we were feeling; he felt the fear and the anxiety. And in that moment, we knew he felt responsible for figuring out what was going on. Doctor Peterson took that moment and removed the "Us vs. Them" and gave us back the care and compassion we had seen from the physician team up to that point.

Two days later, day twenty-seven posttransplant, and day thirty-four in the hospital, there was still no improvement in Kristen, and Doctor Peterson decided to do a lumbar puncture. The tap revealed that Kristen had a certain type of encephalitis and allowed the team to determine the way to start effectively treating her condition. We do not know what would have happened had we not met Doctor Peterson, but, indeed, the doctor may have single-handedly saved her life.

I offer this story to share with you an instance in which a physician took the time to share a moment—a moment that very much impacted how we look back on my sister's sixty-day hospital stay. It was a moment when my mom felt heard and felt cared for, and we experienced real human compassion.

It was moments like these that reminded me of why I love working in the Franciscan Health Indianapolis Family Medicine Residency. I get to work every day with residents and faculty knowing that they may have had that moment with a patient yesterday or last week or maybe last month. I know they are changing lives because I have lived it, and I love being a small part of a program that helps residents to get to a place where they can share those life-changing moments with their patients.

May they share tender moments like my mom and I shared with Doctor Peterson.

Savanna Fox's sister Kristen Jeffries gave her permission to use her name for this story. Fox was raised in Morristown, Indiana. She completed her bachelor of arts at Indiana University–Purdue University, Indianapolis, and her master of business administration degree in healthcare administration at Indiana Wesleyan University. She is a former Family Medicine Residency Coordinator and currently works as a project manager in the pharmaceutical industry. Fox enjoys time with her family and soaks in every minute with her sister, who is currently celebrating one year in remission after her bone-marrow transplant.

Grandpa

ELIZABETH M. HOOVER, DO

"What is the War of 1812?" "Who is Teddy Roosevelt?" "What is thermodynamics?"

I look up from my GameBoy and stare in awe as my grandfather casually answers every *Jeopardy!* question correctly, one after another. When the show goes to a commercial break, he turns to me and explains, in meticulous detail, the backstory behind Rudolf Clausius and William Thomson, outlining the first two laws of thermodynamics in 1850. As a ten-year-old child, I suppose I assumed that all grandfathers just knew stuff the way mine did.

Have you ever had a brain freeze from a cold drink? Just put the drink in the palm of your left hand and press your tongue to the roof of your mouth, and poof—no more brain freeze. Ever wondered where the word "robber" came from? My grandpa could tell you all about the feudal lords in medieval Europe who were deemed "robber barons" and how the term became popularized in America in 1859. As I grew up, I realized that not only is he my grandpa, but he is also Doctor William H. Fulton, MD, and that he has made impacts on countless people's lives.

He graduated from Indiana University School of Medicine in 1958. After completing his internship at Wishard Hospital and before enlisting in the army, he practiced family medicine. During that time, he made house calls and learned how to really listen to patients beyond their primary complaints. He knew how to ask the important questions, and he remembered everything. If he saw a patient once, he could recall what they were wearing, how old their kids were, and what their pet's name was at the next visit a year later. He never saw these details as facts, but rather as pieces of a puzzle or pages in a book that helped illustrate the patient's story.

After two years in the army, Doctor Fulton began a neurology residency. That was a new specialty in those days because neurology was not quite its own field. Neurologic problems were treated by neurosurgeons and psychiatrists. Computed Tomography scans and Magnetic Resonance Imaging scans were not available. The field of neurology developed because there was a need for a physician to have an in-depth knowledge of the brain and its pathways, as well as the skill and patience to take a comprehensive medical history. For someone who had an innate ability and passion for both medicine and history, this was a perfect fit.

In 2004 my grandfather was honored by Indianapolis mayor Bart Peterson to commemorate both his forty-year anniversary as a clinical neurologist and his volunteer work in the community. One would think that a physician who had worked that hard would retire to a condo somewhere warm, but he continued to practice. He was again honored ten years later by Franciscan Health Indianapolis for fifty years of his hospital service there. Still, he kept on running. In total, he practiced medicine for sixty years, retiring at the age of eighty-seven.

William H. Fulton, MD

In April of my third year of medical school, just a couple months after my grandpa retired, I was fortunate enough to complete my neurology clerkship rotation at the very same office where he changed the lives of so many people. Upon learning that I was Doctor Fulton's granddaughter, one of his patients told me that she had been going to him since she was a little girl. "He always remembered everything; he always listened, no matter what," she recalled. This was a common theme I noticed in his patients. Every day I met someone else who expressed how much it meant to them that he would sit and really listen to what they had to say instead of jumping straight to ordering tests, imaging, and medications.

His colleagues in his office kept lists of "Doctor Fulton's Clinical Pearls," and one that I heard quite often was, "If you do the wrong test for the wrong reason, you get the wrong result." He also encouraged medical education by advising his students and colleagues to both "learn something new and teach something new every day." I now have a collection of his pearls, which I will continue to repeat to myself throughout my own career in medicine.

Perhaps my favorite part about rotating at my grandfather's clinic was reading the notes he had previously written for many of my patient encounters. I would walk into the room feeling like I really knew the patient. His notes read like 1920s novels, with sentences like, "This kindhearted woman had a misadventure one Wednesday afternoon while enjoying strawberry ice cream," and "She has, fortunately, overcome this obstacle and has since had no more seizure episodes." His patients were more than a name in an appointment slot or a diagnostic billing code. They were all people in search of medical help who have lives, personalities, hobbies, and families that might all affect their diagnosis.

Within the last two decades, the use of the electronic medical record has changed the way doctors document patient encounters. Today, when medical notes are written, they are done so in an abbreviated, matter-of-fact way designed to increase the efficiency of charting medical records. My grandpa loathed the EMR. With all its boxes to check and formulaic format, he saw it as more tedious and less patient oriented. There are certainly many benefits to EMRs—quicker access to information, looking up past medical histories easily, etc.—but for someone who values personal touches as much as my grandpa does, there is understandable frustration with the EMR system. Medicine is not a fill-in-the-blank, check-the-boxes science. Doctor Fulton's notes were always written like a story because that is the way medicine should be. It is not just about the patient's chief complaint on a given day; it's about the patient's life, their story, and what ultimately led to them to come to the physician's office.

By walking in my grandpa's footsteps for a month, I learned so much about the importance of humanism in medicine and how much of a lasting impact I can have on people simply by listening to them. Meeting his lifelong patient with the seizure disorder was a blessing. I see her in all other patients I treat now. I hear her tell me how much of a difference I can make in someone's life by treating them as a human instead of a list of symptoms.

As I graduate from medical school this year and begin my career in family medicine, I will take Doctor Fulton's Clinical Pearls with me and hope to always remember that patients are people with stories, families and children, fears, joys, and sorrows. I will remember that my job as a physician is much larger than just clicking buttons and prescribing pills.

Elizabeth M. Hoover grew up in Zionsville, Indiana. She majored in biochemistry at DePauw University. She wrote this story while a fourth-year medical student at Marian University College of Osteopathic Medicine in Indianapolis. Hoover is a fourth-generation physician in her family and currently is a family medicine resident.

"Each of you has many stories to tell of patients you will never forget. You will always remember their valor, their dignity, their humor, their determination, as well as their anger and defeats. You must tell their stories. . . . I call the stories that moved you, the stories that will stay with you always, your 'private stories.' I believe that our duties as physicians lie not only in the clinic, in the wards, or in the operating rooms, but in making our private stories public."

Neal Baer, MD, Harvard Medical School and Harvard School of Dental Medicine's 2018 Commencement

Learning from a Centenarian

RICHARD FELDMAN, MD

I enjoy my elderly patients and routinely inquire about their memories of the past and their perspectives on contemporary life. I admire their values and wisdom, the history within them, their understanding of what is truly important in life, and their wonderful sense of time and place.

Their attitudes were often shaped by experiencing the events and challenges of the past that most of us can only imagine; a time that was without the conveniences and the medical and technological advances that we enjoy today.

Most rewarding is caring for my patients approaching the centenarian mark. I was privileged that my oldest patient gave me permission to write about her. Viola Kollmann passed away at 101 years old in Indianapolis.

This elegant woman walked briskly with her head up proudly, her shoulders back, and with a twinkle in her eye. She was bright, engaging, and informed concerning current events and issues. She read the editorial pages, and yes, she had her opinions.

She appeared at least twenty years younger than her age and was truly healthier than many of my patients in their seventies. It was hard to find anything to treat in this spry and spirited woman. Sometimes out of sheer routine and not considering her chronological age, I offered her preventative medical screening tests. She usually smiled and responded, "Now why would I need that test at my age?" I think she humored me in allowing me to treat her for most things.

How fascinating it was to hear her firsthand accounts of times gone by. She grew up in Indianapolis's Fletcher Place neighborhood, where she watched the man lighting the gas streetlights each evening. Viola saw William Jennings Bryan speak at Tomlinson Hall and heard John Philip Sousa at Garfield Park. She recalled the days when you could buy a loaf of bread for a nickel and ice cream for a penny. Viola recalled lying on her front lawn gazing at the millions of stars twinkling in the night sky free of pollution and the glare of electric lights. And she remembered the Armistice in 1918 when downtown Indianapolis exploded in celebration, singing, and throwing confetti because it was finally over, over there.

Viola was the head of billing at Western Electric and was married to her husband, Frank, for fifty-nine years. The Great Depression was a difficult time for her family. They had almost nothing but were optimistic and learned "that good can come from misfortune, and that there is much to enjoy beyond what money can buy."

Viola lived during the time of few medical remedies and before the development of immunizations and antibiotics. Her sister Martha died at the age

of nine from typhoid fever, and other cousins and neighbors died of diphtheria, scarlet fever, tuberculosis, and the 1918 influenza pandemic. Young healthy people routinely dying of acute infectious diseases were just a fact of life.

Viola had volunteered as a guide at the President Benjamin Harrison Home since 1989, doing so until she was 100 years old. She walked up three flights of stairs conducting tours and wondered why anyone would want to take the elevator and miss seeing the beautiful hand-carved woodwork on the stairways.

Viola Kollman

She also volunteered at the Wheeler Mission Ministries Ladies Auxiliary. "It's never too late to start a good work," she noted.

Her family was blessed with good genetics. Three sisters lived into their nineties, as did both her mother and father. Her brother only lived into his seventies, but she was quick to add that he was a smoker. Viola believed that her longevity is more than good genes. She attributed her long life mostly to "practicing the power of the mind and strength of spirit and never losing my childhood sense of wonder and eagerness for learning."

Viola was the healthiest and most remarkable centenarian I have ever known as a patient. She took lots of walks, ate a healthy diet, and watched her weight. But her formula for a long life was all about being young at heart and passionate about life. She teaches us important lessons.

Thank you, Viola for inviting this family doctor into your life.

Viola Kollmann gave the author permission to use her name before her death.

Birdman

CHRISTIE ALICEA, MD

I was well into the third year of medical school by the time I began my internal medicine clerkship—an eight-week stint of taking care of patients on the wards in the hospital. My feet throbbed at the end of each day, the circles under my eyes grew darker with each week, and the ten pounds I had gained studying for step one of the medical licensing boards were not going anywhere, thanks to eating bags of chips and chocolate bars on the go.

Each of the rotations I had moved through so far including pediatrics, psychiatry, and anesthesia only served to further distance my heart from the field—the long hours worked by emotionless physicians, the aching back I arrived home with six days a week, and the parts of my daughter's life that I was receiving photos of instead of participating in. None of it seemed like what I had signed up for.

Internal medicine was the rotation I was most looking forward to. Despite the long hours and twenty-eight-hour call every sixth day, I was hopeful that I could create meaningful connections with patients and start to feel like I was making a difference. I had visions of sitting at the foot of an elderly woman's bed, laughing about stories from her younger years, and bonding over our mutual love of bingo. This proved to be a false expectation.

I quickly learned that the amount of time spent calling consults, crafting progress notes, and crossing off orders left little time for fraternizing with our patients. On a good day, we could spend fifteen minutes diving deeper into a patient's story during morning rounds, and on the best of days, we even found several minutes to check in with patients prior to leaving for the night. But mostly, with patient lists pushing twenty and only a few hours to complete morning rounds, each patient got only around ten minutes of our time, most of which was spent by us talking to them instead of with them.

It seems unsurprising, then, how easily one could become distanced from the humanity of medicine and focus strictly on the bottom line. During staffing one morning postcall, I brought up a question that I had on the care plan for a patient of mine, Sharon. She was a "frequent flier," as our team called them, arriving for chronic obstructive pulmonary disease exacerbations almost every other month. Around fifty years old, her smoky voice gave away her thirty-five-pack-year cigarette history, and her mullet was a nod to her golden years of the 1980s.

Sharon was persistent and vaguely demanding, and she was not completely keen on the idea that her smoking habit burdened her lungs in any way. This bothered my team, who exhaled deeply every time she referenced pollution or allergens as the main culprits of her lung disease, but I felt indifferent. As a medical student, I did not feel like it was my business to pass judgment on our patient's decisions, nor did I feel like it mattered whether she recognized the catalyst for her lung condition.

She already had COPD, and she had been counseled on how cigarettes were harmful and how quitting could benefit her. She had been offered numerous tools to help her put them down. But she was not willing to, and I thought that was okay; it was not my job to be frustrated by her choices, but instead, to meet her where she was in her journey and provide healthcare. I could counsel and guide all I wanted, but at the end of the day, I had a choice too: Was I going to provide unbiased, nonjudgmental medical care as I would for any other patient as I had taken an oath to do? My choice had always been yes.

"Doctor Halder, I know we discussed long-term antibiotics for Sharon Wilks on admission, and I was wondering if we should send her home with a script or not?" I asked my attending. Doctor Halder was not an intimidating man as far as physicians go, but the puzzled look on his face in response to my benign question made my heart rate quicken.

"Who? What antibiotics?"

"Sharon, my patient on five . . . she, uh, we saw her together yesterday afternoon?" I felt my face flush as I scrambled to push my white coat out of the way to reach the patient list in my back pocket. Noisily opening it up, Doctor Halder looked over my shoulder as I pointed out Sharon's name, second from the bottom since she had been on our list the longest.

"Oh, the COPD'er, yeah. We'll send her home on azithromycin," Doctor Halder nonchalantly concluded.

After a brief discussion on dosing, I wrote a note for myself to remember to add the information to her discharge instructions and made a mental note to reference diseases over names, just as my attending had done.

For a few weeks, this worked out just fine. I started seeing patients as lists of problems to solve, labs to normalize, diagnoses to make, instead of people to heal. On the one hand, this created a much easier day for me, with concrete tasks to cross off my to-do list: "Order repeat chest X-ray on room 2310; Trend cardiac enzymes on 5445; Increase Humalog insulin two units for room 2217." If the chest x-ray looked good, or the heart enzymes did not indicate a heart attack, or if the new insulin regimen worked to control diabetes, these patients were fixed from a medical perspective and could go home. But I did not know these patients, in fact, even worse, I thought that I did not care to.

The patient in room 2217, with the uncontrolled diabetes, had been on our service for a few weeks. She was morbidly obese and was not very talkative. I could not tell you anything else about her, except for her lab values. Her fasting blood sugars were in the 300s. We had spent the better part of her hospital stay tweaking her insulin regimen every day until her glucose had stabilized in the range that we were comfortable with: not too low to worry about hypoglycemia, but not too high as to lend itself to advancing the disease at a rapid rate. She was finally, from a medical standpoint, ready to go home.

I got the call from her nurse almost immediately after putting in the "prepare to discharge" order.

"I see room 2217 is ready for discharge. Where is she going, have we decided?"

I shook my head as if trying to rid a thought from my brain. "What do you mean? I guess she is going home. Her levels are normalized and there's nothing else medically to do for her," I said, not very confidently, as I was suddenly reminded of my stature as a third-year medical student.

"She was evicted two days before admission. She has nowhere to go, and no family or friends to stay with. We're working on it, but I thought you knew this," the nurse trailed off.

I did not know this. She had been in my care for weeks, and I knew nothing of her life except what her blood counts could show me. I had assumed things, sure. I had assumed that she was morbidly obese because she did not care, and that her diabetes was out of control due to her poor eating habits. I had not taken a second to wonder if maybe her circumstances had put her into a corner, or if maybe stress was contributing to her outrageous blood-sugar levels. Worse, I had not asked her about her lifestyle, about her situation, about who she was at all.

"No, uh, I . . . my team was under the impression that." That what? That she had a safe place to go postdischarge? That she was just like most other patients with a home and a family? That she did not have her own unique narrative that complicated her medical status?

My senior resident could see I was floundering, so she took the phone from me to complete the call: "From a medical standpoint, she's cleared for discharge. There is nothing more for us to do, and the longer she stays in the hospital, the more likely she is to contract an infection or decondition further below her baseline. Please have case management work on this, in an expedited manner, because this is beyond our realm of expertise, and medically, we are done," she spoke authoritatively with an air of callousness.

I felt the heat of shame creep from the back of my neck up to my ears. I felt that I had failed this patient in some way by not delving deeper into her story and really knowing who she was. How could I expect to heal patients without first taking their hand and being with them in their story?

My clerkship was ending and one of the last patients on my list was Mr. Nash, who I had seen through two admissions in the last six weeks. He was in and out of the hospital on a revolving basis for glycemic derangements, congestive heart failure exacerbations, and COPD flares. He was a hulking man overtaking the hospital bed with his stature, and if you can believe it, he looked just like Santa Claus.

Mr. Nash never talked much, and my team did not spend long enough in his room to encourage meaningful dialogue anyway. Their viewpoint was that this was just another old man on Medicaid who did not understand, nor care, how much he was damaging his health. He always looked defeated to me, sad in a way that told me his mind was deep in thought. I had a sudden idea that if I could just get him to grab hold of the olive branch I was extending, I might be able to find out what makes him tick. So, I asked him why did he want to get better?

"It's for the birds," he said after several painful seconds of wondering whether he would respond. I waited silently, a tactic that I was still learning to master.

"My birds," he continued, "There are so many birds in my yard. I want to make a bird feeder before the winter. When I'm not home, I worry about them. I have a big window in my living room, and I just watch them come and go all day. They're like family," he chuckled and then looked at me shyly.

I smiled at him and nodded my head slightly. "Mr. Nash," I said. "Let's get you home to your birds."

Over the next few days I lingered behind the team on rounds to talk to Mr. Nash. I would look up photos of bird species native to the area and ask him if he had ever seen one. I asked him what seeds he likes the best. We talked about the logistics of the birdhouse he wanted to make. In those conversations, I sprinkled in tips on how to keep his COPD in check in the coming colder months, and we talked about how to replace some of his favorite winter comfort foods with low-carb alternatives.

With each of the patients on my list, I found that I could discover something unique about them, some nugget of humanity that served as a point of connection for us during conversation. There was Virgil with an intricately hand-carved wooden cane who told the story of his more than twenty years in the army. How he loved to tell the story of each notching on the cane and how it all added up to the story of him.

There was Diane, who liked to sing karaoke, but only cappella songs from the 1950s. She would serenade us as we walked out of the room every morning after rounds with a new tune. And who could forget Steve, the nervous man who could not bear to reconcile the fact that his foot needed to be amputated. We finally suggested he bring in his guitar to play to relieve his stress. The music that emanated from his room was not radio worthy, but it led to many conversations about who held the title for greatest guitar player of all time (it is Eddie Van Halen, by the way). Steve's anxiety was notably lessened.

These patient interactions were not groundbreaking stuff, but it felt like the heart of medicine. Understanding my patients for who they were outside of the hospital reminded me how human they were, and what a privilege it was to care for them in their time of vulnerability. I had met them where they were on their journeys. For Mr. Nash, it was not in a hospital bed with nebulizer treatments every four hours and a low-sodium diet. It was on a path full of birds, illuminated by the warm light of human connection.

Christie Alicea was a medical student at the Indiana University School of Medicine when she wrote this essay. She is currently an internal medicine resident at Saint Vincent Hospital in Indianapolis. She is passionate about medical ethics, community outreach, and integrating medical humanities into every-day clinical practice. She is an avid reader and traveler and loves spending time outdoors with her husband and stepdaughter.

Oliver's Story

ROBERT L. WERGIN, MD

As a physician, sometimes in life the best lessons learned are accomplished by listening to our patients.

Oliver was a ninety-four-year-old male patient in my practice for many years. I took care of his family and his wife. The family was a close-knit Mennonite family in rural southeast Nebraska, and Oliver was a farmer and a retired lay minister from a country Mennonite church for many years. His church was a strong spiritual congregation with lay ministers leading them.

Unfortunately, Oliver contracted pneumonia and was quite ill when he came to my office for help. He was fiercely independent and did not want to go to the hospital. But at his age, and with fever and shortness of breath, he finally consented to be admitted to my rural twenty-bed hospital. As his hospitalization progressed, he continued to worsen.

One morning I was rounding on Oliver and commented to him that we still had some options to reverse his declining course. Oliver was resting quietly, and I was not even sure he heard me. In the room his son David and two of his great-grandchildren, who I had delivered, were sitting with their father and great-grandfather.

As I was talking, David got out of his chair and came over and placed his hand on my arm and said, "You know doctor, our father loves you, and we as a family all love you as well. You are as much a part of our family as anyone in this room, but we wanted you to know that our father does not fear death. We have met as a family, and we are ready for what is to come for our father, but we are worried about you. You don't seem to be ready for what is coming for my father."

I looked back at David and told him that I understood, and I went back to the nurse's station and slowed Oliver's intravenous fluids and wrote for some morphine for comfort. Over the next few days, Oliver succumbed to his pneumonia and passed away quietly. I have to say it was a beautiful thing and not a failure of medicine to witness Oliver's last days on this earth.

There was no shift-working hospitalist coming by each day to see him and write orders. There was no pleasant hospice nurse explaining death and dying to this retired Mennonite minister. Instead in his last minutes, Oliver just had his family and his family doctor at his bedside. He was ready for what was to come for him, and he helped ready me as well.

I learned a lot from Oliver about life, dignity, family, and death. It was a privilege to be his family doctor.

Robert L. Wergin is a practicing physician in the community where he grew up, Milford, Nebraska. He practices full-spectrum family medicine in his Mennonite community. He is a graduate of Kearney State College and received his medical degree from the University of Nebraska Medical Center. He is past president and chairman of the board of the American Academy of Family Physicians.

The Awakening

SUZANNE MONTGOMERY, MD

She looked small and frail, almost like a child, even though she was every bit of forty. Her chest rose and fell in rhythm as breaths were forced into her lungs. I reached for her hand. It felt warm but limp in my grasp. My thumb brushed across the bruise that had formed around the IV protruding from her wrist. I know my sigh was audible as I turned to leave. Celia's mother was entering the door behind the nurse. We both watched as the nurse moved to change the bag of fluid that had run dry and exit the room without a word. Only the noise of the ventilator and the constant beep of the heart monitor broke the silence. All this effort for what? Celia remained in a coma with no outward sign of life.

I embraced her mother and we rocked gently in each other's arms for several moments before we spoke. This woman and I had become familiar companions as I made my daily rounds at the hospital and checked in on Celia. Numerous specialists and their entourage of students rotated in and out of the intensive care unit over the course of her stay. As her family physician, I acted more like her cheerleader than her caregiver. I returned daily to see if there had been any change since the stroke. Two weeks passed but nothing.

A decision had to be made today. The endotracheal tube could not remain in her throat any longer since it could cause damage to the tissues. If Celia stayed on the ventilator, a tracheostomy must be placed in her neck. Earlier in the morning, her neurologist ran a scan looking for any brain activity. I held onto her mother's hands as I backed away.

"Did you hear the results of the test?" I asked.

"Yes," she said with tears welling up in her eyes.

"And what are your thoughts?" I responded.

"If there is no brain activity—if Celia is brain dead—I don't want her to stay like this. I don't think she would want it." After a long pause she added, "I've made my decision."

"I understand. I don't believe she would want to remain alive in this state either. You're making the decision she would want."

As I turned to leave, I reached for Celia once more and whispered, "Good-bye." Driving alone on my way back to the office, I cried out to God. "Please, please do not leave Celia in this vegetative state. When the endotracheal tube is pulled and the ventilator stopped, let her pass away peacefully or heal her." As this plea left my lips, I knew in my heart the answer God would give. I expected her to die.

The plan was to stop all life support the following morning after Celia was moved to a regular room from the ICU. To my surprise, when I arrived to do rounds, she was still unconscious but breathing on her own. How could this be? The damage to her brain was extensive; I had seen the MRI films myself. This was impossible. But the next morning, she began to wake up and by the third day, she asked for something to eat. Her mother and I were in awe and amazement.

I found her neurologist and told him what had transpired since her discharge from the ICU. In disbelief, he came to her room to witness her unprecedented recovery. He ordered another MRI scan, and we both marveled that the films showed a very different picture of her brain. It was not normal but much of it was healed.

Celia looked up, greeting me with a crooked smile when I returned to her room to relay this information. Her mother and I stood at the end of her bed watching her. One side of her body remained weak but with her strong arm, she lifted the food to her mouth to eat. Never once did she choke. As she spoke with us, her voice was hoarse and weak from the two weeks on a ventilator. However, her words were logical and clear. I shook my head in wonder.

Her mother turned to me and said, "You and I both know that this was a miracle."

At her words, the Spirit of God invaded the room. I felt an overwhelming sense that we were standing on holy ground. My breath escaped me, and I found it difficult to remain standing. I held on to Celia's bed for stability. God in His compassion and grace had answered my prayer in a dramatic and unquestionable way. I expected my plea to be answered by Celia's death, but God had another plan. She had a long, hard struggle ahead of her in rehabilitation, but she was alive.

"Yes," I said, "this certainly was a miracle."

This story took place in the late 1990s while I was practicing medicine in the Indianapolis area. After these events, she was able to regain most of her normal functioning through rehabilitation, although she needed a walker for stability. More than ten years later, she passed away in 2008. No medical explanation was ever determined to explain her miraculous recovery. This experience dramatically changed my view of God and how He answers prayer. I hope that the telling of this story will move others to a deeper appreciation for the awesome power of God and a realization that prayer does really work.

Suzanne Montgomery is a family physician, practicing medicine in the Indianapolis area for thirty-five years. She and her husband have six grown children and they live on a mini-farm north of the city raising a menagerie of cats, dogs, chickens, and bees.

Accidental Professionalism

JASON MARKER, MD

I had become frustrated with the lack of progress I was seeing in the weight-loss struggle of one of my young adult patients. Her obesity had created all the comorbidities that go along with that diagnosis, but for a variety of reasons she was never able to comply with my well-considered lifestyle treatment plans. I was starting to think she had unspoken reasons why she really did not want to make these changes, and I was frustrated that I seemed to care more about her weight-loss plan than she did. All my motivational interviewing and shared decision making had been unable to yield improvements. Still, I kept at it visit after visit.

As we wrapped up yet another unfruitful visit, she said, "Doctor Marker, I like coming here to see you." Despite the compliment, this only fed my frustration. "I know I haven't lost any weight after all of these visits, but of all the doctors I've seen about this, you've stuck with me the longest, and you never once treated me like I had Medicaid." She smiled as she stepped past me and headed to the reception desk to make another follow-up appointment.

I stood in the hallway perplexed. Her concern that I would treat her differently based on her insurance status had never once entered my mind. Did doctors still do that with patients in 2005? Had I treated patients in that way unknowingly? And what does it mean to treat someone "like they have Medicaid" in the first place? Were there other unconscious behaviors I needed to learn to avoid? I had been taught in residency to avoid knowing a patient's insurance status when making medical decisions; was that still good advice? Were there other nonmedical factors I was ignoring on purpose (or incidentally) and was that okay?

Though I was happy to learn of my act of "accidental professionalism," the underlying issues that it brought up weighed on me in the days and weeks that followed. In retrospect this encounter sent me down a road of discovery about myself, my colleagues, and my profession that has made me a far better physician over these following years. Everything I've learned about diversity, medical justice, microaggressions, privilege, social determinants of health, and health equity stems from a curiosity about how we deliver medical care that led from this encounter.

My patient never did lose any weight during all my visits with her, but what I gained more than makes up for that.

Jason Marker grew up in Mishawaka, Indiana. He received his biology degree from Indiana University Bloomington and his medical degree from the IU School of Medicine. He completed a four-year family-medicine residency at Memorial Hospital in South Bend, Indiana, while concurrently earning a master's degree in public affairs/health services management from IU South Bend. After fifteen years managing a full-scope, rural, solo private practice and engaging in a broad spectrum of local, state, and national medical professional leadership work, Marker transitioned to teaching full time and is currently an associate director at the Memorial Hospital Family Medicine Residency Program.

Doing the Right Thing

JASON MARKER, MD

Some lessons we learn about our role in people's lives are learned through loss and frustration.

I had struggled to really connect with one of my pregnant patients. She came to all her appointments and did all of the things we ask first-time moms to do, but her personality and mine just did not mesh. She held too tightly to some of the old-wives' tales of pregnancy, seemed skeptical of some parts of evidence-based medicine, and obsessed over minor and benign symptoms of pregnancy. By mid-pregnancy, I was dreading what I was sure would be a rocky set of well-child visits if this baby was anything short of perfect.

I was unsurprised when, four weeks before her due date, she began pressing hard for me to help her "get this pregnancy over with." Every weekly visit gave me a new opportunity to explain in a different manner why I would not be meeting this expectation. Delivering early is not good for babies.

A week before her due date I was three hours out of town with my family when my cell phone rang loudly in our hotel room at midnight. "Doctor, I think my water broke. I've had a lot of moisture tonight," I heard her say on the other end.

I had chosen not to make any explicit on-call coverage for this one night out of town, so this was certainly unwelcome news. One of my colleagues was on call for unassigned patients or emergencies—this was neither. As much as I wanted to tell her it was probably just the normal thin discharge of late pregnancy, the voice of all my residency obstetrical teachers was deep in my head. I told her to go to the hospital and be checked out, and then I called the obstetrics unit and explained the situation. I told them, "If she's ruptured and in labor I'll come home. If she's ruptured and not in labor, we'll keep her, and I'll probably be home before it gets exciting anyway. If she's not ruptured, send her home." I went back to sleep listening to the wind starting to whistle outside as a spring storm was rolling in.

An hour later, my phone rang again. Whispering in the bathroom so not to wake up my family, the nurse brought me up to speed. "Well, she's not ruptured, but she's refusing to leave." As my irritation grew, there was more to the story. "She's contracting hard every three minutes, but she hasn't started to dilate at all. The baby's head is low, however, and her cervix is very thin." I knew a thin cervix could be an early sign of labor but willed it not to be so. I told the nurse to recheck her in an hour and only call me back if there were changes. This time I had trouble returning to sleep. Would I have to return home in this developing storm in the middle of the night? Should I call my colleague even though we always did everything we could to deliver our own babies? Was my general irritation with this situation making me dig my heels in?

An hour later and another phone call: "No change, Doc. She wants the medicine to put her into labor. She says you told her you'd do that in a couple of days and so what's the big deal with doing it tonight?" I *had* told her that I would help this process forward once we got to her due date, but not when I was three hours away in a thunderstorm at 2:00 a.m.! If I started the medicine as she wanted, I would have to come home, but worse, she would have "won."

Calling my on-call colleague seemed like a copout when I was going to leave for home in a few hours anyway. Why wake him up, too? A "surprise" delivery in the night would be no picnic for him, even if I had given him a heads-up at midnight. But now it was the wee hours of the night. I was angry. I knew what the right thing to do was, but I did not want to do it—my pride and arrogance stood in the way. There were easy ways out available to me, but even in my anger I knew that was not the "right" path. "Start the medicine. I'll be there in three hours," I said

It was practically a gale as I drove home in bursts of lightening and rain so heavy that I had to stop on the side of the road twice. This did not make me less angry. That whole drive home I stewed in my anger. I was angry at the patient, her cervix, the baby, the nurse, the storm, the drive, my squeaky windshield wiper, and my sleepiness.

As a Christian physician, I was embarrassed to have it finally occur to me that I should probably be praying instead of extending vitriol to inanimate objects. The die was cast. I had decided, and I was going to live with it. Why all the anger still? "Lord," I prayed, "I don't know what you're doing here, but I'd sure like you to share the secret with me."

My faith did not make me less irritated when I got to the hospital and the medicine had not put her into labor yet. Nor did it help me at daybreak, or when I knew my family was waking up from their sound night of sleep without me in the room with them. I kept praying. I smiled over gritted teeth when I talked with the patient, who was thrilled and vocal about having gotten her way with me. I was outwardly pleasant and acted like this was a fine plan when

I talked through it with the nurses. I was the outward appearance of Doctor Marcus Welby with the inner soundtrack of a domestic dispute.

About the time my family was arriving home, the patient was suddenly seven centimeters dilated. Then rapidly—eight centimeters, nine centimeters, completely dilated, and, finally, delivered. I went home, grabbed a shower, and took a nap without a sign from God about why this had all gone the way it had. I continued to stew whenever I thought about how this patient had disrupted "my" plans for her own selfish reasons.

Two days later she and the baby were home. I saw pictures of Dad and the baby in matching shirts and the grins of excited parenthood. I told the story of my irritating night to my staff as if their commiseration would justify my internal behaviors. A couple of days later, on the patient's original due date, I got a call from the hospital. "We wondered if you could come down here and help us out in the ER." That was a new type of request for the middle of a workday, and I inquired further. The new father, while working with a lawn tractor up on a lift in their garage, had been under it when it collapsed onto him, crushing his skull.

The timing of this tragedy was not lost on me as I drove to the hospital. Had I waited to start her labor until her due date, this man would never have seen his son. This woman would never have known the joy that her childbirth had brought to her husband. Those gleeful family pictures would never have populated the baby book or the funeral display. My selfish and minor hardship had created an opportunity for the week of infinite love that would be needed to salve an infinite depth of sorrow.

I am convinced that God smiles when physicians do the "right" thing and not just the "easy" thing. He will test us routinely, and we will not always pass those tests. I sure do not think I did during the night of my long drive home.

Looking back on that time, I wonder what would have happened if I had made different decisions. Maybe nothing. Maybe something—better or worse. I will not know on this side of heaven. But I do know that if I remember to consistently do what is "right," that in the end I will not have regrets, even if I am unhappy during the journey. When I struggle with the inner turmoil that is part of the professional responsibility of being a physician, I think of this case, and it's a little easier to find the perspective to do my best work.

"Story telling is a reciprocal act. In a clinical setting, it is for the teller, an act of reorientation after basic change in his life. For the listener, the story telling, which provides a window on the teller's soul, is often received as a most intimate and precious gift."

Glen W. Davidson, medical humanities educator, researcher, and author

Between Excuses

ALYSSA COOKE, MD

Mr. Sanders was sixty-two years old when we met on the second day of my internal-medicine rotation. He was my first admission of the month. My resident asked me to see him and perform a complete history and physical.

Upon talking to him, I learned many things. I learned the story of how he had been admitted—an infectious-disease doctor had run after him, catching him before he left from a routine follow-up appointment. He had been in the hospital a month prior for an unusually low white-blood-cell count. All his labs (except for his blood-cell counts) had come back normal. As such, it was decided that it was most likely due to a virus and would resolve on its own. For good measure, he was told to follow up with the infectious-disease doctor in a month to ensure that his blood counts had recovered.

They had not. While his white-cell count had made a moderate rebound, his platelets had completely crashed. They were below the minimum number the machine could detect.

What exactly was the significance of this drastically low number? As the infectious-disease doctor explained to him, he was at an incredibly high risk of a life-threatening bleed. He had already been experiencing spontaneous and unrelenting nosebleeds—a frequent sign of this ominous low level of platelets. This was the reason the doctor had chosen to run after him, catching him just before he left. Mr. Sanders credited this doctor with "saving his life." I did not recognize this statement for what it was at the time: an admission of blind faith that he would be healed.

Mr. Sanders loved to chat. I would find myself trapped in his room for up to an hour at a time, unable to find a polite way to leave the conversation. Anticipated quick check-ins continued to drag on endlessly, setting me behind in my work as I tried to cut in with an excuse to leave. Occasionally my residents would notice I had been missing for a long time and would page me, the insistent beeping offering me an out. In between these excuses, both real and fictional, I learned about his life.

I learned that the woman with him was not technically his wife, but nonetheless a woman to whom he had committed the rest of his life. He would tell me much more about this relationship over the next few weeks as I attempted to put together the puzzle pieces of his case. For now, I knew that referring to her as his wife—despite the technicalities—would earn me great favor.

I discovered that he rode motorcycles for fun. The fact that this was an exceptionally dangerous hobby given his susceptibility to bleeding was not lost on me, so I stored this fact carefully in my mind. I wanted to be able to give him proper precautions before discharge. I suppose that I shared his blind faith in our ability to heal.

I learned that he had lost his first wife, a woman that had given him four children. Though he loved her and mourned her loss, he felt that he had been given a second chance at love (and therefore life, to hear him speak of it) when he met his current partner, Deena. He was determined to live this new life to the fullest. This hospitalization was certainly a speed bump in those plans.

As more and more physicians were asked to consult on his case, he began to grow frustrated with his inability to keep them straight. Each one would come in and introduce themselves too quickly or not at all. He could not keep track of the exceptionally complicated titles that they used for themselves: rheumatologist, hematologist, oncologist. That same day, I returned to his room and gave him a typed reference list of his physicians. He would later interrupt each doctor and demand that they point to their name before allowing them to continue.

Mr. Sanders told me that the steroids that we had given him made him feel incredibly strong—strong enough to question whether he needed to be in the hospital anymore. I also learned that those same steroids had given him thrush and it was affecting his ability to speak. This was another major concern of his, as Mr. Sanders took great pleasure in talking. I noticed a common duality of pharmacy: the same medicine that treated a problem could cause another equally distressing problem to take its place.

I discovered that his favorite doctor was one of the physicians who had treated him during his last admission. He told me long stories of how carefully the physician had explained everything they believed was going on, using analogies and metaphors that were easier to comprehend. He felt that the last time he was admitted, he understood what was going on. Now he had no idea.

In part, he did not understand his diagnosis because there was none. There was an awful lot of speculation, but labs stubbornly returned without abnormalities. He did not understand how we were coming up with treatment plans without a diagnosis, and I carefully explained to him the difference between treating the cause and treating the symptoms. I told him about his platelets, his white-blood cells, and his red-blood cells, breaking things down and coming up with analogies as his previous physician had done. He told me once that he thought I was the smartest person on his medical team. I laughed.

Mr. Sanders was not getting better. In fact, he was beginning to feel considerably worse. His platelet counts did not budge, despite multiple transfusions. His arms were covered in bruises from each needle stick, his blood failing to clot. He and his wife began asking difficult questions: When would he get better? What exactly was wrong? Would he ever leave the hospital? If nothing we're doing is making him better, should he just leave the hospital and accept whatever is to come?

We continued to discuss the most likely diagnosis and its treatments and began to discuss other options in case these treatments failed. While we were not out of hope, we also began to discuss the possibility that he might not get better.

One day, a little over two weeks after his admission, my team was notified that Mr. Sanders was having difficulty breathing despite being given more oxygen. He was breathing faster, his blood-oxygen level was dropping, and his lungs developed signs of fluid formation. The cause of the rapid decline was unclear, but even I could see that he would need to be transferred to the Intensive Care Unit. The room was in chaos as my residents worked to stabilize him for the transfer and explained to the ICU team the details of his case. Suddenly his wife, Deena, grabbed my arm and pulled me to the far side of the room.

"I need the truth. Is it bad?" she asked, reaching out for both of my hands.

Out of everyone in the room, I had the least experience. There was no time to talk to my residents, to make sure that my list of possible causes or assessment of the situation was correct. Still my eyes darted quickly around the room trying to find a more competent member of the team to help me. My eyes went unmet. They were all too busy. This was to be my job alone. I looked back at her and held her gaze.

"We are very concerned. He needs more oxygen than we can give him on this floor, so we are going to transfer him to the ICU. The doctors there are very good. There are a lot of steps they can take to try to get his breathing under control, but we also need to figure out what caused the sudden change," I said.

"So it's bad." She said it as a statement this time, not a question.

After he was transferred off my service, I continued to check in on him every so often, though perhaps not as frequently as I should have. When I did visit, it seemed I always stopped in at the wrong times—in the middle of a meeting with a social worker, during a chaplain visit, or when the intensivist was talking with the family. I was still slightly uncomfortable in the ICU rooms—the way they seemed so isolated, hardly any sounds besides the beeping of monitors. In these rooms, I was a white coat without a purpose. His name had been removed from my list of patients. The list dictated a sort of priority, containing the names of the patients whose care I was responsible for; I was no longer a part of his care team. His name on my list had been immediately replaced with the name of another patient. I continued to follow his chart, convinced that when he stabilized, he would come back to my service and reclaim his place on my patient list. Perhaps these, too, were just more excuses.

A week passed, and as I was walking to check on one of my patients, I ran into Deena in the family waiting area. She asked if I had a moment to talk, and I recognized pain in her expression.

"He's getting worse or at least not getting better. He can hardly speak. I don't know what to do. I'm worried I'm going to have to make decisions alone," she said.

"Deena, you have both been preparing for this possibility for a while now. I know this must be incredibly difficult, but you shouldn't feel like you're making these decisions alone. I think you know what he wants," I replied carefully. *Am I even qualified to be giving advice?*

"You're right. I do know. We've talked about it so much. It's just so much harder in the moment," she said. She paused. "Will you come see him? You're still his favorite. I think it would help him to get to see you."

"Of course," I said.

She held my arm with both hands as we walked back to his room. He looked shrunken compared to when I had first met him, with dried blood crusted around his nose beneath the heavy-duty oxygen mask. In the three weeks he had been here, we had not even succeeded in stopping his nosebleeds. Unsure of what to do, I walked to his bedside and held his hand. He smiled and squeezed then looked over to his wife. Deena and I chatted like this for a bit, Mr. Sanders unable to speak around the oxygen mask.

His monitors began beeping and I realized that his breathing had become heavier. The quality changed, becoming ragged and desperate. His oxygen blood levels were plummeting, the monitor beeping more insistently. I called out to the nurse, and after a moment she disappeared and came back with the resident. Mr. Sanders and Deena had discussed earlier that he did not want a breathing tube, and so instead Deena held his hand as his heart rate slowed to a stop.

Later, I looked at his chart. In the death note, I am noted as a "family friend at the bedside."

Mr. Sanders was the first patient to treat me like a physician. In doing so, he taught me an incredible amount about how to be one. He taught me that my patient's problems and priorities may not align with my perception of them. He taught me about the importance of explaining medical concepts in a way that the patient can understand. He taught me about having difficult and emotional conversations with patients and their families. He taught me about having confidence in my assessments. He taught me about the uncertainty that still exists in medicine, and how to be honest with my patients during that uncertainty. He taught me that even after I am no longer responsible for the care of my patients, I can still care *about* them. He also taught me the heartbreak of losing a patient. It is incredible what a patient can teach you in between your excuses.

I will forever be humbled that he considered me one of his physicians, and I will forever be honored that he considered me one of his friends.

Alyssa Cooke grew up in Cary, Illinois, and attended Purdue University for her undergraduate studies. She completed her medical degree in 2019 at the Indiana University School of Medicine. She is currently a resident in the combined IU Internal Medicine-Pediatrics Residency in Indianapolis.

Betrayal

MARINA SHARIF, MD

I stand with my resident at the head of the bed in the operating room. It feels cold and bright. I shiver in my thin blue scrubs as I glance at the clock, wishing I grabbed a jacket from the locker room. On my surgery rotations, I scrubbed in, covered by hospital-issued garb, keeping my gloved hands drawn tightly to myself above my waist. That was not the plan today.

Today, I am on the anesthesia team. Instead of being with the surgeon at the table, I am behind the drapes. I pace the room to warm myself, careful not to go near the dark-blue sterile area guarded by the scrub tech.

Today's case will last several hours, but I do not plan to stay the whole time. After putting the patient to sleep, I will slip out and go home for the day. I am so looking forward to this. My stomach growls. I missed breakfast, and there is no food allowed in the operating room. Not even a small snack! I sighed, restless. I realize I could not even remember what the procedure is. Finally, a nurse peeks her head in the door, "The patient is on his way!"

I had been in operating rooms before and had seen patients enter the room and be put to sleep for a procedure. Adults are usually wheeled in with an IV already in place in their arm, small talk ensuing as we help them onto the bed and introduce ourselves. We attach a few tubes and let the milky white anesthetic flow straight to their veins while holding a mask gently over their face to help them breathe. Typically, they are asleep within a matter of seconds. The whole thing is quite unceremonious.

Things were going to be a little different today. Our patient was a child.

The double doors opened, and the fanfare began. The Disney song "Under the Sea" from *The Little Mermaid* blared from the operating room speakers. A video of Sebastian, the singing crustacean, emanated from screens around the room. We all cheered and clapped.

In waltzed a brown-eyed, brown-haired boy of three years in a colorful small hospital gown and blue hospital socks. He was grinning—lured by the music into the operating room. Behind him, approaching much more cautiously, was a woman in a white paper suit, cap, and mask. She nodded at us politely.

"Mommy, look! I love this song!" he cried, pointing at the screens. My resident nudged me as he moved to turn the volume up and gave me a wink. I nodded. As the medical student, I was assigned the task of interacting with the child and getting him in the correct position before surgery. I walked over and began to sing the words I knew so well from my own childhood. He laughed and began to dance. His mother remained still. I led him, through dance, toward the operating table. I asked his mother if I could pick him up to get him on the table, and she consented without turning to me. "Weeeeee!" I jeered as I swung him into the air. Quickly and skillfully, the nurses began fastening multiple body belts over him to keep him in place. His mother took his hand. "It's going to be okay, sweetie." His eyes locked with mine and he giggled.

"Do you have your mask?" one of the nurses asked him.

"Right here!" He proudly held up a small clear triangular mouthpiece that would be used to help him breath in the gas.

"What flavor did you put in it?" my resident asked playfully. With the body belts on and machines beginning to whir, he remained smiling, but this time looked to his mother instead of answering.

His mother answered the question, but toward her son. "You put strawberry in, didn't you sweetie?" He nodded his head yes, eyes trained on his mother, still calm, but no longer as excited; I gently placed the small mask lined with strawberry flavored Chapstick over his mouth and nose.

"Breathe deeply, sweetie," I said. He obeyed. His mother held his hand tighter.

My resident began to draw up the medication. The boy caught site of the needle, and immediately his demeanor changed. He began to blink faster, his eyes darting around the room. He looked at his mother in confusion. He tried to reach up for the mask, and one of the nurses held his arm down. The music stopped. He kept shifting. The mask would not stay on with him squirming like this.

"We need him to keep breathing gas through the mask," I said to the mother. She did not move. The boy began to struggle; he let out a yelp. I came to the head of the bed with my resident.

"Grab his head from the angles of the mandible, hold him up, and push the mask down with your other fingers." I knew this as the correct airway maneuver to deliver the gas, but the boy was clearly still awake. I could feel the team waiting for me to continue. I pushed the mask down hard over his face, and he screamed loudly.

One of the nurses started to lead the mother away, "We have it now, you can wait outside from here." My heart was pounding.

One of his arms escaped the belt and his nails dug into my wrist. The nurses restrained him. He yelled again, his face turning a deep red from his effort. I held the mask down harder. Tears streamed down his face and our eyes met. This time, he held an undeniable look of anger and betrayal.

"Help! Mommy!" he managed to shout. This plea caught me off guard, and I felt my seal on the mask loosen. Suddenly, there were two stronger hands on mine pulling his chin up again. I turned. It was the attending anesthesiologist. Amid the chaos, I had not noticed he entered the room.

"Push the mask harder. It's okay" the anesthesiologist said in a calm voice. I did as I was told. The boy began to hyperventilate, his whole body vibrating from the effort of breathing. "Be steady," he encouraged as his hands held mine in place. The boy passed out. I held on as I felt his muscles relax. His breaths became more rhythmic.

My resident slid in gracefully and took over the airway for me, telling me I did great. Our attending guided me toward the side of the table and told me I could put the IV in now. I looked around for the mother, but she was nowhere in sight. The scrub tech was helping the surgery team into their gowns and gloves. The boy's gown had been removed and he lay naked on the table now. A nurse began to scrub his abdomen with an orange iodine solution while the tech arranged drapes ready to cover him. I felt distracted by them as my attending gently encouraged me to continue.

I tied the tunicate tightly around his arm, searched for a good vein, and started the IV. He did not fight me at all during this part. My attending patted me on the back. The struggle was over, but I felt ashamed. I had held down this child much like a kidnapper might have with a rag of chloroform. I had garnered his trust and then, almost immediately, betrayed him. I knew ultimately, this was all being done to help him, but I still felt dirty about it.

Unable to process the experience and no longer hungry for snacks, I stayed for the duration of the surgery. Upon waking, he was groggy and unaware. I helped the resident wheel him into the recovery room; our attending joined us.

On the way back, I noticed the mother waiting outside in the family lounge. She had a man with her, his arm wrapped tightly around her. She had been crying. She saw us coming and we locked eyes—hers just as big and brown as her son's. Her cheeks reddened, and she buried her face into the man's shoulder. I wanted to say something to her, but I did not know what or how. "I'm sorry that seemed awful?" or "It was what we needed to do?" I looked to my attending and resident who had also caught a glance of the couple.

I watched my superiors closely, hoping for some hint of recognition or hesitation. There was none. My attending walked past her without a word. Behind him, my resident did the same. I was a relatively inexperienced medical student and, unfortunately, I took their lead and made no move to speak to the mother.

Medical students are taught by example. Role modeling is such an important part of medical education for both clinical and professional development. But regrettably, all too often, we are taught to be less empathetic throughout medical school and likely during residency training as well. It is not directly taught; it is a subtle, gradual unintended process that diminishes our human sensitivity. Maybe it is a defense mechanism that protects physicians emotionally from the difficult medical decisions they sometimes must make or the tragedies of seriously ill patients we witness.

But I have learned there are also so many empathetic and kind physicians, and with further experience, I have been able to regain some of that; however, it was a long time before I recognized what I had lost.

In retrospect, I consider that encounter in the surgical waiting room a great lesson learned, but also something I will always regret. I made no move to speak to that mother that day. I followed them.

Marina Sharif was born in Canada and moved around while her father completed his medical training. She grew up mostly in Marion, Indiana, where her father is a cardiologist. She wrote this story while a medical student at the Indiana University School of Medicine. From an early age she gained an appreciation for reading and writing from her mother, who took her and her sisters to libraries and bookstores, encouraging them to read whatever they could get their hands on. She is currently a resident in internal medicine at the Virginia Commonwealth University Health Systems in Richmond, Virginia.

Courage

RICHARD D. FELDMAN, MD

As with virtually all practicing physicians, I have had patients die through-out my career. These are difficult experiences, especially with those patients I became very close to and cared for over many years. I remember the loving older couple who brought me a big jar of cookies they baked very Christmas. She died of a melanoma, and he died of renal failure just a couple of years later. I remember the grandmother, the matriarch of the family, who died of COPD and congestive heart failure. There was the old man who died of liver cancer and patients who died of lung cancer. I recall the woman with pancre-atic cancer who chose to die without treatment and without artificial means of nutrition or hydration in a nursing home. There were, of course, many others.

I am struck by the fact that nearly all my patients with terminal illnesses faced their end with dignity and courage. They accepted their fate bravely and expressed that they were fortunate to have lived such a good life. They were thankful for what they had. They had no regrets. Some were more concerned for the loved ones that they were leaving behind than for themselves. Such was the man who died slowly of a progressive degenerative neurologic disease. Near the end, he met with me privately to discuss the future well-being of his wife, Karen, after he was gone, and to thank me for the care I had given them over the years. They had no children, and I promised him that I would make sure Karen was doing okay. Courage and love.

There was another individual and friend, Jim Shrack, who lived in my hometown. Over the years he would call me for medical advice and opinions. I was in a way his "part-time" physician. Jim was in my wedding and was one of my best friends since college. We even lived together for a time when I was in medical school, and he was working in Indianapolis. Many years later, he de-veloped an unusual and incurable gastrointestinal cancer. He called me for my opinions and advice, and I provided him with what information I had to offer and explained aspects of his disease and potential treatments he did not fully understand. I consulted with some of my oncology and surgical colleagues to give him the best advice possible. Along the journey of this final illness, I reviewed his treatments and medications and helped him make decisions regarding the best medical center choices to consider for his treatment.

Jim Shrack with his daughter Erika

He underwent chemotherapy and two surgeries. Initially his oncologist was hopeful that with treatment he could live a few years. After his round of chemotherapy and abdominal surgery, his doctors were more hopeful for even longer-term survival given the specific type of cancer found on his pathology report. Unfortunately, the cancer progressed with a vengeance, leaving him with extensive intestinal obstructions. Further chemo would be of little help, and further surgery was impossible.

Jim was left with only the ability to drink water and some sugary drinks. He could receive no real nutrition. He was advised that he would essentially starve to death. And indeed, he did. He died a week after I last saw him. He had lost sixty-five pounds in ten weeks and was essentially skin over bone. He really was not in excessive pain, although he took some opioids and nausea medications during his terminal illness.

Jim was Catholic, very religious, and belonged to a charismatic community. He was a good husband and father to his nine children. He worked hard, was responsible, and was a good citizen. He was a good man—the best.

When I last saw him, I told him that I envied both his courage and his faith. He had no doubt that in passing, he was entering the next phase of his life, and that he would be with God. He had no interest in anything that would extend his life and was not afraid to die. He thanked me for being such a good friend over so many years.

He told me that after he was gone, if I ever was in a difficult situation and needed God's help, to let him know and he would do his best to help me. This was not a reflection of a sense of superiority or specialness; he was a humble individual. He just believed he had a personal relationship with God and Jesus, just as everyone believed in his religious community. This was an unusual conversation for us to have because although a very religious Christian, he never wore it on his sleeve, at least with me, his Jewish friend.

My friend's courage, character, and faith carried him through. I think of my courageous friend often.

Jim Shrack's wife, Jeanie, granted the author permission to use his name.

Privileged

DANIELLE YIN, MD

Most of us who go into medicine are privileged. Of course, not all of us have the same amount of privilege, but undoubtedly it takes a certain degree of it to get to where we are. Personally, I had the advantage of having two supportive parents who were devoted to helping me succeed. From extra Scholastic Aptitude Test prep books in high school to bringing me dinner when I was too tired to cook after a long day in the hospital, I have been blessed with the privilege of having an unrivaled support system. Perhaps my entitlement is why my first pediatrics patient left such a lasting impression on me.

Carrie was a teenage girl with some of the normal teenage girl problems, such as catty friends and unrequited crushes. But for the past six months she also had some very abnormal teenage girl problems. Occasionally, she would collapse to the ground with her limbs jerking wildly and her eyes rolling back into her head. The episodes happened at home and at school. They occurred in the presence of her friends and her aunt, her legal guardian. Each time she looked as though her body was violently seizing. But to her medical team, something was off. Her seizures looked more like what an actor would portray in a movie than a true seizure.

The "seizures" never happened when she was alone. She woke up confused from her episodes but quickly regained knowledge of medicine's tell-tale signs of awareness: where she was, who she was, and when it was. Her presentation did not add up to a seizure disorder because she did not have a true seizure disorder. Her symptoms were caused by something that is arguably even more complex—psychogenic nonepileptic seizures. Instead of a misfiring of neurons, her symptoms were caused by her mind's repression of unmanaged stress.

The stress powerful enough to cause psychogenic nonepileptic seizures often requires a traumatic event. It is hard to verbalize the emotions that grasp me when I come to understand that my patient's past contains a traumatic event so horrible that her mind literally cannot handle it and manifests it through a physical outlet. "Devastation" might work, but it is not enough.

An important part of interviewing an adolescent patient is the HEADSS assessment: home and environment, education and employment, activities, drugs, sexuality, and suicide/depression. As you can imagine, some of those are the exact topics that most teenage girls shy away from talking about. But with Carrie the conversation flowed. She confided about her life to *me*, a brand-new third-year medical student who still was not entirely sure she put the earpieces of her stethoscope in the right way.

We discussed her family, her friends, her favorite classes in school, her hopes, and her dreams. She told me about her mom who had been in prison for drug-related charges since she was a little girl. Sometimes she got to visit her. She told me about her dad, who she watched being handcuffed and escorted away by the police a year prior. She talked to me like she had no one else to talk to in her life, like I was the first person who had ever asked her about these things.

It turns out that I was. When I asked her who her sources of support were, she merely shrugged. She just moved to a new school and was not that close with any of the girls there yet. Her grandparents cared for her but never talked to her about subjects like this, she said. Her younger sister was her best friend, but she could not live at her aunt's house with her because she could not afford it. So, she lived with different relatives in a different state, and now they hardly talked. She said she felt alone all the time. What I had taken for granted slapped me in the face as I listened to this strong, resilient girl tell me about how she has none of what I did. One conversation with her taught me gratitude, which I never forget.

My favorite part of her interview was when she told me she wanted to be a doctor. To Carrie, medicine seemed like the perfect job for her. Science was her favorite subject. Most importantly, she wanted to help people like she had been helped. She may not have shared the same privileged life that I had, but something told me she would be wearing a white coat one day.

Danielle Yin is from Indianapolis, Indiana. She attended Indiana University, Bloomington, for her undergraduate studies. At the time she wrote this story, she was a medical student at the IU School of Medicine. She is currently in a radiology residency in Pittsburgh, Pennsylvania.

A Survivor

JULIE SAUNDERS, RN

I am a registered nurse at Franciscan Health Indianapolis. I work "PRN" (as needed) on two units at Franciscan: Geriatrics and Palliative Care. During the COVID-19 pandemic, I devoted most of my days to Palliative Care. I feel God inspired and committed us all in Palliative Care to meet the needs of our patients and staff. As we were present in most every unit of the hospital every day, we consulted on most all coronavirus cases, witnessing stress, strain, heartache, joys, and victories.

The hospital did a great job in preparing for the crisis and the onslaught of critically ill patients. However, understandably, issues "cropped up" that needed to be addressed as soon as possible—unexpected things that were crucial to good, meaningful patient care in such an unusual hospital environment. For example, our house-wide "restricted visitors policy" required some swift decisions for us to uniformly control visitation. All patients were only allowed visitors at end of life.

Consequently, many patients no longer had contact with family members. I know it is hard to imagine today that any patient would not have access to family via phone or tablet. But in Palliative Care, we saw many patients on ventilators and even BIPAP masks, which do not allow patients to speak on the phone. So, no family could call and talk to them, let alone see them. Many patients were elderly and did not know how to use a cell phone. Others were just plain sick or confused. While non-COVID-19 patients at end of life were allowed only two visitors, a coronavirus patient was allowed only one. What about all the family members who wanted or needed to see these patients for the good of their relationship or to assist in important decision making?

And so, some immediate decisions had to be made. To provide the means to do Zoom video chats with patients and their families, older computer tablets in the hospital were used, most of which were "confiscated and commissioned" primarily by Palliative Care staff who stepped up and acted on the need. The Zoom app was downloaded on each one, and all were put into use for the hospital with their home base in Palliative Care.

I will never forget the first video chat that I coordinated. A palliative-care patient who had had a stroke and had been in the hospital for one week was on a ventilator. His family had not seen him since being in the emergency

Angela Rodgers

room. His left side was flaccid, but in this much-needed video chat he opened his eyes to his family loudly cheering him on from the tablet, shook his head to their questions (all while intubated) and gave "thumbs up" with his right hand as his bedside nurse panned the tablet to show his hand to his family. It was a huge success, everyone involved, including myself, were sincerely blessed and thankful. It was truly one of the greatest moments of my thirty-eight-year nursing career. And it was all just getting started.

Early on, since I had some video-chat experience, I was asked to spend the day going to different units to do video chats with patients. The bedside nurses were understandably busy, and patients needed to see their families. I gladly agreed. It just so happened that the hospital also had made another quick decision that day: to train a "displaced" employee from a closed hospital department to do Zoom video chats during the crisis. So, this employee, Susan Hicks, joined me to shadow for the day to learn the process.

As with many things surrounding COVID-19, we just jumped in and started working on behalf of all the patients. I did not have much time to get the "background story" on Susan. I did manage to quickly tell her how crucial the video chats were in providing an important link between patients and family. And she was about to see for herself. Soon our phone started ringing with calls from all over the hospital requesting Zoom video chats. Part of the job was just staying organized.

After a few video chats, we were called to a COVID-19 isolation room in the Intensive Care Unit. This was also a great opportunity to teach Susan about the coronavirus isolation procedures. So off we went. I methodically told her how to connect with the bedside nurse to get a short synopsis of the patient and family and to invite the nurse to be involved in the chat if needed.

This coronavirus patient, Angela Rodgers, had been on the ventilator for three weeks. Angela's husband immediately shared with us on the chat that he had not seen or spoken to his wife in those three weeks. The bedside nurse told us that the patient had not been responsive until "her family showed up in the room" on the Zoom video. Lots of cheers, hellos, and "We love you Grandma!" from her grandchildren, plus some tears. I positioned the tablet for her to see her family clearly, as she could not move her head while on the ventilator. Suddenly, Angela began heaving with tears and crying, all while ventilated. Her nurse entered the room and took time to speak to her husband about his wife's future, which was really an unknown. The nurse conveyed that her condition was very serious, and that difficult decisions may be needed for the patient regarding the extended use of the ventilator or taking her off to provide comfort care at the end of her life.

Susan and I ended the chat and removed our isolation garb. Just outside the room Susan stopped me. She said, "Let me get this straight. This patient has coronavirus, and she might die?"

"Yes," I responded.

We sat down to chart and she stopped me again saying, "I'm ashamed, and I have a confession to make. I was just talking to my husband this morning saying this coronavirus thing is all a bunch of crap because it just didn't seem real. I had no idea what was involved with this new job today. God put me here, today, for a reason."

Fast forward a couple of weeks. While seeing palliative-care patients on a med/surg unit, a nurse shared with me that she thought she had a "Code Rocky" that day. Code Rocky was initiated by the hospital to provide a tunnel of clapping and cheering staff while a COVID-19 survivor is wheeled out to be discharged. We briefly talked about how the Code Rocky process worked, as we had yet to ever hear one announced overhead. In speaking to the hospital operator to initiate the event, it was clear this was possibly the hospital's first Code Rocky because the operator was unsure what we were asking for. The excitement on the med/surg unit was palpable; this Code Rocky would be as much for the staff as it was for the patient.

I stood in the throngs of hospital staff in the hospital lobby waiting for the patient to be wheeled by for the Code Rocky. When she arrived, it was such a release of emotion to cheer and witness a success story! A win! A survivor!

I was so caught up in yelling and jumping up and down, I hardly noticed the patient behind her mask. After she left the building, something compelled me to go to the window and watch her being greeted by her family. I recognized her husband and grandchildren from that video chat with Susan in the ICU. It was her! Angela Rodgers was getting up from the wheelchair and walking to the car! I was amazed and speechless, so grateful and thankful to have been a part of this huge success story. But I was not the only one. The lobby had emptied behind me; everyone had gone back to work, except one person who stood back behind me in the lobby looking out the window. It was Susan. She said with tears in her eyes, "It's her! She survived!"

I have learned so much from my experience in this crisis: How to be bold and "do the right thing" when one sees a need, the importance of family and relationships, and being grateful for every day with my husband and sons. I learned so much listening to COVID-19 patients crying in thanksgiving to their loved ones on video chats after they had been taken off the ventilator and survived. I was thankful to be God's hands and feet, in a little way, in this big world, for such a time as this.

Julie Saunders grew up in rural southern Indiana. She received her associate's degree in nursing from Indiana Central University and later her bachelor's degree from the University of South Florida in Tampa. Saunders has been a med/surg nurse most of her career in pediatrics, neonatal, school nursing, hospice, and now palliative care. She enjoys her family, running, tennis, bible study, and helping her husband's ministry as a pastor.

The patient, Angela Rodgers, gave permission to use her story and her name for this book. Susan Hicks, a surgery scheduler at Franciscan Health Indianapolis, also gave permission to use her name in this essay.

Cecilia

MARY MAHERN, MD

I do not remember ever asking a patient of mine before (or since) for a photo, if one does not count the occasional rash or other skin abnormality, that is. Cecilia was happy to let me take a picture of her with my cell phone. I wanted the photo because she was the youngest looking ninety-eight-year-old-woman I had ever met. Her subtle, engaging smile made her quite photogenic.

I was always pleased when I saw her name on my schedule. Her medical issues were straightforward for the most part, uncomplicated blood pressure management as I recall, allowing time for simply chatting. She was the kind of elderly patient who was so healthy for her advanced age, that as her physician, I had to be particularly careful not to prescribe anything that could create a new problem.

I was captivated by her stylish and youthful appearance. She wore her hair in a casual bob and often had a scarf of muted colors tied loosely around her neck. She frequently had a social event in the works at the retirement home where she lived.

As the years went by and she turned 100, Cecilia's ability to get to my office declined, so I began visiting her in the nursing facility, where she received the increasing care and support she needed. She was able to remain active in some aspects of her social life for a while, but eventually her world grew smaller as she was less able to get out of her room. Still, visiting her was like visiting a friend.

Cecilia had the means to have a private room that she had curated to be a lovely, albeit very small, home. She had retired as an art teacher several decades earlier and had collected many beautiful works of art over the years. When she moved to the nursing facility, she let go of all but the select items in her room. As an appreciator of art, she had an aesthetic for the simplicity of a few fine pieces. The portion of her room closest to the window had two simple armchairs arranged to invite comfort and intimacy. A floor lamp created a warm glow. She had three of her favorite paintings displayed on the wall and a small sculpture on a stand under one of the paintings. On a small table near her chair, she kept the machine that she used to play the books on tape provided by the Library of Congress. Her vision was very poor by then, but this did not prevent her from enjoying great works of literature. I was able to appreciate the décor that she had created, which she could no longer see clearly.

As she gradually declined further, Cecilia could no longer get out of her bed and could not communicate verbally. I continued to enjoy her chosen favorite things and honored her at each visit by taking in the beauty of the items she found most precious to her.

Cecilia impressed upon me that it does not take many "things" to appreciate beauty and cultivate a love of the arts in our lives. Since she passed several years ago, I often consider what few works of art and beauty I would choose if I were to make a home in one small room. Thus far, I have selected an oil painting of lilacs painted by my grandmother.

A lifetime Hoosier, Mary Mahern has been a family physician in Bloomington, Indiana since 1991, except for four years away to accompany her active-duty husband to Panama and then to San Antonio, Texas. She feels enriched by the long-term relationships she has developed with her patients and continues to learn from them every day. Mahern enjoys her teaching role with the Indiana University School of Medicine, influencing the next generation of doctors who spend time with her in her office.

Gertrude's Prescription

MARY MAHERN, M.D.

Gertrude had been a patient in my practice for several years. She was in her late seventies with osteoarthritis, mild emphysema, and was thirty pounds overweight. Life was getting to be a bit of a struggle for her.

She came to me one fall with a dilemma. The holidays were approaching, and she simply did not feel she was going to be able to cook the Thanksgiving dinner her family had come to expect. For the past fifty years she had enjoyed cooking a big traditional dinner for her family that had grown to include at least twenty people by the time you counted her kids, their spouses, grandchildren, and great-grandchildren. This had always been a source of pride and joy for her. She was coming to terms with the inevitability that she could no longer put on the family feast. Her family, however, did not seem to be picking up on the clues that hosting the annual dinner was getting to be too much for her.

There is a transition that those of us who are fortunate enough to have parents who live into advanced age must face. The always-capable parent is no longer as strong and vibrant as they once were. The father who took care of all the household fix-up chores and was able to split and carry in firewood, rearrange furniture, and lift heavy grandchildren, may no longer be able to safely change a light bulb. The mother who has always enjoyed culinary arts may no longer have the stamina to prepare and serve the holiday meal.

I had thought this sort of thing might be obvious to the family, but I have observed more than once over my thirty years as a family doctor that some folks seem to be blind to these changes. Perhaps it is a denial of their own sense of growing older that they cannot see the slow decline in their parents. Could it be that their lives are simply too busy to see that mom can no longer undertake the heroic task of planning, shopping, cleaning, and cooking the biggest meal of the year?

Sometimes the family doctor needs to intervene on behalf of the patient and instruct the family that things are changing, and their parent can no longer be expected to do things they have always done in the past.

I still remember Gertrude sitting in one corner of the exam room while I positioned myself to make eye contact with her as well as her fifty-five-year-old son and another family member who she requested come to the appointment.

"Your mother can no longer manage the Thanksgiving dinner," I told them. "Someone else in the family will need to take over this task. Perhaps she can contribute a dish or two but everything else will be up to the rest of the family. It's time for the next generation to take over." Gertrude seemed visibly to be relieved by my professional proclamation. The son understood instantly.

Sometimes what our patients need more than anything is for us to advocate on their behalf and explain simple facts to their families. There are prescriptions that doctors provide other than for medications.

"The practice of medicine is an art, not a trade, a calling, not a business, a calling in which your heart will be exercised equally with your head."

Sir William Osler, MD,1903

Lessons from Mr. Brady

ALLISON MUI YEAMAN, MD

During my third year of medical school, I had the privilege of being a member of the hematology team for four weeks of my internal-medicine rotation. This rotation came about midway through my clerkships. At this point of my career, I had not yet decided on a medical specialty and had not yet experienced an intensive inpatient experience. As a medical student, I was responsible for following two to four patients. I was encouraged to learn as much as I could about each patient and was expected to know every detail of their medical history, hospital course, and treatment plan. This allowed me the unique opportunity to grow close with these patients and their families, spend more time with them before and after rounds, and truly dive deep into the physician-patient relationship.

I spent almost every day of this short month with Mr. Brady and his wife. Over his hospital course, I learned about diagnosing acute leukemia, neutropenic fever management, chemotherapy treatments, and more. These, however, were lessons I could have learned from any of the various patients I followed. Ultimately, the most important lessons I learned during this month were the ones from Mr. Brady. He truly was the most valuable teacher of all.

I visited with Mr. Brady every morning before 7:00 for six out of seven days of the week. Without fail, he was always awake, bed made, sitting in his day chair, and awaiting my visit and his breakfast. This routine struck me. I had grown accustomed to waking patients up, presumably often after they had just fallen asleep after a sleepless night filled with countless interruptions. Mr. Brady's discipline was inspiring. In a way, Mr. Brady making his bed daily was a testament to how seriously he took his hospital stay. He was frequently seen during our team rounds walking the halls with his wife. He was careful about brushing his teeth, eating the right foods, and letting us know if anything about his body changed or felt differently.

Seeing Mr. Brady's neatly made bed every morning reminded me of the sage lesson of Admiral William McRaven who said, "If you make your bed every morning, you will have accomplished the first task of the day. It will give you a small sense of pride, and it will encourage you to do another task, and another, and another."

One of my favorite moments was when I told Mr. Brady that his absolute neutrophil count went up to 0.1 from 0, and his response was, "Bubble Boy is making a move!" His optimism and spirit through this challenge and chapter of his life continue to inspire me even today. He taught me to always look at the bright side and the importance of optimism, especially in the setting of the dark hospital room. Mr. and Mrs. Brady were always grateful for the blessings they did receive, like being with each other, having a supportive medical team, and persevering through the complications in his hospital course. I cannot recall a single morning when Mr. Brady displayed a broken spirit. Even when he physically looked his worst, his attitude was unblemished. I was inspired daily to always be hopeful and enthusiastic, even for seemingly insignificant victories. His cheerful disposition reminded me that there is always something in life to celebrate and for which to be thankful.

Mr. and Mrs. Brady grew to become so much more to me than just a patient and spouse. They were the first people who revealed to me the most incredible aspect of practicing medicine: the honor of being a part of my patients' lives. Throughout our month together, I learned about their lives, their jobs, their families, and more. We discovered that we were all from the same region of Virginia. I spoke to them about applying as a couple for residency training with my medical student fiancé, deciding on a medical specialty, and even wedding planning.

My relationship with the Bradys was critical to my realization that I belong in family medicine. I can confidently say that being a small part of their lives is one of the greatest privileges I have had, not just in medical school, but in my life. I never cease to be humbled that patients allow themselves to be vulnerable; they invite me into their lives and share their hopes and dreams and their greatest weaknesses and fears. The privilege of experiencing an incredible relationship between physician and patient is easily the most important lesson of all I have learned in medicine.

When I find free moments throughout my days and nights in the hospital, I occasionally check in on patients I have followed and provided care for in previous clerkships and rotations. For Mr. Brady, I cannot wait more than one or two days without satisfying this curiosity and more importantly, temporarily refreshing my hope that he is continuing to thrive and recover. Whenever Mr. Brady is readmitted to the hospital for complications, I value the opportunity to revisit him and his wife and to check in on how they have been doing and feeling. He always reassures me that coming back to the hospital is like returning home to his second family. He is always so thankful for the help and medical care he receives, but I am truly grateful for the lessons I learned from Mr. Brady.

Allison Mui Yeaman was a resident at the University of Virginia Family Medicine Residency Program in Charlottesville, Virginia, at the time she wrote this essay. She grew up in Newport News, Virginia, and earned her bachelor of science degree in chemistry from Virginia Commonwealth University in Richmond. She stayed in Richmond and earned her medical degree from Virginia Commonwealth University School of Medicine. Yeaman's interests within family medicine include working with underserved populations, preventative medicine, and palliative care.

The Bittersweet of Being Your Doctor

ERRIN WEISMAN, DO

In caring for my patients, I have myself encountered the broad spectrum of what it means to be alive. From the most tender and touching to devastating and brutal, being a physician is bittersweet. Being a part of the magic of new life, healing, and health has been paired with intimate dances with death, disease, and illness. We become key players in critical life moments and authors of a few sentences in the stories of our patient. I have found that when I can truly embrace the bitterness of being a doctor, I can more closely hold the sweetness that is somewhere deep inside.

During my residency training, I had the privilege to care for Mr. Rogers, who was in the late stages of ALS, commonly known as Lou Gehrig's Disease. He was wheelchair-bound and developing weakness in his speech. At our first "establishing care" office visit, he already was nearing the end of his life; he knew it and I knew it. We continued to see each other monthly knowing the end was coming but also because it gave him a sense of purpose to get out of his home and to be involved in what he called, "a real conversation." We would talk as much as time allowed in the hustle of the office setting. He always wanted a hug saying, "Come here, kid" raising his chin and motion with his hand given he could no longer raise his arms at the shoulders.

I remember the call one evening from one of my resident colleagues that Mr. Rogers was in the emergency room, and she said, "He's not doing well. No one is here with him, but your name is his emergency contact. The attendings are talking about whether or not to intubate him prophylactically."

Mr. Rogers had talked extensively about his end-of-life wishes, hence why he probably made me his emergency contact. He had told me that if he came to the hospital, he did not want to be intubated; he wanted to go peacefully understanding his diagnosis.

At the time of this call, I had picked up my two-year-old son and we were driving home. I was thirty-seven weeks pregnant with my second and had been cramping all through the work day. I told my colleague, "I can't make it in tonight" and went on to explain Mr. Rogers's exact wishes along with explaining his advanced directives were already scanned into the electronic medical record.

I was just exhausted that evening but promised to make a special effort to come to inpatient rounds the next morning.

The next morning's rounds never came. In the early morning hours around 3:00 a.m., cramps turned to contractions. Membranes ruptured on their own and I had my second baby son forty-five minutes later.

I called the morning hospital team after I got myself together enough from delivery to get an update and get one on Mr. Rogers.

That is when they told me, Mr. Rogers had died around 4:00 a.m.

He did not have a spouse, friend, or anyone else to advocate for him, just me. Whether it was destiny or sheer coincidence that Mr. Rogers's death and my son's birth coincided, I will never know. But the bitterness that I felt because I was unable to see my patient in his final hour still bothers me years later. The sweetness comes from knowing Mr. Rogers would no longer struggle against the body that was failing him. Guilt and joy all rolled together.

Bittersweet.

Another bittersweet experience involves a lovely patient I picked up in my first year of practice; her first visit with me was a hospital discharge follow-up. She had had some acute shortness of breath related to her end-stage chronic lung disease with an extremely complicated hospital course with almost every complication that could possibly happen. Her chart was literally chapters long and took me several hours to review. Through her chart review, I began to read between the lines that this woman was a fighter.

We developed a beautiful doctor-patient relationship that stretched beyond diagnoses and treatments. She was such a joyful person, always with a smile even amongst the gasps for every breath.

When she died, I went to her viewing and met her family. It was beautiful to hear their stories about her, to say good-bye, and experience the joy that she was no longer suffering. But I also felt the bitterness of her death, the realities if she had just gotten care sooner or made herself a priority like she did with so many others, her light would still be present.

Bittersweet.

When I left my first practice, it was unlike any experience I had had to date. I felt as though I was getting divorced from thousands of souls. Leading up to my last day, the good-byes with my patients were gut wrenching.

One of my patients, Mrs. Retherford just bawled when I told her of my departure. She came to see me every month before I left just to "see me one last time." She had been pushed through the system of healthcare and labeled "malingering and non-compliant." But by taking time to fully listen to her story, we had developed an understanding. She explained that she had never felt so cared for.

There was such bitterness in that—to know that I had to give up being her physician because of the issues at that practice. And there was also a sense of accomplishment and joy that because of me, she had felt heard and desperately wanted to stay my patient. I felt gratified.

Bittersweet.

The practice of medicine can make physicians hard and stoic. We are constantly inundated with emotional situations that if not dealt with become emotional baggage like barnacles building up. Without clearing them and working through them, they encase and destroy us. Resistance to experiencing fear, anger, shame, or sadness, only morphs these emotions into something much darker: burnout, depression, aggression, and violence.

Processing through the bittersweetness of these experiences have taught me to honor all my emotions as a physician. No more swallowing them down in avoidance because they just fester into larger pathology. Instead, by progressing through and being present in all emotions allows for the sweetness to trickle through every doctoring experience.

Errin Weisman is a life coach, speaker, and fierce advocate for wellness in medicine. She faced professional burnout early in her career and speaks openly about her story to help others, particularly female physicians. Weisman wholeheartedly believes to be a healer you must first fill your own cup. She lives and practices in rural southwestern Indiana and loves her roles as a farmer's wife, athlete, and mother of three.

The Craftsman

RICHARD. D. FELDMAN, MD

One of my most valuable lessons in professionalism was from a house painter many years ago. His name was Lube Rusomarov and he was the closest thing to an old-world craftsman that I have known. This middle-aged man from the former Yugoslavia spoke in broken English. He was highly recommended to me by a couple of friends who had used him. Like a couple other contractors that we had used during our historic-house restoration, he came to see me professionally a few times for specific acute medical issues.

If it was painting, plastering, or working with wood, he was very accomplished. He was a perfectionist and always insisted on quality work from himself and those who worked for him. Lube (pronounced Loo-bay) had an unusual passion for the beautiful old houses he frequently worked on, the materials he worked with, and the people for whom he worked. He took great pride in his trade and had a deep appreciation for true craftsmanship that is increasingly more difficult to find these days.

Amid restoring our historic old house, Lube showed me a door. As he hugged it, he said, "Doctor Richard, you can't buy a door like this anymore." He took me outside to admire the intricate raised timber work fitted together with wood pegs. "Doctor Richard, you can't find craftsmanship like this today," he said. Lube was right. It is hard to find the old-time craftsmanship and the fine materials in modern construction that were once commonly used.

There was an interior door that had a big imperfection. I decided to fix the defect myself and one day I proudly presented my "restoration" to Lube to evaluate. In horror, he said, "Doctor Richard, who did this?" After I admitted that I had done the work he responded, "Doctor Richard, from now on let me do it!" I did. I left it to the craftsman from that moment on.

Toward the end of the restoration, the house suffered a huge fire. The next day, I found Lube in the house crying. He was crying for me but also for the house that he loved so much and invested so much of himself in. For months, Lube would not accept any money for his work until he was assured that Doctor Richard was okay.

Lube and I would talk from time to time about things other than the house restoration. I recall he once spoke about his memories as a young grade-school boy in Yugoslavia. The Nazis were occupying the country and he saw his Jew-

Lube Rusomarov

ish classmates disappear one day, never to be seen again. The children understood what that meant and knew not to ask questions. I could see the sadness and anguish in his face as he related what happened many years before.

I also remember the time that I was caring for a Native American patient at the hospital. He was a Sioux from South Dakota who found himself in Indianapolis, alone, feeling isolated in an unfamiliar environment and without a job. I inquired what past employment he may have engaged in, and he responded that he had experience as a house painter. The next day I called Lube and asked him if he would take him on. Lube said that he had a full crew and did not need any additional help. He paused and then told me that if this man showed up at 8:00 a.m. the next morning at the jobsite, he would put him to work. Lube was, indeed, a sensitive and compassionate person.

When Lube died many years ago, he left me with more than paint, plaster, and wood. He left me with a sense of professionalism that should exist in any occupation.

Concern has risen within the medical profession about maintaining our long tradition of professionalism in this era of escalating pressures and regulations and the corporate-like business ethic dominating the healthcare industry. There is continual apprehension regarding medicine becoming increasingly depersonalized.

Our reimbursement system is not structured to value doctors taking the necessary time with patients to develop therapeutic relationships and to know them as individuals because physicians are increasingly pressured to see more patients. Patients easily become widgets, and pride within the profession erodes in the process.

Professionalism in medicine is far from dead, but we have tough times before us. As we now create the future healthcare system for all Americans, we must preserve "craftsmanship" in the medical profession and, in doing so, the time-honored doctor–patient relationship. It should be a system invested in personalized, compassionate, and humanistic medical care that only true professionals can deliver.

When I was in medical school, I spent some time with my father, who was a family physician in South Bend, Indiana. One day we saw a patient who could not afford to pay for my father's services. He already owed a sizable amount, but my father continued to see him and his family for their medical needs. His receptionist later told me that my father arranged for this patient to pay $5 a month on his account. Turning her head from side to side, she said that it cost the office more than $5 to collect this small payment every month.

That evening, I asked my father why he created an arrangement that made no business sense. He replied that it was not about the money. What was more important was maintaining the patient's sense of self-worth and dignity. My father, like Lube, loved and took great pride in his profession, and he cared about the people he served. A doctor and a house painter had much in common.

Lube Rusomarov's wife, Angelina, and his family gave the author permission to use Lube's name.

Alberto

LYDIA R. DUVALL, DO

"They also will answer, 'Lord, when did we see you hungry or thirsty or a stranger or needing clothes or sick or in prison, and did not help you?' He will reply, 'Truly I tell you, whatever you did not do for one of the least of these, you did not do for me.'"
MATTHEW 25:44–45

While shutting down our makeshift clinic for the day, we received a phone call concerning a man who had fallen and was no longer able to walk. The team decided to travel twenty more minutes into a more remote and barely accessible area to meet with the man. Mark, an American internist, and the translator were led into the home, which was no larger than most American closets. I stood in the opening, watching the examination, and within minutes it was over. The man, Alberto, had visibly suffered a stroke, half of his body paralyzed as a result. When asked how long since the man fell, the family's response was eight years ago. Alberto had not moved from that bed for almost three thousand days.

When Mark emerged from the shack, he relayed the prognosis to Alberto's sizable family. Not a single family member understood the significance of a stroke. Due to the obvious lack of an accessible healthcare system in rural Nicaragua, our only option was to leave the last bottle of aspirin as a preventative measure for future stokes. My heart sank. Tears began to fill my eyes. He was now alone in the one room-shack, lying on a tarp that was stretched to give tension between a wooden bed frame. He cried out, trying to form words, but his vocabulary was limited to incomprehensible groans. I entered the shack and sat by his side, resting on the hard-wooden panel; I stroked his head and held his hand as he looked into my eyes. Neither of us spoke, but we understood that the only thing I could offer him was love and attention.

Approximately fifteen minutes later, I was called by the other team members; it was time to go. As I made it to the doorway, Alberto began to cry out and his wife rushed into the room. When I turned around, I saw that Alberto had tried to get out his bed, half hunched over and one leg outside of the wooden panel. I asked his wife what was happening, what was wrong? She said, "He wants to go with you."

My story of Alberto is one of many that have kept me on the path of medicine. It granted me the opportunity to see another side of medicine. International service work and serving the poorest of the poor revealed many stark realities within the healthcare field, not only abroad but also in my own backyard. Although many do not consider this the alluring or glamourous side of medicine, for me it has been highly rewarding.

One of my leading takeaways from my experience with Alberto is that the common phrase of "help yourself before you can help others" is not true. Instead, it has been through service and dedication to others that I have found myself. As a result, I developed a better understanding of my place in the world and my responsibilities to others. Consequently, my medical journey, although not without challenge, has cultivated my strength of conviction.

Additionally, through this gained perspective, I have grown to believe that to those who are given much, such as education and other opportunities, much is expected. This is where I truly feel called to give back, specifically to the underprivileged. Therefore, my service to others has only validated my greatest aspiration of being a physician. I have learned that sympathetic care is a staple of human dignity and allows us to care for the well-being of others.

The conclusion from my story of Alberto and my medical experience is that the healthcare field is universal; in either a multimillion-dollar research hospital or a shack in a rural third-world country, the face-to-face interaction between patient and medical provider forms the basis of the healing process. I look forward to carrying these lifelong lessons into my medical career.

Lydia R. Duvall was raised in Kentucky. She attended Thomas More University for her undergraduate studies and later completed a master's degree at the University of Kentucky. Duvall perused a career in cancer research, and most recently was an adjunct professor at the University of Cincinnati. At the time of writing this essay, she was a medical student at Marian University College of Osteopathic Medicine in Indianapolis. She plans to pursue a career in pediatric and global medicine, and to be an advocate for the poor and underserved populations. She dedicates all her successes to the intercession of Mary, Mother of God.

A School of Love

KATHARINE A. CALLAGHAN, MD

Emergency Medical Services was wheeling in a new patient. They moved this gentleman, Mr. Irwin, into the bay, transferring him off their gurney and onto ours. They were anything but gentle with him in the process. He groaned and appeared in some distress, unable to explain what hurt but clearly in pain. Assessing him from head to toe, the first thing that grabbed my attention was the blood oozing out of this man's scalp. The blood saturated the dressing placed haphazardly atop his wound and stained the collar of his ragged white T-shirt. As he attempted to situate himself in his new bed, the edge of his khaki pants lifted over his right ankle and there emerged the second thing that caught my eye: a black, plastic tracking bracelet.

Immediately, I began making assumptions. I thought to myself, "He's a criminal. He can't be trusted." Suddenly, his groans of pain meant less to me than they had moments before. The internal dialogue continued: "You're in pain, huh? I bet you are." I began to disbelieve his distress, building a wall between the two of us, wondering less about who he was and how to care for him and more about what he had done to earn himself twenty-four-hour monitoring.

Amidst this inner swirl of thoughts, I asked a few basic questions and was informed that EMS was called because he had a ground-level fall during a fainting episode. His still-oozing scalp laceration was impressive, a U-shaped wound that would require significant repair. I finished my exam and left the room to consider the best way to address his injury. I was quickly offered the option of stapling it, given the extent of the injury and its proximity to Mr. Irwin's hairline. However, things continued to move slowly in the emergency room that morning and honing my suturing skills was one of my goals for the rotation. So, I requested that instead of stapling the wound I be allowed to give most of the rest of my morning to sewing it up. The emergency department attending agreed to my proposition.

When I returned to the trauma bay that had become this patient's room, his pain had settled out some. He remained uncomfortable, but he was now speaking in full sentences and able to better describe his discomfort and his experience of the day. Thankfully, amid his articulating his fears surrounding his fainting episode, something in me softened. He became more than a ground-level fall, more than a scalp laceration. He noted significant pain with my initial efforts to locally anesthetize his wound, but I quickly discovered that if I could engage him in conversation, the discomfort was less burdensome for him.

"What do you like to do for fun, Mr. Irwin?" I asked, hoping this question would simultaneously distract him and further soften my all too easily hardened heart.

"For fun?" he repeated back to me, a little shocked that I had asked the question. "Well, I like to watch football," he ultimately replied.

"College or pro?" I questioned.

"College."

"What schools do you most enjoy watching?" I asked, knowing this shared interest of ours was building a bridge between us where I initially had erected a wall.

"Notre Dame and Boston College," he replied.

"Not very often that I hear someone say they like watching both of those teams, sir. What's your draw to them? Have you lived in South Bend all your life?" To that he stated that he had not. He was a Notre Dame fan long before he moved to South Bend.

"Neat," I replied. "So, what's the draw to Boston College?"

"Well," he said, "that's where I got my Masters of Divinity."

The needle driver nearly fell out of my hand. Divinity school? Really? This guy with a tracking bracelet had once been a divinity student? I was stunned and now eager to know more of his story. A theology major myself as an undergraduate, the conversation took off from there.

He shared with me that his favorite courses as a divinity student were pastoral care and spiritual direction, the courses I imagined would have been my favorites as well had I pursued graduate work in theology. He went on to tell me that he was an ordained Eastern Orthodox priest. "I bet you don't believe that coming from a guy like me. Yeah, before I got myself into my current predicament with tax fraud and house arrest, I was a practicing priest," he said.

He was right. I could not hardly believe it. But as I asked him more and more questions about Eastern Orthodoxy, about Advent (the season we found ourselves in) in that Christian tradition, and about his theological studies, I knew the story was too elaborate and had too much depth to be anything but true.

As I continued to listen to him, all the while placing each of the twenty-six interrupted stitches it would require sewing up his scalp, I could not help but marvel at the gift I had been given in getting to spend time with Mr. Irwin that day. Here was a gentleman I had so much in common with. We shared a common faith in Christianity. We shared a favorite pastime (watching college football) and, as it turned out, even a favorite author (C. S. Lewis).

As I discovered each of these connections, I encountered the reality of our shared humanity and our shared belonging to one and the same community, a community he found himself cutoff from amidst his legal issues and subsequent house arrest. And yet, on this day in the emergency room as part of my job, I got to sit with him for nearly two hours. When so many communal ties were severed, my work in this profession gave me a path in to sit with this thoughtful man. I was given the opportunity to do something with my hands to help him heal, all the while knowing it was my own soul that was being most truly set right in the encounter.

As I sat with Mr. Irwin, I was struck by how precious a gift it is to be a part of this profession. This work intrinsically draws me out of myself. It brings me into contact with people I might bar myself from in other contexts. It gives me opportunities to build relationships with individuals who I would otherwise never could know. And it is presently equipping me with tools to meet those individuals' needs.

In short, the work of medicine is a School of Love, my patients some of its best professors, and Mr. Irwin among the greatest of them.

At the time Katharine A. Callaghan wrote this story, she was the chief resident at the Memorial Hospital Family Medicine Residency in South Bend, Indiana. She earned her undergraduate degree from the University of Notre Dame and her medical degree from Vanderbilt University. Upon residency graduation she will complete a one-year fellowship in Health Services Management at Memorial Hospital. She envisions staying in South Bend to practice.

The Lens of Humanity

Prior to medical school, I worked at a hospital for several years as a nurse technician on a medical/surgical floor that was part oncology. My basic responsibilities included answering call lights, taking vitals, drawing blood, providing patient care, and other tasks. There was an inherent and heavy sorrow that accompanied taking care of patients who were fighting with everything they had to beat an invasive cancer that had taken hold of them. This was especially true for those who required chemotherapy in the hospital; they were the ones who had to fight the hardest. This was my first real exposure to the medical world, and I saw it all: conquering disease, succumbing to illness, family drama, ethical dilemmas, intractable pain, confusion, anger, hope, and despair. I watched the spectrum of the human experience unfold before me with wide eyes.

Once, we had a patient come to our floor from out of state, looking for a second opinion from our oncologist. She was a thirty-five-year-old female who had been diagnosed with an aggressive breast cancer and was admitted to our floor to run tests and potentially begin treatment. She came in with her husband and their five-year-old son. I took care of her for her stay with us, which ended up being a few weeks. When I first met her, she was what we called a "walkie-talkie," someone who could generally take care of themselves and would not require a lot of assistance—in other words, the ideal patient. Her husband was very doting and did whatever he could to make sure she was comfortable.

Unfortunately, she declined rapidly. Due to my position, I was not privy to her exact diagnosis or prognosis, so all that I know is from what I witnessed firsthand. It happened gradually; she went from being fully independent to needing some assistance to get up to go to the bathroom. She became unsteady on her feet, and eventually we decided that it would be better if she used a bedside commode. She started sleeping more and talking less. She stopped asking to go to the bathroom and would just quickly jump out of bed, which would set off her bed alarm. Confusion began to develop, and she became slow to respond to verbal commands when I would try to help her get up. After working on a cancer floor for a period of time, one begins to recognize the signs of brain metastases easily.

When she had to go to the bathroom, she sometimes waited too long and would not make it in time. As the days went on and the cancer insidiously spread, she simply stopped trying to get out of bed and became incontinent. I would go in to clean her up and change her gown and bed. Her husband was always there to help and would apologize despite explaining to him that it was part of my job. Cleaning up incontinent patients truly was part of my day-to-day responsibilities; with a ten-to-twelve patient load on a med/surg floor, at least two-to-three patients were bound to be incontinent. It was never something I bemoaned or thought much about.

True to that situation, I brought in a couple of adult diapers one shift to use when I was called to get her cleaned up. I had a patient who was becoming more and more unaware of her bodily functions, and I was changing her bed several times a shift. So, I thought if I put a pair of diapers on her, I would only have to change the diaper and not the whole bed every time. To me, this was logical and made sense for the patient.

I brought them in and broached the idea to her husband that maybe it would be easier for us if we put these adult diapers on her. I will never forget the look on his face; it was a look of utter bewilderment, disbelief, and perhaps a realization of what was really happening. I immediately rescinded the idea.

I then realized that up until this point, I had been viewing the patient through my own lens. I saw her as a young cancer patient who was declining fast and needing more and more support to make her comfortable. I was giving her the best care that I could in my position. But I was not seeing her through her husband's lens—that this was his young wife, mother to his young son, who up until only a couple of weeks ago was walking, talking, and laughing. Now she was not eating, was mostly sleeping, and currently was unable to tell when she had to go to the bathroom. Shortly after this incident, she ended up entering home hospice to spend her last days in a more comfortable setting surrounded by family and friends.

I think it is easy for those of us working in the medical field to get caught up in our own medical world—all the jargon, the acronyms, the analytical reasoning. It can be difficult to proverbially step outside our white coats and view things from not only the patients' perspectives but also from those of their families. To take off the medical lens and put on the humanistic one is not always intuitive, especially after spending so many years studying to develop this medical approach. It is, however, essential to never lose sight of the humanity before us in medicine. We should not let all the science, physiology, lab results, and imaging blind us to the person right in front of us.

The human aspects of our profession are exactly why most of us choose medicine to begin with—to treat and heal people.

Doctor Wolverton is from Indianapolis and is a graduate of Indiana University and Marian University College of Osteopathic Medicine. She plans a career in family medicine with special interests including hospice, addiction management, and underserved populations. Doctor Wolverton enjoys watching movies, doing yoga, traveling, and enjoying time with her fiancé and their animals.

"Let the young know they will never find a more instructive book than the patient himself."

Giorgio Baglivi, Armenio-Italian physician and scientist

Trusting Your Judgment

PETER CAPELL, MD

I am positive I shared a problem facing many young physicians starting out in practice: How do you make a patient feel secure when you look like someone just getting out of high school?

Several times during my residency training I encountered disbelief that I was really a physician. Comments on first presenting at the bedside, either from the patient or the family, mostly expressed surprise I was not there to deliver the newspaper or bring in a food tray. Fortunately, when an older resident or the attending physician appeared, patient anxiety dissipated. Upon completing my training, I was chronologically older but had changed little physically. How can you gain a patient's trust, so key in the doctor-patient relationship, when the very idea you look old enough to offer healthcare solutions seems farfetched?

I met Dorothy Hammond during my first year in private practice. I had joined a multispecialty group of fourteen physicians. Naturally, I was frequently given the "opportunity" to take emergency calls on weekends. The veteran physicians knew how to stay away from any means of communication (this was the era of pagers and the telephone). Dorothy was in her sixties and on postmenopausal estrogens. She called the office on Saturday morning saying she had awakened with her left arm swollen. I asked her to come into the office so I could go over her exam. Her history and exam were as reported over the phone with her left arm swollen to the top of the shoulder. A puzzling presentation, but I was sure she must have a blood clot obstructing her subclavian vein, likely related to her estrogen. But, of course, there were other more concerning possibilities. I related my hunch and indicated she needed to be in the hospital for an evaluation and to start on anticoagulants. I mentioned that treatment was necessary now and could not wait until Monday when her attending physician returned. I was pleased with myself until I looked at her and her husband who both showed signs of overt panic. I recognized the appearance from the times I encountered a similar look during my residency training.

Dorothy asked me if I could possibly reach my colleague who served as her primary-care physician, and if he could come in to see her. I responded this was a very good idea. I called our answering service and asked to be put through to my partner. I reached one of his children who explained that he was out of town and not expected back until late Sunday night. I told her he was not in town but had left a message to call me when he returned.

Dorothy then mentioned she had been cared for by another of my partners when her primary-care physician was out of town. She asked if I could try to reach him. I realized she needed reassurance that I knew what I was doing, so to gain her trust I would go the "extra mile." Anticoagulation has potential side effects, so even more reason to show I had no problem seeking additional opinions. My call to physician number two also failed to get a response.

We were all in the same room, so she and her husband were able to see my disappointment in not getting a response. I could tell the wheels in Dorothy's mind were still turning. She then mentioned she had seen another of my partners on one occasion. Before she could ask me to contact him, I looked at her and said, "Dorothy, you will have to sink or swim with me." I promised I would let her primary-care physician know she was in the hospital and would make sure he saw her as soon as possible after his return. With that pledge, she agreed to hospitalization. Fortunately, all went well, and her problem was likely due to estrogens. Her primary-care physician did see her early Monday morning and then said he would stop in periodically, but he wanted me to continue her hospital care. Upon his retirement, she and her family members became my patients.

Trust must be earned. I believe there is a danger in thinking that all your experience and education should automatically lead to a patient's buy-in. Time spent to ensure that the patient knows you will do what it takes to assuage their anxiety is key to a meaningful relationship. Promising to go the extra mile, especially if you are mistaken for Doctor Doogie Howser, will always be a great asset in delivering quality healthcare—at least until your hair turns gray.

Peter Capell grew up in Rochester, New York, and now lives in Seattle, Washington. He attended Purdue University and the University of Rochester School of Medicine. He completed residency training in internal medicine with a subspecialty in endocrinology. Capell spent twenty-three years in private practice and fourteen years at the University of Washington School of Medicine. He retired as emeritus clinical professor of medicine.

Learning on the Job

PETER CAPELL, MD

The fog of time obscures many of the details involved in my early years of practice. What remains very clear are the lessons one patient taught me that influenced my career and patient interactions for the next few decades.

Before introducing you to my patient, Jane O'Neil, it is useful to briefly review my experiences from typical training as house staff. My residency training focused on several aspects of patient care. There was naturally an emphasis on learning differential diagnoses; how to construct, organize, and interpret diagnostic testing; treatment decisions; and evaluation of progress and communication skills to obtain both an accurate history and develop patient rapport. House-staff training provided uncomfortable but useful experiences in managing time, dealing with pressure, and experiencing disappointments.

There were, however, areas that residency training did not deal with. First and foremost was the issue of cost. I had no idea what a typical hospital stay added up to. As far as what medical tests, X-rays, or medications cost, as they say in New York, "Forgeddaboutit." I did not learn that 25 percent of prescriptions patients were asked to buy were never picked up from a pharmacy. I was unprepared for the impact copayments have on families. I did not even know there were diabetic patients unable to afford the healthy diets that were emphasized as being so important for their treatment. I assumed everything is always taken care of by insurance.

Jane was a fifty-eight-year-old single mother of one who came to see me after her prior physician had retired. I had recently finished my formal medical training and not only had openings in my schedule but also time to get to know her. She was employed doing low-level clerical work, and I knew she had healthcare coverage. But I had no knowledge of what was covered and if there were significant copays. Her primary medical issue was hypertension that required medication treatment. For the first few years of our professional relationship her blood pressure was under satisfactory control. She, however, presented one day with an urgent call of experiencing headaches. I found her blood pressure to be quite elevated. I have a vague recall of it being around 190/115. I reviewed in my mind the differential diagnosis of accelerated hypertension, began an intensive investigation, and started a more aggressive treatment plan.

On her return to clinic, her hypertension was better controlled, but her routine blood tests did not disclose a cause. I continued a diagnostic workup that now included more extensive and expensive blood, urine, and radiological testing. I never did find out why she experienced a sudden increase in her blood pressure, but I did learn some disturbing news.

My discovery started when on a follow-up visit she asked if I could cut back on her medication doses or find a less expensive way to treat her. I learned she had been reducing her dose of medications on her own. She eventually related that her insurance company declined to cover some of the expensive tests I had ordered. Further, I did not know her company insisted on prior approval before agreeing to paying for the tests. She was unable to afford to pay her bills or even the medications. I knew that the testing I ordered was exactly what my medical training advised. I also knew my patient was in no position to argue the case with her insurance. I had to be her advocate.

Reversal of the insurance company's payment denial took several appeals, a direct confrontation with their medical director, and quite a bit of time, but it worked. What surprised me was not the resentment I felt toward the company (although that was clearly present). I felt satisfaction that my intervention provided my patient with relief from a financial crisis that had caused her great anxiety. I am convinced the relief was as important for keeping her blood pressure under control as were some of the medications.

After the experience, I realized that part of a primary-care physician's job is to serve not only to diagnose and treat a medical problem, but also, if needed, to be a patient's advocate. The complexity of medical care has greatly increased since my early days in practice. Navigating the system often requires help not only in dealing with cost but also such mundane issues as getting appointments to see a specialist, or how to get an X-ray scheduled, or asking if the medication you ordered is being covered by their insurance carrier. There is a great service a primary-care physician can provide by reassuring a patient you can help to navigate the healthcare system if there is a problem with something you ordered or suggested.

I was fortunate to learn the need for patient advocacy at an early stage of my career. Jane was one of many patients who were penalized by the medical/insurance system for following physician orders. Without this patient experience, I may not have appreciated the value of this aspect of medical care. The value of advocacy to overall medical care, let alone patient satisfaction, is incalculable.

Bluebird

ALAN FERREIRA, PhD

This is a story of a young woman, Margaret, I came to see as touched by God, and not in a loving way. Let me tell you why.

Margaret carried the finest credentials one could ask for: bona fides of an emergency room doctor's worst nightmare. Jagged scars up and down both arms, scars on her thighs, and scars across her belly. She exhibited a tolerance for pain and painkillers that had become legendary in most of the local emergency rooms. Generations of interns and residents told tales of sewing up her multiple lacerations without anesthesia, sometimes purposely jabbing her just to see if her defiant attitude and cocky smile would falter. Never once, not even when they used a stapler.

But if a telltale smirk or rolling of the eyes ever crossed the face of a nurse, physician, or social worker treating her, there would be hell to pay. Miraculously she stayed out of jail despite the commotion she could create simply by showing up a bloody mess in the middle of a shift. Those who recognized her would go to great lengths to avoid having to treat her yet would crowd around outside the curtains to hear how those who were too new or too gullible to know better would cope with her. She was at the top of the assignment list for senior residents who subscribed to what the old psychiatrist said to each new class of interns: "Every new doc needs at least one Borderline."

While Margaret was outwardly a hard case, almost burly in appearance with close-cropped hair and a menacing demeanor, on the inside she was still very much a wounded and terrified child despite her thirty years. The first day I ever saw her she entered my office with her assigned resident doctor for a little cocounseling, a requirement of the residency for which I was the staff psychologist. When I saw some of the residents' toughest patients, I would not take over their mental-health treatment. I consulted with the young physicians, demonstrating how such treatment is done and learn to refer or manage such cases themselves. Usually this was a relatively painless and predictable process, but not so on that day.

I began with something like, "Your doctor has told me you've been having a difficult time lately. Can you tell me what that's been like for you?" There followed ten minutes of total silence. No eye contact, no change in the downcast stare nor movement at all beyond a furtive glance in the direction of her resident doctor. After an increasingly noisy monologue inside my head I finally ventured, "Something is keeping you from being able to speak?" It was a safe guess, but also a weak one, because even a "Yes" could easily be followed by another ten minutes of silence. This would not be my finest hour of therapy. In response, her eyes once again slid toward the doctor, then for the first time in my direction, then back to the doctor. At that moment I made a fateful decision that would deeply affect me for the next six years and beyond. Against my own stated policy, against at least half of my instincts, and against the sage advice of my mentor psychiatrist at the medical center, I asked her, "Do you want Doctor Haskell to step out of the room?" The answer was unequivocal: a couple of quick nods and a deep sigh.

For the next five years I saw Margaret once or a week or so, sometimes at the residency office and eventually in my private office, often fielding many enraged or tearful phone calls in between. I had missed a chance to model for my medical resident how to treat such a patient. But I had instead inherited an opportunity for a once-in-a-career relationship with a young woman who was more deeply wounded and yet as remarkable a human being as anyone I have ever known.

Throughout this time, I broke another rule by never asking her to pay for our sessions. In doing so, I guaranteed she would never go away if I was there to listen. But my goal was to keep her from giving up on our work together because I had decided early on that I would not give up on her. The theory behind such a rule against free services is that a person who pays nothing at all will not value the treatment enough to "do the work," and will only become dependent on the therapist. Guilty as charged.

The standard view of those who suffer from borderline personality disorder is that they often do not recognize the usual boundaries between persons. Sufferers often experience an ongoing pattern of extremely variable mood, behavior, and self-image. Relationships are fraught with fear, anger, and distrust. Anyone who attempts to engage in a helping relationship with such a person may experience all kinds of double messages, such as, "Only you can save me!" and "You will fail!" This is often accompanied by, "I hate you; I need you!" All this was true enough with Margaret, except it was not me she seemed to hate, but worse, herself. At times she appeared to dissociate in the middle of our sessions, losing her connection to where she was, and I began to suspect that she was struggling with long-repressed traumatic memories.

Treating Margaret was excruciating. Rule number one: always maintain appropriate professional boundaries, though some patients may not make it easy. One day they may make a noisy scene in your waiting room, show up in your home's driveway on Saturday afternoon, proudly tell you of the loaded revolver under their pillow, confide that they are falling in love with you, or leave a session so angry that they drive around the city beltway at seventy-five miles an hour, tempting fate. Each time Margaret did such a thing, I tried my best to remain calm and gently remind her of our special relationship; I was her caring and committed therapist. Nothing more, nothing less.

Recommended psychotherapies are designed to help patients challenge and replace their irrational and self-defeating thoughts, as well as teach acceptance, self-awareness, and emotional regulation. Patients are also encouraged to engaged in such expressive or creative activities as art or writing—anything to help them let what is inside come out in a nondestructive way. This of course requires trust and commitment between patient and provider, qualities that are especially hard to maintain for a person who may never have felt truly safe in any relationship. With Margaret, simply helping her feel protected and calm in my office was sometimes more than I could accomplish.

Although there were times that I desperately tried to invent some lame strategy for getting her out of my life, including very early retirement, I never seriously considered sending her away. Against my training and perhaps all good sense, I had entered into the most dreaded of contracts: I would Never Give Up on her as long as she would Never Give Up on herself. As any beginning counselor trainee will tell you, I may have let myself become more responsible for Margaret's life than she was herself. A dangerous boundary to cross.

One might consider it a spiritual boundary crossing if that is possible. In my defense, I can only ask: When a human soul is deposited on your doorstep screaming in agony and terror, what do you do, sneak out the back door? Through the years, I slowly came to see Margaret as touched by God, if there is a God who touches some for purposes beyond our understanding. As I listened to the searing details of her story, she seemed to me branded, like Job in the Bible, in a brutal test of faith. Satan claimed that Job was a man of faith only because he had everything a man could want: perfect health, a loving wife, many children, great wealth, and the respect of his community. God agreed to take all this away from Job to prove that he would not turn away from Him despite the advice of friends who urged him to "curse God and die." I could only hope that like Job, Margaret would be rewarded in the end for her perseverance.

She was so deeply injured yet so incredibly strong just pulling herself out of bed each morning that I marveled at how she kept her sanity. Not that she always did. More than once, she battled a murderous demon who visibly walked straight through the locked door of her apartment. Many times, she drew a knife across her flesh in a desperate attempt to feel something when she feared she had already died and needed some proof of life that only blood could provide. There were times when her demons seemed to have won control of her, finally turning a pot of scalding cooking oil over her own head, as though she could burn away the mental pain with the merely physical. This act led to months of hospitalization, numerous surgeries, and though I did visit her in the hospital, the end of our regular therapy sessions. Yet, through it all, I came to see a sweetness and innocence in her that was both lovable and heartbreaking. During her short life, Margaret never dared to form a friendship with another girl, never let it be known that she yearned for a boyfriend, never knew the touch of a lover. She seemed unable to escape the stagnant backwater of her past. Though she was never fired from a job, she left several, convinced that everyone hated her and would eventually betray her.

Through our years together, I heard Margaret's story and began to see evidence of the creative and ambitious mind she had hidden from the world. What emerged was sheets of poignant and heart-rending poetry that described her dreams and her visions of beauty and love. For a time, I dared to hope that she was finally finding her way out of the past and into a more whole and healthy future. But then the day came when Margaret hit a wall for reasons I will never know. Did something happen in her family? Did I miss some vital clue that she had suddenly lost her grip on reality? Did life drop one more burden on her that was too much to bear? When Margaret died, by a heart attack according to the physicians, she was so far past my reach that I could only wish her a better existence beyond the grave than the one she knew here.

Looking back, I hardly know what to make of the stories that slowly emerged during our time together. She spoke of torture, sexual violence, and threats of murder. She told me that as a five-year-old she was dangled over the railing of a bridge by her father, who promised to drop her into the river if she failed to behave. She was brutally molested by her father's drinking buddies with his approval. Her own brothers were allowed to treat her as a punching bag, while she was expected to cook and clean from an early age. All this with the apparent consent or willful ignorance of her mother. How could such things happen in an outwardly normal family? In my office there were hours of sobbing, then stoic silence, and then screams of rage. She brought me pages and pages of stark testimony to a childhood of unspeakable horror. Most of the time all I could do was hold her hand while she cried. I never knew for certain what was factual, but of course it did not matter, because the effects of her torment were evident in Margaret's broken life, her avoidance of friendship or affection or trust in any other person, and her addiction to self-injury. Only my role as listener, insulated from anything like an ordinary relationship, allowed her to let me see her inside reality. All I could give her was my compassionate attention.

At the prefuneral visitation there was a closed casket, as Margaret's face was terribly disfigured with burn scars. I had met no one in her private world before, but as I glanced around the room her father was impossible to miss, an imposing man with a haggard look and pasty skin. I got some curious stares from the twenty or so people standing around. After a time, I was approached by a woman, Margaret's mother. "We are so thankful that you were there for our little bluebird," she said. I could only manage a smile and nod before leaving, my own faith shaken to the foundation. Now, whenever I think of Margaret, I am taken back to the Book of Job and I wonder about the story of a God who takes a bet with the Devil and touches that ancient Hebrew's life like He touched hers. But in Margaret's case without the happy ending.

Did I help Margaret in any way? As far as I can tell, only by letting her know that she was not alone and sharing her story with medical residents who might otherwise fail to see her as so much more than a one-word diagnosis. Especially with self-inflicted injury, it is vital that someone recognize a cry for help and listen for the story behind the physical wounds. Sometimes one must risk breaking the rules to make that happen.

There is one thing more: I now have a bluebird house near my home so that every spring I can watch the miracle of birth and remember the sad beauty of one special life.

Alan Ferreira and his wife Elizabeth live in Indianapolis, where he worked as a psychologist in public and private hospitals, in private practice, and for seventeen years in a family-medicine residency. After retirement, he discovered his love of writing and performing songs, doing carpentry, and found a new love, pickleball. Ferreira has published two novels, The Year of Not Knowing *and* The Weatherman's Son. *He is currently working on a book of short stories and essays.*

Mr. Wolfe

RICHARD D. FELDMAN, MD

I have always addressed my patients by their first names. Some in the medical profession consider using first names disrespectful to patients. But for me, it just feels comfortable and right. After all, as a family physician I get to know my patients extremely well over many years. Not unusually a warm personal rapport grows between a doctor and a patient. And that is how it has been with me.

But there was one patient who I always addressed by his last name. That was Mr. Wolfe. There was something about him that made me a little uncomfortable. Was it the way he looked at me? Were there subtleties in what he said or the way he expressed himself to me? A cautiousness? A distrust? I really could never put my finger on it. He was an imposing figure, tall and slim with carved facial features. Although a bit formal and stiff, he was never unfriendly, always cordial, and not unpleasant. But I just knew somehow that it would be more appropriate and certainly more comfortable calling him by his last name.

I took care of him and his wife Anne for years. One day he came in the office with obvious changes in his right leg consistent with arterial vascular disease. His pulses were absent in his foot and the skin color was a violaceous-blue. He was having increasing difficulty walking without developing calf pain, and it was obvious that he had a blockage in the arteries to this leg. I recommended diagnostic imaging and proceeding with an urgent consultation with a vascular surgeon for an arterial-bypass procedure.

In the hospital he did well postop for a day or two, but then the lower leg became cyanotic and cold. The surgery failed, and all attempts to save the leg failed as well. For several days before his amputation, I came in to see him on rounds and expressed how sorry I was about the poor result. Although I did not express it to him or to myself at the time, I think there was an element of personal responsibility for recommending the surgery. He finally looked at me sternly and said, "You know doc, it doesn't do me any good to have you come in here every day and feel sorry for me."

I just nodded and acknowledged his wishes. He was a strong person and accepted the unfortunate situation; it was time for me to do the same. In that moment, I understood that sometimes patients do not want sympathy from their physicians but only their best advice and support. That certainly was the case with Mr. Wolfe. I think it was the first time (and fortunately one of the few times) that I experienced the emotions of having recommended something to a patient that ended in a bad result even though I knew it was the best course of treatment. Every doctor comes to know that some patients will unfortunately experience poor outcomes even if everything was done correctly. It comes with the practice of medicine.

I continued caring for Mr. Wolfe for a long time and worked successfully through other health issues that he developed. One day in the office he looked at me squarely in the eye and said, "You really do care about your patients, don't you." It was not really a question but a judgement he had carefully considered. And this time when he looked at me, there was a certain warmth to his face with the slightest of smiles.

I finally felt like I had gained his respect and responded, "Of course I do." Nothing more was said. I continued addressing him by his last name.

Fred Wolfe eventually came in my office with an unusual presentation of lung cancer with some odd facial lesions and chest pain, mostly when he stretched his arms straight out in front of him. He died a short time later. A few months later, I saw his wife, Anne, in my office. Toward the end of the visit she said, "I want you to know that Fred really liked you and he thought you were an excellent doctor." That was one of the greatest compliments I have ever received as a physician.

Anne asked me, "Did you know that Fred was an artist?"

"No, I had no idea," I responded.

"I brought something to show you." From a bag she pulled out one of the most beautiful, delicate, and sensitive landscape paintings I had ever seen!

"Fred painted this?" I asked.

"Yes, he was a wonderfully talented painter, wasn't he? He painted for many years. He just loved to paint. I just wanted you to see this." She went on to say that he was generous person and much loved by his family and friends. She missed him very much.

I had to earn Mr. Wolfe's respect and trust. He was obviously a good man and a warm, sensitive individual. Patients are not always what they seem.

Remembering You

AIMEE KABALA, MD

Must others die so we can start to live? We bury our heads into our books. We think it is an inconvenience to stop for a moment and entertain others. We learned early on as medical students that success in the study of medicine can only be achieved with the outmost concentration. So, when we were assigned to visit Mrs. Cooper as part of our medical humanity assignment, we were profoundly annoyed at the prospect of spending time away from our studies. We reluctantly contacted Mrs. Cooper and scheduled a weekly meeting at her home for the entire semester. She was an elderly female in her late seventies with a medical history of recurrent breast cancer, among other diagnoses.

She lived alone and was eager to meet us. She insisted we bring our stethoscopes to practice listening to heart and lungs on her even though we were merely in our first year of medical school. We knew absolutely nothing about auscultating the human heart. For us, it was a fine prospect to attempt our first physical examination.

Our first meeting with Mrs. Cooper was on a sunny Sunday ablaze with heat. As we were parking our car, she came to meet us. Much to our astonishment, she had on a black winter coat with a pink hat embroidered with white lilies. It must have been about eighty degrees inside her house. We dropped our bags full of books on the floor next the door and sat on the couch as she motioned with her long slender fingers. We conversed for an hour, and then she broke the conversation by asking if we would like to listen to her heart. We hurried to unfold our stethoscopes. She removed a heavy coat to reveal a short-sleeved gray t-shirt. Her alabaster skin hung loose to drape her 206 bones. In horror we stared, our hands full of life afraid to touch her. Would our touch cause our first fragile patient's bones to break? She reminded us of death, but we dare not mention it. When we finally summoned the courage to place our stethoscopes on her chest, we found life again in the drumbeats of her heart.

After a few visits Mrs. Cooper proposed that we bring our notes and study at her place. But as much as we wanted to study, we found ourselves tending to her garden or enjoying the sunshine in her wild backyard or listening to her stories, a collection from a life well-lived. In those moments the light on her face stood in contradiction to the darkness covering the rest of her body. She often asked us about her health issues: back pain, loss of appetite, recurrent cancer, and regrets. We did not know the answers to many of her questions, but it pleased her when we dug deeper in medical literature to find the answers.

At the end of our visits, she handed us fresh tomatoes from her garden. She said, "Do something with them. Anything!" We joked once that we should probably make ketchup or salsa from them. But like the pile of tomatoes that grew higher in our refrigerators, anatomy and biochemistry piled on. We promised we would visit again, but we did not.

There was always something that was more important, like a microbiology exam, a neurology exam, or studying for boards. Although we had expected Mrs. Cooper's imminent death, we were shocked to learn that she had died. But more than the shock, it was the shame of unfulfilled promises that hung heavy on us. Did we disappoint her? And amid tackling the overwhelming medical school workload, were we neglecting our families and friends? Ourselves?

In a panic we called our friends and our families. We reconnected. We made plans to pursue our hobbies. We both rekindled our love of dancing. As always, you listened calmly to my complaints about my clerkships, my last break up, or my perceived bad luck in love. But somewhere between my disapproval of your exaggerated Cuban dance hip motions and your obsession with overly sentimental poetry, time passed, we forgot and fell back on common familiarity—studying hard and making empty promises.

When I heard of your passing, my dearest medical school friend, time stopped for a while, then resumed with the pounding echoes of my heart, a reminder of yours silenced forever. In panic, I again called my friends and my family to check on them. I must have called a hundred times, and they began to wonder why.

I would like to tell them that the picture of death I had in mind has disappeared, metamorphosed into an ambiguous image I scarcely recognize, but I know they will not understand. At your remembrance, someone told me that it does get better. That in time one forgets. Oh! The shame and guilt I felt at the thought of faded memories and leaving you behind, just as we left Mrs. Cooper behind, our first patient and the one who brought us closer.

So, on these pages, I lay your memories. In eternal ink I lay that beautiful day in August. How next to Monument Circle in downtown Indianapolis, a crowd of aspiring physicians converged into the golden double doors of Hilbert Circle Theatre for our first-year medical students' "White Coat Ceremony" and disappeared on top of the grand stairways. You were sitting next to me, a perfect stranger, became my brother, an ally in this marathon that is medicine. Our faces were hopeful and bright like born-again believers; we had found our religion.

With the recital of the Hippocratic Oath, we sealed our fates for eternity.

Aimee Kabala was born and raised in the Democratic Republic of the Congo. After high school her family immigrated to the United States. She attended South Dakota State University for undergraduate studies, majoring in chemistry. Kabala worked as a chemist before attending the Indiana University School of Medicine. Dancing and reading are her main hobbies.

An April Fool's Joke

LEENA ALJOBEH, MD

"Any allergies to any medications?" I ask, my eyes making their way down the acronyms I had written in rushed, capital letters on the white loose-leaf sheet on my clipboard—there to remind me of topics to cover during the visit. I look to the middle-aged woman seated across from me, a slight smile perpetually upturning the corners of my mouth.

"Nope," she says, without even a hint of impatience, although I am sure she probably has more important things to do than be questioned by a medical student, especially since she had only come in to the office for a medication refill.

I move to my next acronym and continue with inquiries about her diet, exercise, alcohol intake, and smoking. So far our conversations have been comfortable and moving quite swiftly. It is only with my mention of smoking that we derail a bit.

"Do you currently smoke?"

"No." She pauses. "I quit seven years ago."

"That's great!" I say, my smile edging up a bit higher. I am about to glance at my notes when she continues.

"Quitting was going to be an April Fool's joke, you know." She looks down, then back up. "They asked me at that one clinic to pick a day to drop the smoking, and I picked the first day that popped into my head." Here, she shakes her head. "April 1st was only a week away, and if I quit, great, but honestly, I wasn't really planning on it." She pauses. "So, I'd just say that it was just a joke." She looks earnest somehow, in such a way that I cannot tell if she is retelling this part of her story for the tenth time or if she is just now sharing it for the first time here with me. "My mother puffed out her last breath on a ventilator later the next day after five years of lung cancer. That's when I quit."

We are both silent for a bit, as if letting her words gently swirl and fall around us. Somehow, we both manage to maneuver our way through the rest of my questions, the memory of her words like colorful leaves that try to capture our attention if we fall silent, again.

Before I leave, I clasp her right hand warmly, my slight smile etched once again on my face, erased before only momentarily. "Thank you for speaking with me," I tell her.

"Of course," she replies. "Good luck."

Though I know she was wishing me luck with my studies and my career path, in retrospect, I feel as if she had meant so much more with that statement.

Sitting in lecture the next day, my laptop open in front of me, my eyes following the professor's gestures without concentrating on his words, I still hear my patient's story twirling in my head. I glance at my laptop screen. Opening a new document, I quickly transcribe the conversation I had just had the day before, not wanting to forget the words that seemed to have imprinted themselves in my mind. The irony was threefold: Knowing while she was setting her day to quit smoking that her plans were in jest, smoking years off her life while her mother spent her last years wilting from lung cancer, and, finally, achieving her goal to quit smoking only after, or perhaps because, her mother exhaled her last breath on a ventilator. The patient's story resonated with me and I found myself realizing that the irony extended to myself, as well.

For years I have set life goals and have rushed through weeks and months in their pursuit. However, my personal goals have always been the ones with the extended due dates. Each year, I have a certain set of "New Year's Resolutions," goals that include healthy habits that I have resolved to finally, *finally* have time to achieve. Unfortunately, for the past three years of medical school, my resolutions have been the exact same since at the end of each December, I think, wryly with a surprised overtone, "Oh. Well, there's always next year."

I have been playing an April Fool's joke on myself.

The saying goes that it only takes sixty-six days to form a new habit. With November looming in sight, giving me a bit over two months until the end of the year, I revisit the goals of healthy living that I had set and reset for myself for the past three years. Just like my patient, I had picked my personal goals without planning on following through with them; they were an ideal, a platitude that I had already rehearsed so that if I ever felt down about my day-to-day lifestyle, I could look to my resolutions and think, "Well, I've been *meaning* to do that. I just don't have the time," or perhaps, "It's on my list of things to do. I'll start tomorrow." Then, I could conveniently forget until the next time I needed a placation that I was trying to change.

Sitting in my classroom seat, her words come back to me as if they are the key I needed to open the gate of forgotten resolutions and shake off their dust of insincerity. That same afternoon I grabbed my running shoes and headed to the campus gym, a routine that would be continued well pass the requisite two months.

Leena Aljobeh was a medical student at the Indiana University School of Medicine when she authored this essay. She is from Valparaiso, Indiana, and attended Valparaiso University. She balances her passion for medicine and literature by combining the two as often as she can. With a special interest in poerty, Aljobeh has published and performed various poems regarding medicine and social justice and hopes to continue to do so in the future. She plans for a career in family medicine with special interest in underserved populations.

Empowerment

KATIE MCMASTER, MD

As a medical student on the internal-medicine service, I was assigned a patient admitted with chest pain. What an exciting case, with so much to learn! That was a heavy dose of sarcasm in case that was not coming across. He was a textbook "non-ST elevation myocardial infarction," in other words a relatively mild standard heart attack. Urgent, but not emergent.

At this point in my medical training, I understood that patients were not to be ignored when they say, "This feels like my heart attack last time." I thought to myself, "You sir, would know." He had a history of eight cardiac catherization's with stent placements but had not been able to maintain a change in lifestyle. He was the first to say he still ate junk food, did not exercise, and smoked on occasion. As part of his healthcare team, I dutifully informed him about the modifications that could lengthen his life. I guessed that at this point he knew more about it than I did. He had heard this speech more times than I had given it.

The cardiology team determined that he required not simply stenting, but a multivessel coronary artery bypass graft at this point. He knew this meant open-heart surgery. He agreed and we planned for his transfer to a hospital that performs this procedure. Due to a lack of beds, it would take days.

The day prior to transfer, after I had spent so much time arranging it all, I got a page from the nurse. When I returned the page, she said, "Mr. Brant is having second thoughts. He's asking to speak to a doctor." Second thoughts! I had talked to this patient at least twice a day for almost a week. Why now? I went to see him in the afternoon when I had spare time and sat down with him.

He greeted me as he always did, "Hey, Doc." We talked for several minutes. Eventually, his concerns started coming out. He felt unsettled that he was not going to meet his new team of physicians until he was transferred. He told me, "I don't even know what they look like. I hope they have gray hair. I need experience on my team." I was sure, based on the amount of training they had, they were probably gray, but we could find out. I had to try something. I was told by my team to solve this problem. I promptly began to Google images of his team at the other hospital. He laughed. I could see some of tension fall away from his shoulders as he peered at the screen.

He leaned back in bed and revealed his hidden fears. He had two family members who had died in the cardiac intensive-care unit in that hospital: his uncle and young nephew. He was fearful. He tried to convince himself that it was not the same situation and was trying to rely on his faith. He was acutely aware that the procedure was necessary. But how was he supposed to know if the surgeons were good?

How could I get this man to trust someone who he had not met? And to be honest, I had not met them either. But that was my job; I needed to get the patient to agree to the plan. I told him that the doctors he had gotten to know here trusted the doctors at that institution. This was not uncommon for the healthcare team to transfer a patient for this operation. But he remained unconvinced.

I informed him that he had a choice. Our team could not do anything without his consent. He had a right to revoke his consent whenever he chose. If he felt better about another hospital for whatever reason, then we could try to transfer him there. The decision was up to him.

He looked at me with appreciation. He said, "You know, Doc, no one has said that to me. I've been here for many days, and no one has said that. Thank you." Somehow that conversation was enough that he was once again okay with the transfer to the other hospital for the operation.

In the days prior to his transfer, he assured me he was planning on changing his life around. He was finally going to change his diet, exercise, and stop smoking. I hope so.

Sometimes patients just need to feel empowered and to have control of their lives.

Katie McMaster is a native Hoosier from Zionsville, Indiana, and attended Xavier University in Cincinnati, Ohio, for her undergraduate studies. She was a medical student at the Indiana University School of Medicine when she wrote this essay. After her graduation in 2019, McMaster entered the IU General Surgery Residency.

"Health care will always be about personal relationships and be an emotional arena to work in. As Hippocrates himself said over two millennia ago, 'It is more important to know what sort of person has a disease than to know what sort of disease a person has.' It was true back then, and it's still true. Every doctor has stories to tell about incredible patients they've met and been inspired by."

Suneel Dhand, MD, internist and author, Salem, Massachusetts

Sunshine

BRIAN S. BACAK, MD

I first met Maria as her newly assigned primary-care physician. In her late fifties, she came to me with the business card of her mental health center psychiatrist, Doctor Merchant, who had taken care of her for years and who would subsequently become my "phone a friend" as we navigated Maria's conditions together. Maria was a kind, somewhat disorganized, schizophrenic with a somatoform disorder and numerous chronic health conditions. I took care of her for more than ten years.

Maria's best friend, who was always at her office visits with me, was Sunshine, a stuffed plush rabbit with floppy ears. She claimed to know that Sunshine was "just a stuffed animal and not real," but she spoke to him and counted on him during all the scary times in her life. Just like Maria, Sunshine suffered from a three-pack-a-day cigarette habit; although I think his issue was more one of "secondhand" smoke.

During hospital admissions our residents would work with Maria so that Sunshine could get his "own" procedures, which pretty much consisted of a wash and dry that left him much cleaner, and I would guess, a little happier, than when they came in. He sat by quietly during important discussions, sat in a chair during the exams, and hid in her large purse-like bag she carried around when the going got particularly scary.

I spent lots of time talking with Maria during her office visits. Sunshine was always brave in offering up himself to receive the first taps of the reflex hammer and proving to Maria that the physical exam would not be that bad. He sat by when Maria brought in her college photo album to show me containing a picture of herself as an undergraduate that she, at this point, could not quite connect to. Her graduation from college, I am pretty sure, was the thing she was most proud of.

Many years later, a collection of assaults, falls, mental-health disorders, and poverty had taken their toll and pulled her from the anchors she had as a young adult. Sunshine, the ever-willing partner, marched on with her as we battled her woes together (including a bad case of bedbugs). Over the years I became sensitive to whether her abdominal pain was a reason to chat or an indication for admission, whether her shortness of breath was a reason to chat or COPD necessitating treatment, and whether her confusion was a reason to chat or an indication for medication adjustment.

During one office visit, Maria, who was almost in tears, showed the medical student and me the aftermath of some horrible accident. Sunshine was in the bag, almost torn in two. His head lopped aside, which kept him from joining in our usual exam routine. I had our medical assistant grab some 3-0 monofilament suture, a needle driver, and a pair of scissors. Once donning sterile gloves, the student and I sutured Sunshine together. Resuscitated from the brink of death, Sunshine appeared to beam as bright as the smile on Maria's face.

Years later, the student with me that day, who subsequently became a resident in our family medicine residency program and later a colleague, told me that being part of Sunshine's resuscitation cemented him on our residency as the place he wanted to train. He said it was obvious we cared and lived how we preached. I am still not sure whether or not he counted Sunshine as a suturing event in his procedure log.

Without a doubt, I feel like this experience encapsulates the joys of teaching and humanistic patient care that is family medicine.

Brian Bacak grew up in the suburbs of Dallas, Texas. He attended Trinity University in San Antonio and then the University of Texas Health Science Center at San Antonio for his medical degree. He completed his residency in family medicine at Fort Benning, Georgia, and worked as a family physician in the U.S. Army for six years, stationed both oversees and in the United States. For the last several years he has been involved in medical education at the University of Colorado Anschutz Medical School, working as a residency program director, a leader in clinical operations, and seeing patients at the University Health System.

But What Did She Say?

BRIAN S. BACAK, MD

At the time that I saw them, the Navarros were in their early to mid-seventies. He was my patient, and she was his witness. Mr. Navarro was retired, afflicted with a stooped shuffling gait, and was experiencing the early challenges of dementia. The dementia was labeled Alzheimer's, and in hindsight it was possibly Parkinson's. His ongoing challenges were twofold. First, he had coronary artery disease and had undergone stent placement. His angina (chest pain) became intermittently ever-present. His second challenge was his expensive interactions with the healthcare system.

Mr. Navarro was anxious about many things, and his anxiety manifested in a bunch of ways, most notably as complaints of chest pain. To the novice emergency department, he had a "fast pass" into the depths of technology—EKG's, echocardiograms, laboratory testing, repeated nuclear medicine treadmills, and myocardial infarction "rule out protocols." These evaluations occurred repeatedly despite the many cardiology notes in his chart, despite the negative testing, and despite his wife's accompanying, calm narrative that her husband "insisted on coming into the emergency department because of chest pain, but he's fine." Such visits were a regular occurrence.

Some days Mr. Navarro was not anxious. On those days, however, they would still show up at the emergency department. The confused front-desk clerk would try to figure out why they were there. "Is he having chest pain?" the clerk would ask. "Okay, no, then why is he here? No chest pain? No shortness of breath? No wheezing?"

A concerned Mrs. Navarro would tell them, "Well, he's just different. He's in trouble. I know it." On more than one occasion, begrudgingly done EKG's showed marked abnormalities with evidence of coronary insufficiency. These visits cumulated with a panicked and somewhat delayed entry back into the depths of technology and subsequent treatment for progressive coronary artery disease.

Invariably, I became their situational translator. Paged to the emergency department, I would call them. As the physician gave me the report about their planned disposition, I would listen for that crucial piece of information: "But what did she say?"

The ED physician would report: "He came in complaining of chest pain. We're going to admit him for observation." They would continue, "Oh, his wife, she says that he's fine and we're doing too much."

I would reply to the Emergency Medicine physician, "Well, trust her. Send him home. He's fine."

On other occasions, I would return the page and an exasperated emergency medicine physician would tell me, "I'm not even sure why he is here. He says he is fine. No chest pains. He's got a really anxious wife. She keeps telling me that her husband is very sick, and she's refusing to leave, even though his EKG is negative and he's not even complaining."

My response to the emergency physician was urgent and unwavering, "I know this couple." I would tell them, "By gosh, admit him now! Get cardiology involved! Stress test him!" Invariably, the testing would come back abnormal with subsequent treatment and stents. As their family physician, I felt like I understood them well. I knew they spoke for each other. I knew that her sense of his wellbeing after sixty years of marriage was an invaluable diagnostic tool that was too important to be ignored.

Years later, after this scenario had played out multiple times, this "always-together" couple separated out of necessity, not because of his heart disease. Rather, it was a result of his dementia. Specifically, it was his hallucinations, his ongoing and chronic abuse toward his wife, and his threatening behavior with a gun he kept at home. This was not part of the narrative that I knew or part of their story that I had weaved together in my mind. I never picked up on her fear and her struggles with his behavior; I did not create the safe space she deserved.

Sometimes listening is hard. As a family physician, I strive to be a complete and comprehensive ally for my patients to give them the care that they need and to give families what they need and deserve. I try always to listen. As I look back on this patient, it is not just the question I asked the emergency department that was so important. It was the question itself that still haunts me: "But what did she say?"

Controlled Chaos

BRIAN S. BACAK, MD

Jose and Camila were always together. A matching set if you will. They were linked by their chronic illnesses, doubly afflicted with diabetes, obesity, hypertension, and the stress of modern life. Both were taking almost the same medications. Both were invested in the same exercise, diet, and treatment recommendations to the same degree (or not invested as the case may be). Although their illnesses linked them, their illness did not define them. Rather, they were defined by their love of life, their love of family, and their love for their ten-year-old son.

Juan had a developmental disability and was a bundle of energy, always in motion. Jose, Camila, and Juan were always together at their visits, and Jose and Camila provided what could best be described as a "zone defensive bubble" around their child. His well-child visits were frighteningly disordered, always in motion, and infectiously fun (at least from a family doctor's perspective). Jose's and Camila's diabetes visits were equally as lively and similarly tinged by a palette of color and motion. Typically, our medical assistants and I would double up in the room, the medical assistant watching Juan and keeping him safe (along with our medical supplies, the computer, and the supposedly endless roll of exam-table paper), while I attended to the more "traditional" elements of the visit. Chief complaints were shouted and scrambled. Chests were auscultated and ears were peered into, and pronouncements about diabetes control and blood sugars were made. Growth charts were checked, and shots dispensed. Always room to improve. Never enough time.

Early on in medicine we learn how to use a SOAP format to organize a visit and the documentation starting out with subjective complaints, moving to objective findings, developing an assessment, and then creating a plan for care. Their SOAP became waves of OASP and SPOA and every other combination of letters. Documenting was never in real time and always cresting toward their patient handout and the visit finale, until we would meet again.

I always presumed that such visits would have been terrifying to a medical student. A true test of faith for students who commonly value order, progress, documentation, and fitting the world into a neatly treated box. The visits instead were controlled chaos, punctuated by stories about family in Ecuador, careers in Denver, relatives in Florida, and volunteer hours spent making their community better. The challenges of raising a son, working, and keeping track of their own issues and medical odyssey were other frequent elements of discussion. For our office staff, such merged/mashed together visits created an inordinate amount of angst about when the appointments started, when they would end, and how in the world the staff would document their role in the care of this family.

To me, however, the visits were secretly thrilling. Energy and passion captured and confined into a block of time and walled-in space. They came alive with Jose's and Camila's love for each other, their love for their son and their family, their stories about their homeland, and their plans to follow up in the future, telling me, "I'll make a follow up with you doc. I'll do better. You're the best. You listen to us, and we feel heard."

One day a medical student who was working with me and joined in on the fun said to me, "Wow, that was exhausting. But they were great. So interesting. So cool to see them all together. I don't think you'd have a visit like that in any other specialty." I do think she was right about that.

Memories

BRIAN S. BACAK, MD

Sophie stands out to me against a tableau of my memories of individual patients. Impressive in her resolve in overcoming adversity, I doubt she was an inch taller than five foot, two inches. My first conversation with her as a new patient concerned her tattoo. More specifically, the number stenciled on her forearm that she had carried with her for fifty-eight years.

An elderly lady, now in her late seventies, Sophie had been imprisoned in a Nazi concentration camp during World War II. She relocated after the war to the southern part of the United States and by the time I first met her she had been an established patient at our clinic for many years. As a family physician in the U.S. Army, I saw her once every couple of months in our office for several years. We discussed her hypertension, osteoporosis, and her knitting. We discussed a few details from the war as time went by, notably the death of her sister and other family members at the hands of the Nazis. Understandably, our conversations drifted around many of the specifics, but what came through time and time again was the utter fear she experienced during that time in her life and how it shaped her present-day reality. During the time I worked with her she was very active in her synagogue and took great pride in her heritage and relationship with God.

During the time I took care of her I learned about her thoughts on growing older, the things that made her laugh, and the things that made her angry. One event that made us both laugh was the unfortunate time she became trapped in her synagogue. Specifically, Sophie became trapped in the bathroom, set off the burglar alarm, and emerged from the bathroom after the conclusion of temple services and everyone had left the building. While she could appreciate the humor, the event also unmasked a deep fear. The local police department, responding to the alarm, wrenched her arms behind her and handcuffed her while awaiting the rabbi. The episode was profoundly terrifying for Sophie, as this represented a loss of freedom she had not experienced since the days of her imprisonment. We spoke often about this incident and about her overwhelming desire for freedom, and to never again to be put in captivity, imprisoned, unable to move, and forced against her will to do the bidding of others.

One day while teaching in the clinic, the residents on our inpatient service let me know that Sophie had been admitted to the Intensive Care Unit after suffering a massive stroke. Rounding on her in the hospital, it became clear to me that her prognosis was indeed grim. Unconscious, she had radiologic evidence of significant damage and had lost the ability to breath on her own. At this point we normally would have called a family conference to discuss the patient's prognosis and disposition, consider the family's wishes, and determine what they thought their loved one would have wanted.

However, Sophie had no surviving family, and she did not have clear advance directives. She also had not discussed her wishes with her rabbi. As the ethics consultation we requested evolved, however, it did become clear that she had expressed her wishes for care to someone, and that someone was me. It was as if she had been preparing me for what to say and what to do when she no longer had a voice.

I was able to speak for Sophie that morning. I spoke up against imprisonment, against being held in a suspended state of animation against her will, against being strapped down, and against the forced indignity of being without clothes and without control of her bodily functions. I had no doubts and no hesitation of expressing how she wanted to depart this world.

They say that a great value of family medicine lies in the relational continuity with patients over time. It is this continuity that fills the emotional void and helps patients feel safe in the very private of spaces with their family physician. I would like to say that I fulfilled the role that Sophie deserved from her personal physician. I can say with certainty that never have I been more humbled in my calling as a family physician than I was that very routine but singularly unique hospital day.

Afternoon Tea

BRIAN S. BACAK, MD

I first met Charles in a hospital bed, but not in a hospital. It was the hospital bed in his living room, where he lay, day after day, due to the ravages of Parkinson's disease. As a U.S. Army medical officer assigned to his family by our geriatric medicine coordinator, I began a several-year relationship with Charles and his spouse of more than forty years, Carmen.

His life was one of drama and one for the history books. Years before during the 1950s, he was responsible for debriefing defectors from the Soviet Union. Secretly, apparently, for years. By the time I came to know him, his past, not available through the history books, was relayed to me by his wife and by the heirlooms in their house.

Carmen would invite me into the house for tea about every three months or so. We would chat for a bit about how Charles was doing, and then Carmen would walk me through the latest events and proceed to show me every inch of his skin, pointing out the things she was concerned about. She would describe how she administered his medications through a gastrostomy tube, how she kept track of his medical information in a chart she kept by his bed, and how she would roll him over to make sure he did not develop a bedsore. That part was particularly impressive because Charles must have been six feet, two inches in height and weighed 180 pounds; she likely weighed 130 pounds after a heavy meal.

Carmen had a complicated dance perfected, dropping the head of the bed as she pulled on a sheet and rolled him over, all in one fluid motion like a choreographed olympic routine. At the end of all the commotion he always appeared as if a team of ten of the best long-term care nursing staff had swarmed over him, crisp and clean in perfectly folded sheets and laundered pajamas. It was amazing to see the love she showered on her husband.

After this medical odyssey was complete, we would sit at her kitchen table and talk. With tea in hand, Formica and vinyl chairs reflecting a spotless kitchen, we would chat about anything and nothing at all. Mostly, I provided assurances that the care she was providing was second to none. I always had my black bag with me, but rarely did I do more than check his blood pressure and pulse and study his intact skin. Always, a cup of tea and conversation.

When I received new orders and a change of assignment, they were one of my first patient-families that I told. After that last cup of tea, she handed me a part of Charles's uniform he wore during the "interrogation years," a major's cluster, gold and shiny. Carmen presented it to me with a request that I carry a piece of Charles forward in the army that he loved.

I cannot remember who became Charles's physician after I left. I do not know if the afternoon teas continued in their home. I do know that as I moved on in my career I held on to that insignia. His major's insignia became part of my uniform three years later upon my promotion. I wore it every day. For me, it became my badge of honor as a physician. More than twenty years later, I still have that major's leaf. It is on display in my office, still my badge of honor and my tribute to my patient.

Where the Poppies Grow

RICHARD D. FELDMAN, MD

Frank Shaw was a combat veteran of World War I. He was an elderly man who became my patient in the very early years of my practice. He was born into an Indiana farm family just before the turn of the twentieth century. Frank was probably a couple of years out of high school in 1917 and working on the family farm when the United States entered the war. He was tough, full of patriotism, and the spirit of adventure. He enlisted in the army because he wanted to do his part to serve his country and to help save the world from what he saw as Germany's evil aggression. Frank was engaged to his high school sweetheart, later becoming his wife of more than sixty-five years. But that marriage would have to wait until he returned "from the war to end all wars."

Frank was obviously a hearty man in his youth; I could see it in this elderly man even still. He was a big man with that "all-American jaw." Frank was muscular and tall and still standing straight. He said in his youth that he was very strong and athletic and figured that he had "a better than even chance" in any fight with a German.

I probably never would have known that he was a World War I veteran if I had not asked him. He was not the type to talk about it much unless he was asked; he did not wear his military service on his sleeve. As we came to know one another better, he progressively opened up about his war experiences because of my continual questioning. I was fascinated. It was the historian in me who just wanted to know.

Although he told me of horrific events, he did not seem terribly traumatized from the war in any lasting way, at least that he showed. He had a very calm demeanor. He was a pragmatic, humble person who just did his part for his country so long ago. He told me that while he was on the front lines in France, he was no hero. He was proud to serve, but said more than once, "The heroes were those that didn't return home."

Frank was a typical "doughboy" of World War I. He described himself as just an enlisted man with a rife in his hand, a pack on his back, and carrying a few hand grenades. He entered the army and was given some training in the states and then additionally when he arrived in France. He voyaged to Europe on a large ship full of troops and worried all the way they might be hit by a torpedo from one of those German "U-boats." But the trip was uneventful other than the crowded conditions, poor food, and some seasickness. He was awfully glad to get off that ship and arrive at a camp in England, but the conditions there were also far from adequate. Finally, landing in France, they were warmly welcomed by the French people. He was ready to fight.

Frank recalled the devastation of the French towns and countryside along the way to the frontline trenches. It was not long until he found himself in the thick of things. This certainly was not what he imagined when he enlisted. His naive thoughts and images of gallantry, duty, and triumph began to fade. His eagerness to fight without the real fear of being killed or wounded soon gave way to the reality of the war's brutality, death, and destruction. It was not going to be as easy as was anticipated to defeat the Germans.

He soon experienced the filth, mud, insects, and rats in the trenches and the stench of the dead. The conditions were terrible and unimaginable. In some areas, the dead from both sides remained everywhere. There were times that there was hardly enough to eat, and his socks and boots were wet for days. Disease was all around him. It was common for troops to die of disease rather than wounds suffered in battle, maybe more common, he said. Pneumonia, dysentery, tuberculosis, influenza, and other infections were always near. Frank recounted that he would look to the sky and see the American combat biplanes overhead. He envied those dashing airmen who flew above the mud and filth and returned in the evenings to their bases to hot meals, comfortable barracks, and clean beds.

I do not remember the battle fronts and the campaigns he engaged in, I only remember that he fought in France, probably mostly in the spring, summer, and fall of 1918. Americans fought in coordination with the French and English. He might have been at the Toul, Chateau-Thierry, or the Meuse-Argonne offensives. But I do recall his description of the fire and thunder of the Allied bombs that proceeded their advances to the German frontline trenches to soften the enemy and their obstacles and barbwire defenses. I remember his descriptions of the anxious waits before being ordered to go "over the top" out of the trenches and running toward the German trenches in "no-man's land." It was here that the most terrifying aspects of the battles took place: Running through a hail of bullets whizzing around them and the earth-shattering shelling that fell on them with deafening and disorientating impact. Intermittently, they would jump into bomb craters for protection and then get up and run again. He saw friends blown apart by those bombs and others slowing dying of

A Poster Used for the Marine Recruiting Campaign

their bullet and shrapnel wounds. A few became debilitated and trembled with emotional "shell shock." They always worried about being gassed.

Finding his way to the German trenches, he engaged in some hand-to-hand combat with bayonets, knives, and firearms. "I killed some Germans," he said reluctantly as he looked down at the floor. But he recounted that he was fortunately only involved in intense hand-to-hand fighting a few times. Overtaking a German trench was many times more of a round-up of prisoners with sporadic fighting, as the enemy was overwhelmed with the effects of the preceding trench bombing and the resulting disorganization. He recalled, "We were certainly attacked by the Germans too, but we were never overrun. Overall, I was fortunate, it could have been much worse."

Frank reflected that somehow, he amazingly got out alive and without a major injury. He suffered a relatively minor shrapnel wound in the leg that earned him a Purple Heart. He showed me the scar: "I was so lucky, unlike the many of my friends who fought along with me. I guess surviving was a crapshoot. I will always remember those young boys who were robbed of living their full lives." He recalled that there were times in battle that the justifications and reasons for fighting the war left him. He was merely fighting out of anger for those Americans who were brutally killed to avenge their deaths, I suppose. It was in those times that fear totally left him on the battlefield.

Frank was proud of his service and put it in terms of, "We did what we had to do." He believed in the cause to save the world from tyranny. But that experience, I believe, also gave him the ability to view the world with the eyes of a much more mature man who more fully appreciated freedom, family and community, and the value of life. And always, he realized that war is a tragedy, a waste of human life, and something horrific that no one should have to experience. He seemed torn between the necessity and the senselessness of war.

He did not normally display or disclose is service to his country to others. But every year around Armistice Day, he did something I thought was a little out of character. He would give his friends and acquaintances he happened to encounter a little red paper poppy with a small, attached card. I received one of those poppies. The card contained that famous poem by Lieutenant Colonel John McCrae, MD of the Canadian Army, titled "In Flanders Fields":

In Flanders fields the poppies blow
Between the crosses, row on row,
That mark our place; and in the sky
The larks, still bravely singing, fly
Scarce heard amid the guns below.

We are the Dead, Short days ago
We lived, felt dawn, saw the sunset glow,

Loved and were loved, and now we lie
In Flanders fields

Take up our quarrel with the foe:
To you from failing hands we throw
The torch; be yours to hold it high.
If ye break faith with us who die
We shall not sleep, though poppies grow
In Flanders fields.

Remarkably, I think the poem precisely reflects the tension that Frank felt in his soul: Believing in one's duty and the rightfulness of fighting the enemy in that great conflict yet lamenting the necessity and irrationality of war with its tragic enormous losses. I believe giving out the paper poppies was his tribute to his unforgotten fallen friends. I can only begin to imagine what his wartime experiences were like. But he gave me a glimpse.

Frank gave me a unique understanding of patriotism, sacrifice, courage, bravery, and commitment to something greater than oneself. All these things revealed in a person of great humility, selflessness, sensitivity, and humanism. A good combination, I think.

One day I asked him if he knew the song, "Mademoiselle from Armentieres," so much associated with the English and American troops in World War I. How I was familiar with it escapes me. He responded assuredly, "Of course!" To my surprise, he proceeded to sing the first verse in a whispered voice, so no one would hear him outside the exam room:

Mademoiselle from Armentieres
Parlez-vous
Mademoiselle from Armentiers
Parlez-vous
Mademoiselle from Armentieres
She hasn't been kissed for 40 years
Hinky-dinky parlez-vous

At his next visit, he invited me to sing it with him. We sang together in whispered voices, and we smiled.

Frank eventually left Indianapolis to be closer to his two sons in his advanced age. We hugged at the conclusion of his final office visit, and he thanked me for the medical care he had received from me. I never heard from him again. I am proud to have known him. He always wanted to return to France to visit the battlefields and the American cemeteries. I hope he had the chance to do so.

Frank gave me many gifts from the heart along with one of those paper poppies. I have it to this day.

On Being My Patient's Student

ELIZABETH PETERS, MD

Mr. Paulson had been admitted to the inpatient psychiatry unit for an episode of acute mania. A sixty-year-old gentleman, he was currently homeless, in a state of fluid overload due to decompensated heart failure, and had little insight about his mental and physical illnesses. Mr. Paulson had been assigned to me, a third-year medical student, on my first day of an inpatient psychiatry rotation at the Veteran's Administration Hospital. Over the next weeks we spent countless hours together which, for my part, were mostly spent listening. He spoke quickly and often circuitously about his challenging past, losing friends and family, and his faith that kept him going.

In turn, I explained why he was in the hospital and stressed the importance of various interventions, among them wearing his compression stockings. He refused this request repeatedly, as well as most other recommendations I made. Despite his lack of support for my suggestions, Mr. Paulson seemed to enjoy talking to me. At first, I attributed this to the mania. Over days and weeks his mania began to improve, but I noticed he was still waiting in the hallway when I arrived each morning and seeking me out on the unit throughout the day. The more I got to know him the clearer it became that Mr. Paulson desperately desired to be heard.

Like so many patients, Mr. Paulson sought more from the healthcare system than medical care. To begin, he needed relationships he could trust. I learned he had felt betrayed recently by "friends" who had stolen money, food, and clothing from him during his recent episodes of mania. I learned he had been living from group home to group home for the past five years. He often wandered through neighborhoods on foot for hours or days when he was manic. He shared that he had not eaten regular meals since leaving the group home a week before admission.

Over the past year he had felt manic much more often than in prior years, which was likely related to several recent changes in his case-management staffing as well as medication noncompliance. As I listened to Mr. Paulson, sometimes for more than an hour at a time, I realized he was disillusioned by a history of many hospital admissions, office visits, rotating healthcare providers, and social workers. Although he could not necessarily articulate it, I could tell that he craved stability and trust. Before my team could address his other needs and compromise with him on our recommendations, I would have to find a way to gain that trust.

After two weeks his mania had improved significantly, and our team had identified a safe-living environment for him. We continued to struggle with his leg swelling. One morning the attending physician asked Mr. Paulson, yet again, if he would give the compression stockings a try. Without responding, his gaze fixed on me. I could not help but smile as I realized after all this time he was looking for my advice. He asked what I thought about the compression stockings. Through my grin, I told him he already knew how I felt. A smile spread across his face as he exclaimed, "I'll give them a shot!"

During the first two weeks of my relationship with Mr. Paulson I had envisioned myself as a teacher. I described various interventions—diuretics, mood-stabilizing medications, compression stockings, dementia screenings—at length. I spent time counseling him on medication side effects and working with him to identify places where he would agree to live following discharge. However, as he grinned broadly at me in that moment, finally agreeing to wear those compression stockings, I realized that in fact I had been the student. For all that I may have taught Mr. Paulson, he taught me more. He showed me that often in medicine, we become better teachers by first being good students.

From Mr. Paulson I learned that a patient's emotional needs often far supersede his medical needs. Without addressing the needs of paramount concern to our patients, we fail them. Often, as in Mr. Paulson's case, a key component of the care our patients need is a listening ear. Finally, he showed me more clearly than ever that I was destined for family medicine. Though I was distressed when I left the rotation, often wondering how he was doing, this was my sign that I needed to enter a field focused on follow-up and longitudinal relationships with patients. I welcome the challenge of many Mr. Paulsons in my hopeful career as a family physician. I cannot imagine a greater privilege than to be a constant in my patients' journeys through life.

Elizabeth Peters is from Cincinnati, Ohio. She completed her undergraduate studies at Miami University in Oxford, Ohio, and completed her medical degree at the University of Cincinnati College of Medicine. She is currently training at The Christ Hospital/University of Cincinnati Family Medicine Residency. Peters plans to provide primary care for underserved populations in her future career as a physician.

"Every patient has a 'why.' We need to listen. We need to hear it, so we can help them with the 'how' so they can achieve it. You will learn about each person's unique 'why' they want to live, that gives them the strength, the will to persist, to survive, to recover from life-threatening illness. Your soul will be enriched by each person you care for. Pursue your calling with vigor, with commitment, with kindness; and whenever in doubt, remember the 'why' that's in your hearts today."

Thomas Nasca, MD, president and chief executive officer of
the Accreditation Council for Graduate Medical Education,
Georgetown University School of Medicine, 2018
Commencement

Max's Legacy

LAUREN GNAGY, MD

"He has made everything beautiful in its time. He has also set eternity in the human heart; yet no one can fathom what God has done from beginning to end."
ECCLESIASTES 3:11

My Mom had been commenting on the increasingly yellow tinge of Great-Uncle Max's skin for weeks. When Max mentioned vague one-out-of-ten-level pain in his belly, she urged him to see a physician immediately. Her concern grave and her motherly intuition right yet again.

As Max was without a wife or children of his own, my mother accompanied him to his first appointment with the surgeon at the cancer center. Meanwhile, I was just down the hall, probably straining my brain in a first-year medical school anatomy lecture. By this point we had learned the vasculature of the abdomen and location of the pancreas, but this knowledge did not prove to help much in assisting my family with Max's diagnosis of pancreatic cancer.

My Mom relayed to me the competence of the surgeon. His candor, confidence, and willingness to draw diagrams of the Whipple procedure had made an impression. A good one. An eye was not batted as my family proceeded with the plan for a laparoscopic intervention. But, when their eyelids began to flutter days before the impending hospitalization, I recall citing statistics from the doctor's biography to quell their nerves. A Johns Hopkins graduate, fluent in three languages, and 4.8/5 rating. Even in the face of a risky surgery, who could question that? And who were we to question the doctor?

From here on out, my memory becomes blurry with peculiar moments of clarity, like watching a VHS tape with intermittent clicks of pause, play, and fast forward. With hesitation and trembling thumb, I depress the rubbery black button emblazoned with a white triangle. Click.

One day, Max is recovering well from surgery. The next he is slightly delirious, mumbling with eyes open, and working with unmatched effort on the incentive spirometer. Max's mental status continues to decline. And my mother's concerns become magnified by Doctor Google's input as the days pass.

She eventually musters up the courage to confront the resident with a concern for sepsis. She is met with resistance.

"Well, he doesn't technically meet the criteria," he flatly states.

"Something is wrong," she pleads.

I can all too easily imagine the internal, reactive dialogue of the resident, "Just another anxious family member," and his subsequent regret when the attending physician walked in later that morning, yelling: "This man's shit smells awful. He's septic! What the hell have you been doing?"

Max is moved to the Intensive Care Unit, and thereafter I spend my evenings studying at the bedside with my family nearby. The attending physician takes the time to speak with my mother often. They talk about his scuba diving adventures and their own children. Upon hearing that I was in my first year of medical school, he invites me to tag along during rounds, handing out his personal cell phone number. He says, "I wouldn't do this for just anyone. This is a big deal." I am caught off guard by both is arrogance and his humility. I briefly wonder if this is okay—to play the role of medical student and family member all at once, and for Max to play the roles of both patient and kin.

The next day, I showed up at 6:00 a.m., bright-eyed and wearing black. Black heels. Black collared dress. We start what I have come to know as the typical morning routine of rounds. Huddling outside each patient's room, proceeding down the hall, time seems to fly. In retrospect, this seems odd. It is, after completing my clinical training in medical school, the only time that rounds did not seem to drag on endlessly.

Before I know it we are standing outside of Max's room. I turn away from the group and wave secretly yet proudly to my Mom sitting on the tan couch in front of the window. I think to myself: "She's brilliant. It makes sense that he made her the power of attorney." I feel an instant pang of regret for all those times I thought that her intelligence was going to waste as a stay-at-home mom. Sitting at the bedside of my uncle for hours on end, I see my most exhausted but beautiful mother with servant-like radiance.

Reality snaps back into place as I hear the attending say that Max has made a remarkable recovery from sepsis. Click. I take the first step in the room. Smiles become shock. Peace to panic. People are already on edge. Click. Blood filling the nasogastric tube and the drain exiting his abdomen. Click. And the urinary catheter too. What is happening? Click. My Mom's face-all smiles and pride. Click. Tears, fear, my arms around her.

"You need to sign this pink paper, so that we can go to interventional radiology."

"Mom, you must do this. It's the only way that we can save him. "

Click. Click. Click. To the interventional radiology room.

"We'll try to plug this vessel. I'm not sure if we can."

My Mom reflexively signs a paper handed to us in the dingy room. Even if we had been experiencing less than emotional shock, I do not think we could have read the consent form in such lighting.

Click. Click. Click. Click. I am in the lobby, extended family surrounding me, trying to explain with my limited anatomy knowledge in hand and colored pencils sprawled across a coffee table. Drawing and drawing. And looking in Netter's anatomy book. I point, "See here? This is what vessel broke. See, right here. They are trying to fix it." Was I trying to teach them or teach myself? Somehow, I do not think it was about teaching at all. Click.

My Mom tells me to go home. I refuse. We think that we have lost him. And then we have not. My Dad prays over us all in a circle with so much certainty in his voice. "God is with us even in death," he says. Even if I want to, I cannot doubt that this is true. As the nurses bring hugs and pitchers of water, calm and peace become reality. My mother insists that I go home—her attempt at sheltering me from darkness and my grandfather's impending cardioversion for atrial fibrillation secondary to stress.

I am sitting in the anatomy classroom the following morning when I receive a text message from my Mom. Click. Max died. The VHS tape ejects.

I grieved for our loss, and even more so for the suffering of the rest of my family. There are traditional things that Max will always be remembered for: the seat he occupied at my family's dinner table many evenings, his love of horses, his typically inappropriate jokes, and his passionate commentary full of swear words at basketball games. But, more than any of this, I remember his legacy of generosity. I recall that he allowed my brothers and me to borrow his convertible in high school and his generous donations to the Danville High School basketball team. In his will he left a ranch to his best friends and enough money to me to cover most of my medical school education.

I have never been to another funeral that was standing room only. I watched as people filed in—former high school basketball players; coaches, Max's high school classmates, the old men who drink coffee together at Hardee's each morning, principals, pastors, and my parents' friends who had only seen Max in passing. It was a semblance of community that I have been attempting to re-create ever since I left the small town of Danville at eighteen years of age. Yet, there is this beauty: a community in which a person is known well enough to be cared for and knows others well enough to serve them, requires sacrifice. A subtle surrender to being known beyond comfortable boundaries. Something more difficult, perhaps, than being removed from city luxuries and entertainment. If this funeral was a good indication, I decided, such living is well worth it.

As I sit on my childhood bed typing this paragraph, my cousin, Lilly Maxine Coleman, is pestering me to do a craft with her. The beauty of this is not lost on me. It is the same truth that I saw in my Mom's sacrificial heart, in the physician's invitation to shadow him, in my father's prayers, the joy Max once experienced when watching my brother Luke dunk the basketball, the times Max lent me his car, the overwhelming support and stories of camaraderie at the funeral, and the surprise of funds for medical school.

It is the same truth I see prospectively in the deep impression this experience has left upon my own heart—the empathy-inspiring experience of having seen through the lens of physician and family member simultaneously, my decision to pursue a rural-focused family medicine residency, passion for end-of-life care and walking with patients through life-changing decisions, increased understanding of the fragility of life, and plans to invest professionally and personally in a small town.

My Dad later told me about something that my then eighteen-year-old brother Zach said around the time of the funeral, "You know what Dad? I know that Danville isn't very cool, but Mom's family has stayed here a long time, and they really love one another. They would do anything for each other. I think I want that too."

In an instant, my brother went from my annoying youngest sibling to a man embodying maturity beyond many of my own peers. And I was reminded that we are all characters in this tale with our own perspectives and potential growth derived from hardship.

This story, this reality, even in the cloudy face of bodily death, physician mistakes, and heartache fills my spirit with hope. It is hope for a continued redemptive process, not simply for myself, but for a community. Separation from those we love can be an experience of discovery. And, even if I want to, I cannot doubt that this is true.

Lauren Gnagy grew up in Danville, Indiana, and wrote this essay during her final year at Indiana University School of Medicine. She credits becoming a physician and her inspiration for writing to her heavenly Father, loving parents, church family, and hometown community. She enjoys anything from sewing to, in true Hoosier tradition, playing basketball with her three younger brothers. Gnagy is training to become a family physician at Ball Memorial Hospital in Muncie, Indiana.

The Healing Power of Humanism

LINDSAY RENZ WILLIAMS, DO

It was 5:00 p.m. on a Monday. The nurse handed me the intake form and I walked into the room of our last patient for the day. As I listened intently to the patient's story, I felt every emotion she described—anger, sadness, fear, and frustration. She had been from doctor to doctor who sent her home with medicines that they told her would ease her pain. Not only had it not improved, but it was also getting worse.

My attending doctor entered the room. When he examined the patient, he told her that he was afraid that he would have to take her to the operating room immediately. I could sense the alarm on the patient's face, so I offered my hand to her. Tears ran down her face as she squeezed my hand. The attending stepped out of the room to schedule the case. As I held her hand, I asked her what I could do for her. The patient explained to me that her biggest concern was for her children who were with her in the waiting room. So, I went to the waiting room and played with her children while she got dressed. I thought about that patient all night long.

The next morning I immediately asked the surgeon how the surgery went. His answer was what I had feared; what he found was suspicious for cancer. My heart sank into my stomach as I thought about this young mother.

She returned to clinic, and we discussed the results of the biopsy. Her face turned white as she heard the diagnosis and could not keep the tears from streaming down her face. As she listened intently to the doctor's plan for her, I could tell that she was not processing the information. Nothing could keep her from thinking about what this diagnosis would mean for her children.

As we waited for her questions, the patient could not find the words to speak. When she finally spoke, the words that came out of her mouth were, "but my kids." In that moment, I knew that what she needed from me was a hand to hold and an ear to listen. I could not cure her cancer that day.

What this experience made me realize was that true healing does not only come from treatments or cures but also from the love and compassion doctors extend to their patients. As the healthcare landscape is changing in our country, doctors all too frequently feel more pressure from hospital administration or other employers to increase their productivity. This can interfere with providing an attentive humanistic approach, so important in the healing process.

Patients seek out care for many reasons, but no matter what the reason is, they want to be listened to and cared for.

Our society needs doctors who understand disease processes but more importantly understand their patients and what matters to each person who walks through the door. As I continue my journey to become a doctor, I will never forget the healing power of humanism. I will be mindful of each patient's unique story including the patient's fears, concerns, emotions, and interests. I will continue to lend a hand, an ear, or a shoulder to cry on for my patients. One of the most rewarding parts of being a doctor is to share these intimate moments with patients.

Humanism is the secret ingredient in the recipe for healing.

At the time Lindsay Renz Williams wrote this account, she was a medical student at Marian University College of Osteopathic Medicine in Indianapolis. She is a graduate of the University of Notre Dame and a native Hoosier. She loves to play euchre, Settlers of Catan, and other games. She is passionate about promoting physician wellness and humanism in medicine.

Humbled

THOMAS KINTANAR, MD

In 2000, when I was a hospice medical director in Fort Wayne, Indiana, I was asked to make a house call on an end-stage Alzheimer's patient. I went to the home accompanied by one of my hospice nurses to make a near-terminal assessment on our patient, Gerald.

Gerald had a robust life, a loving wife, and a son in his mid-to-late thirties. After exchanging pleasantries, I greeted Gerald and began his evaluation. After I finished my exam, I noticed that I was being heavily scrutinized by his son, who was standing in the corner, which made me feel a bit uncomfortable. I thoroughly examined Gerald and found no major changes from his last evaluation.

I finished my notes and charting and discussed his case with his wife and son. Then, I turned to his son and asked if he was living in Fort Wayne for me to touch base with him in the event of a terminal situation. I was duly informed by his mother that he was a priest and had been serving with Mother Theresa for twenty years or more. Being Catholic, I was accordingly humbled and asked if the bishop was aware of his presence in the community. Before he could answer, his mother shared that there was nothing high profile about what he was doing, and they would prefer that this visit to his family be a private event. However, she proudly pointed to a large wall of photographs of Gerald, along with the rest of the family including her son, all taken with Mother Theresa.

Gerald's wife went on to share that when Mother Teresa was on tour in Chicago, they all accompanied her. During the tour Gerald unfortunately became very ill with a virus, and Mother Theresa admonished him to stay at the hotel and convalesce. While he stayed behind at the hotel, she called to check on Gerald to make sure that he was complying with what she had requested.

As I gazed upon the photographs and listened to anecdotes and this and other stories, I was truly humbled and, in some way, recognized the presence of God and Mother Theresa in the room.

This experience was a very spiritual reminder that we not only serve our patients but also the people who love them. And if we care to dig deeper, we can understand the magnitude of the lives that we touch and that touch us in kind.

Thomas Kintanar is a family physician in Fort Wayne, Indiana, where he has practiced in various arrangements for more than thirty-three years. He is a graduate of Indiana University, Bloomington, and Southwestern University Matias H. Aznar Memorial College of Medicine in Cebu City, Philippines. Kintanar also attended the Fort Wayne Medical Education Program's Family Medicine Residency. He has practiced full spectrum family medicine with special interest in endoscopy including teaching these procedures to residents and fellows from across the country. Kintanar is a past board member of the American Academy of Family Physicians and is a past president and chairman of the board of the Indiana Academy of Family Physicians. He and his wife Erin have five children.

Blisters Everywhere

NIMISHA BAJAJ, MD, PhD

"Look at what happened when I fell off my bike!" exclaimed my seven-year-old patient, Ronny. Like many young boys, he loved riding his bicycle around the neighborhood and would repeatedly try new tricks on his skateboard, so he was covered in bumps and bruises. However, unlike most young boys, any trauma to his skin had severe consequences, as he had epidermolysis bullosa.

Epidermolysis bullosa is a rare genetic disorder that affects about nine out of every million people. It is characterized by exceedingly sensitive skin, as patients with this condition have missing connections in one of the layers of the skin, compromising their ability to maintain intact skin. Therefore, even slight trauma, such as pressure from vigorously washing their hands, can cause the layers of the skin to separate and form large fluid-filled blisters.

Not only are the blisters painful, but the disruptions to the skin layer also means that the patients are at higher risk for infections that would be quite rare in individuals with normal, healthy skin. Ronny had come into the general pediatrics clinic for antibiotics for a pseudomonas bacterial infection on his abdomen. Pseudomonas can be a rather difficult infection to treat and can become serious. He was sitting excitedly on the exam table, clad in a long sleeve T-shirt, track pants, and gym shoes. Under his clothes, he had patches of blistered skin all over his arms and legs. He lifted his shirt and removed his bandages to show me patches on his belly that had started to discolor around the edges.

Though it looked suspicious for pseudomonas, we could not be sure unless we did a few more tests. Ronny was my preceptor's only patient with epidermolysis bullosa, so she was hardly an expert. We were not sure exactly what was going on, but we wanted to halt the infection early to prevent its spread to other parts of the body. There are specific treatment regimens tailored to these situations based on published guidelines, and we recommended one of them, but Ronny's mother opposed our suggestions.

Ronny's mother, Cora, had long blonde hair pulled back in a ponytail and was wearing jeans and a black t-shirt from the Dystrophic Epidermolysis Bullosa Research Association that said in white and red letters, "I fight the worst disease you've never heard of." She had an air of confidence and defiance that came from constantly advocating for her child who was regularly in and out of children's hospitals.

Cora and Ronny had been managing his diagnosis for years. They regularly went to the epidermolysis bullosa clinic at one of the large children's hospitals a few hours away. She knew the ins and outs of her son's disease much more than my preceptor did. They lived with it every day, so they knew his patterns. She knew what pseudomonas looked like because she saw it a few times per year. She knew what happened when they followed the guidelines; he was not adequately treated for long enough, so his infections came back. And Cora had worked with the specialists at the clinic to come up with a dependable approach for Ronny's infections that was consistently successful in treating them. But the specialty clinic was several hours away, and his primary-care doctor, my preceptor, was perfectly capable of prescribing antibiotics.

We prescribed the antibiotics but also probed further into how Ronny was handling his illness with all the trials and tribulations of being seven. The constant skin turnover in patients with epidermolysis bullosa leads to severe complications in addition to infections, such as skin cancer and even strictures of the esophagus, which can lead to malnutrition. They can get mouth sores and develop anemia. They live with chronic pain. The life expectancy for someone with this disease ranges from death during infancy to early adulthood to in some cases a full life. As one can imagine, this typically leads to significant limitations in the lives of these patients, especially children, and they are commonly affected by bullying, which leads to high rates of depression as well.

But Ronny was not depressed, and he seemed to be living as full of a life as he possibly could. He was out riding his bicycle, running around with his friends, and taking age-appropriate risks. He was enjoying his life. He seemed completely normal and developmentally appropriate. If I had not known about his life-threatening illness, I would have thought he was a normal, healthy kid who had gotten into some nasty scrapes on his skateboard.

In fact, his normalcy was by design. The physicians at the specialty clinic had made it their goal to help him live like a child his own age. It was not to prevent skin breakdown or infection at all costs but to balance the risks of his disease with his desire to live a normal life.

Old and new technology helped them achieve this goal, of course. Benefiting from old wisdom, he was the only little boy running around in long pants and a long-sleeve shirt no matter what the weather. But new innovations had also been instrumental in allowing him to be a kid. Ronny's bandages had to adhere to his skin somehow, lest they fell to the floor, but most adhesives applied friction that caused blistering of his skin. He gleefully demonstrated to me how his new bandages had an adhesive that allowed them to stick to his wounds without applying this friction. He had clearly lived through many iterations of wound-care technology and had an appreciation for any new developments that came along.

Despite his young age, Ronny possessed wisdom well beyond his years. He taught me how to appreciate seemingly inconsequential things, such as new bandages. He took risks, even though for him they could have more serious consequences than for his peers. He took appropriate precautions but was not handcuffed by his diagnosis. He enjoyed his life and with the help of his mother and his doctors, found a way to live how he wanted, despite his disease.

Cora was also admirable. Despite everything she had seen—the hospitalizations, the infections, the skin breakdown—and read about her son's diagnosis, she did not keep him from learning and exploring like his peers. She was willing to prioritize her son's overall happiness, fulfillment, and growth over the elevated risk to his physical health. And Ronny benefited because of it.

Mother and child were accepting of a serious chronic disease and were determined to triumph over it. I will always be amazed by the strength of the human spirit even in a young boy who despite his illness lives life to the fullest.

Nimisha Bajaj grew up in West Lafayette, Indiana. She studied biomedical engineering at Purdue University and then entered the Indiana University School of Medicine. She took a leave of absence from medical school for five years to pursue a PhD in biomedical engineering at Purdue before returning to the IU School of Medicine to complete her clinical rotations. Bajaj is currently in a pediatrics residency.

Don't Touch Me!

NIMISHA BAJAJ, MD, PhD

I spent several months of my third year of medical school caring for very sick patients. Some of the sickest patients I had the privilege of meeting were hospitalized on the hematology-oncology floor of the Indiana University Hospital Simon Cancer Center.

Some of my patients had good prognoses, and they were just coming to the hospital for maintenance chemotherapy to prolong remission. As far as cancer therapy is concerned though, it requires hospitalization to monitor for and treat side effects, but it is mild. These patients were almost always in good spirits. They had gotten to know the oncology staff on the floors and were always amenable to the teaching mission of the hospital. One of these patients even graciously let me practice comprehensive heart-and-lung exam techniques on her while my senior resident gave me pointers.

Even the sicker patients were patient and kind to me as a young, bumbling medical student who had yet to master any sort of clinical practice or communication. I fondly remember a young patient in her thirties, barely a few years older than me, who had young children at home. She had been diagnosed with a form of leukemia with a poor prognosis, and had gone through induction chemotherapy (the first, really debilitating round that kills the most cancer cells) once before, but the cancer came back, so she was back again for another round. I remember her struggling with all the side effects of strong chemotherapy: secondary infections, terrible mouth sores, diarrhea, weakness, fatigue, and more. And even through all her misery, she never once ceased being incredibly polite to her entire healthcare team and was generally a joy to be around.

Experience with these patients led me to the false conclusion that the normal response to a life-threatening diagnosis is to be as polite and amicable as possible to the people around you. And why wouldn't they be? We were just trying to help, and we deserved nothing less.

These were my assumptions until I met Andy. He had been diagnosed with a form of leukemia that can present with cancerous white blood cells in the blood in concentrations fifty to a hundred times higher than the normal, healthy white blood cells. These high cell concentrations lead to pain, visual changes, difficulty breathing, and many other symptoms because they get stuck all over the blood vessels in the body. Andy presented with all these symptoms when I met him. And he presented with these symptoms after he had already been in remission and had come to the clinic to be checked out for a hopefully curative bone-marrow transplantation. He had been feeling better and had hope, and when he came back to see us, he was back at square one.

The structure of a teaching team depends on the service, but in this case each patient was being seen by a staff physician, a fellow, a senior resident, an intern, and me, the medical student, every day. Each member of the team assigned to the patient goes and checks on them multiple times per day. We justify multiple interruptions to the patient's day by saying that everyone at different levels needs to learn and that patients appreciate the fact that we show so much concern for them. For the most part, patients like that we check in with them multiple times per day to make sure that we are giving them the best care.

Andy, however, did not feel the same way. For the first few days, he barely spoke to us except to give short answers to questions. For the next few days, after he was moved out of the step-down unit to the oncology floor, he was extremely irritable. Any time any of us went to do a quick exam and see how he was doing, he snapped at us, gave passive-aggressive answers to our questions, and refused to be touched

Initially, I was incredibly annoyed by this and took it personally. I assumed he must just always be an unpleasant person. We were just trying to help him! I was determined to find a way to make him nicer to me, not because I thought that he deserved to be treated well, but because I wanted him to treat me better. The intern and I decided to only check on him once a day, and together at that. We minimized all contact with him except when necessary and when he explicitly asked for it. He also loved to ride his bicycle, so we got him a stationary bike so he could ride it in his room while he looked out the window. We tried several things just to make his long stay in the hospital a little more bearable.

After a week or so of us trying to meet his social and emotional needs, his mood changed, and he thanked us for taking care of him. Finally! We had been showed the appreciation that we deserved. However, that is when I realized what Andy had been dealing with. He thought he was on his way to a cure and found himself even sicker than he was when he was first diagnosed. Anyone would be irritable in that situation. In fact, I looked back and was surprised at how agreeable my previous patients had been considering everything they had been through.

My experience with Andy taught me about the role of the doctor as more than just treating a disease. It is not the patient's job to stroke our egos and show gratitude. It is our job to take care of the patient as a whole human— someone with hopes, dreams, hobbies, a job, and a life that has been completely turned upside down by their illness. Andy was distressed, a reasonable response to his diagnosis. Only by tending to his emotional needs were we truly able to care for him. It is my goal to do that with all my patients, now and in the future.

He Can Hear Me, Really

RICHARD D. FELDMAN, MD

This story is about the strangest experience that I ever encountered in my forty-year career. I was an intern on the intensive-care rotation. I was assigned to an unfortunate gentleman, Mr. McGuire, who had attempted suicide. He failed in his very serious attempt but was left with severe brain and kidney damage. He was unresponsive and thought to be comatose. He did not move his arms, legs, or head. He laid in his hospital bed unmoving with his eyes slightly open. He was certainly critically ill and would most likely die of his self-inflicted injuries.

I made rounds and examined him each morning and usually visited him a couple of additional times per day. During my visits I greeted him by name and informed him of what I was doing. I told him that his wife has been at the hospital most of each day, and that I met with her every morning. I offered some small talk not expecting a response and never asked him a question. After all the attending neurologist told me that his brain was gone and that he was completely unaware of his surroundings. Indeed, doctors and nurses would talk about his condition, prognosis, and treatment plans around his bed without any belief that he could hear what they were saying.

Several days after his admission, I thought what the heck, I would ask him a question to see if he could hear me and respond to me in some way. "Mr. McGuire, if you can hear me blink your eyes twice." He blinked his eyes twice. So shocked, I ran out of the room. I reentered the room and asked him, "If you can hear me, smile." He pulled his mouth back tightly in a smile. He could hear me! He was not comatose. He was severely brain damaged, but he could hear and comprehend. He probably had what is called "locked-in syndrome," aware but severely limited in responding in any way. One might say he was "locked in" his own body.

I found his nurse and told her what had occurred. She went to his room and asked him to blink his eyes. No response. Then I asked him to smile. No response. She looked at me like I was a nut case and left the room. I really did not think I was suddenly losing my mind. Later that day I returned to see him and asked him to blink his eyes twice. He blinked his eyes twice as before.

The next morning on rounds I told the neurologist what had occurred the day before. We went to the patient's room and he asked him to blink his eyes.

No response. "Mr. McGuire, smile for me," he asked. Nothing. I tried as well. No response. The neurologist looked at me in the same manner as did the nurse the preceding day and reported, "His brain is squash, he can't hear you. Believe me!" Later that day I returned to Mr. McGuire with my same requests and clearly received the same responses of blinks and smiles. No, I was not a nut case. I could not explain what was going on, but it was real. Was he playing with us? I asked him why he was responding to me only when I was alone with him, but of course he could not reply.

I met with his wife daily to update her concerning his clinical course and any progress he was making. I told her that although he would only respond to me for some reason, he was aware and could hear. I asked her to see if he would respond to her. At first, he did not respond to her either, but eventually in the coming days he did and also to some of the nursing staff. He never did react to the neurologist's requests. Unfortunately, Mr. McGuire eventually died in the hospital of renal failure.

Why did he respond to me and not others? Did he trust me and not others for some reason? Did he sense something about me in my voice? Did he appreciate my little one-way discussions with him during my daily visits? Did he appreciate the simple respect for his dignity I displayed for him? I really do not think I will ever know for sure. But we did in some unusual way develop a relationship. Doctor-patient relationships may develop in unfamiliar ways.

But I know one thing for sure: Healthcare providers (or anyone for that matter) should be very careful about what they say to "comatose" patients or to any patients thought unable to hear what is said in their presence. They may be hearing every detail.

Mr. McGuire certainly did.

HIPPOCRATIS COI
Genuina effigies ex antiquo numismate
graeco Constantinopoli reperto

"Wherever the Art of Medicine is loved, there is also a love of humanity."

Hippocrates

Giving Needed Attention

SHEIKH RAHMAN, MD

In 1985 I was treating an older woman for diabetes, hypertension, and several other chronic diseases. One day her eight-year-old granddaughter tagged along with her for her office appointment. After I finished the office visit, Grandma said, "Doc, can you check my granddaughter? She's getting Ds and Fs on her report card, and her teacher thinks she may have ADD and needs Ritalin."

So, I checked her out. She seemed to be a brilliant little girl; she just did not like to do her homework. I counseled her for ten minutes and emphasized to the girl that if she did her homework, she would be at the head of her class. We really had a nice little chat, and she listened attentively. I told Grandma that she should sit with her every school night and help her until she finished her homework.

She was a normal little girl. All she needed was just some attention. I did not give her Ritalin. But I did routine bloodwork including her thyroid profile and lead levels. They were all normal.

She never came back and time passed. Twenty years later, the day I was retiring, the grandmother came to the office and showed me the graduation picture of that now grownup little girl. She was pictured in cap and gown and was the valedictorian of her graduating class at the University of Pittsburgh School of Nursing.

She was now the chief nurse in a pediatric intensive-care unit. Grandma and I both had tears of joy as we hugged each other. She said, "Doc, see what your ten minutes of warm kindhearted counseling achieved! That office visit was the turning point in her life. I cannot thank you enough!"

I was very grateful to the Lord for His guidance.

Sheikh Rahman is a family physician in Aurora, Indiana, and is affiliated with High-point Health, Lawrenceburg. He received his medical degree from Dow University of Health Sciences in Karachi, Pakistan, and has been in practice for more than twenty years. He has practiced medicine on three continents.

Bologna Sandwiches

GREGORY G. GRECCO, MD, PhD CANDIDATE

I very rarely interacted with patients as a second-year medical student. Most of my time was spent in lectures, in the library studying, and taking examinations. However, once a month, I headed to the hospital to observe a neurologist, practice taking a patient history, or perform a few physical exam techniques. The monthly visit was the only "real medicine" I was involved in at this point in my young medical career.

As I met with the attending physician that morning of my monthly clinic visit, she explained that we would be consulting on patients in the Intensive Care Unit. One of these patients, Mrs. Jones, had a massive left-sided hemorrhagic stroke the day prior. Her brain was herniating, a deadly process that occurs due to increased pressure within the skull that compresses the brain. The attending physician explained that the only treatment option was emergency surgery to relieve the pressure in her skull. However, this would not reverse the devasting consequences of the stroke. The stroke had likely produced a loss of most motor and sensory functions on her right side including the ability to speak and possibly comprehend language. Many families feel this is not a life their loved ones would have wanted to live. The other option was to withdrawal care and allow the patient to pass without intervention. I had only been a part of a conversation like this in practice, invented scenarios in my clinical education classes, which prepared me for the anger, shock, and sorrow experienced by the families of these patients. I had never seen a dying patient with a distraught family surrounding the bed.

"Do you have any pixie dust?" Mr. Jones, the patient's husband, asked the attending physician and me as we entered the room. The physician responded that we, unfortunately, did not. "Well, I guess I don't need much else," he replied disappointingly.

After explaining the options to Mr. Jones and his daughter, they ultimately decided to withdrawal ventilatory support and allow Mrs. Jones to die. Mr. Jones then explained to us his own complicated medical history. He had been in a coma for some undescribed medical reason and near the brink of death. After this scare, he spent a lot more time with his wife.

"I guess it's her time. The day of her the stroke was going so great; right before she was stricken, she was eating her favorite meal, a bologna sandwich.

Not that fancy stuff, but Oscar Meyer Bologna. That's her favorite," he said. Mr. Jones directed most of this conversation to his wife on the hospital bed while the attending and I stood by in the room. I was shocked by his remarkable poise and clarity during this horrible moment. He asked if they could play her favorite Pearl Jam song while her life support was withdrawn, to which his daughter agreed Mrs. Jones would have loved. Mr. Jones then looked at the attending and me and said, "But seriously, unless you can bring her back, we're ready."

Afterward the attending physician asked me if I needed to debrief. I expressed my amazement regarding Mr. Jones's response to the impending and unexpected death of his wife. The attending agreed that his response was not typical of most spouses during a situation such as this. I understand that many physicians who frequently see death acquire an ability to emotionally detach themselves from conversations such as these. Yet, this was my first conversation about death with a patient and the family. I could not help but see myself as Mr. Jones, in my late fifties, at the side of my wife. How would I compare to Mr. Jones?

The attending and I discussed how Mr. Jones's experience with facing death probably explained, in part, his composure during our conversation. He clearly cherished the mundane and ordinary moments like eating bologna sandwiches on a Sunday after church with his wife. He remembered that nothing would comfort his wife more than her favorite Pearl Jam songs. He already seemed to be transitioning to a stage of acceptance and peace with this devastating situation as he recounted Mrs. Jones's happiness with her bologna sandwich. I have wondered if his uncommon response to withdrawing care was related to his ability to live in each present moment, allowing him to deeply appreciate the ordinary moments of life.

I do not know my wife's favorite sandwich. I am not quite sure I could find a favorite song that she would want played if she suffered a hemorrhagic stroke. I do not know these things even though I have eaten lunch with her countless times, and she controls the radio on most road trips. I suspect these shortcomings of mine are because I do not live in the moment. I find myself constantly thinking and preparing for the future, asking myself, "What should I do next?"

This approach in life has undoubtedly contributed to my current success in medical school and will likely prepare me well for residency and a future career in medicine. I believe this mindset is a common personality trait among many trainees in medicine as we have long, difficult roads ahead of us with many important milestones along the way for which to prepare. However, reflecting on my conversation with Mr. Jones, I wonder if there is a cost to my own "forward" thinking. Am I missing out on the opportunity to cherish the delightful mundane and ordinary present moments of life in exchange for a more competitive and successful career trajectory?

I imagine if I was in Mr. Jones's position, I would also want to trade places with my wife. But, unlike Mr. Jones, I would voice some regrets. I now realize I would be willing to trade any future career successes for those "bologna sandwich" moments I often neglect to experience. This is an issue I will likely need to confront throughout my medical career, and the conversation with the Jones family challenged me to experience the present moment I am so often overlooking.

Gregory Grecco grew up in Akron, Ohio, and received his bachelor's degree in neuroscience at Bowling Green State University. He and his wife, Katherine, currently live in Indianapolis with their dog, Charlie. Grecco wrote this essay while a MD, PhD student at the Indiana University School of Medicine. With his combined degree program, he anticipates receiving his medical degree in 2025. His PhD will be in medical neuroscience in the field of addiction neurobiology. He wishes to continue in a medical career that will allow him the opportunity to interact with patients, mentor students, and write.

Why I Do What I Do

FRANK LUCAS, RRT

In my role as a clinical specialist in our Respiratory Care Department of the hospital, I get to see many types of patient situations, both good and bad. During the early stages of the COVID-19 pandemic we were tasked with caring for extremely sick patients who were requiring very aggressive forms of therapy. Many of these patients succumbed to the disease, but there have been some success stories as well. What follows is one of these success stories that stood out in my mind.

Kimberly Biddle is a fifty-three-year-old healthcare worker who tested COVID positive prior to her admission to our hospital. She was initially recovering at home after her diagnosis was made but had rapidly worsening shortness of breath and was admitted to an outside hospital. Ms. Biddle's condition continued to deteriorate and eventually was transferred from the other hospital to our Intensive Care Unit.

She arrived to us encephalopathic, very hypoxic, and requiring ventilatory support. She was also found to be very acidotic and in diabetic ketoacidosis. Her initial ventilator settings were quite average, but eventually her oxygen needs increased to a point where very aggressive measures were required to maintain adequate blood oxygenation. Kimberly's increasing oxygen requirements necessitated use of an alternate mode on the ventilator, use of a special bed for prone positioning, and paralytic medications to facilitate all these interventions. These more aggressive tools can quite often cause other complications, such as pressure ulcers as well as long-standing neuropathy issues.

Kimberly had a very slow improvement and ultimately continued to require ventilator support for a total of twenty-six days! The day-to-day improvements kept her from requiring a tracheostomy, and eventually she was extubated and taken off the ventilator. She was transferred to our Medical Progressive Care Unit and then discharged from our facility.

This pandemic has brought many challenges for healthcare personnel and there were times where we felt overwhelmed with the number and severity of these coronavirus patients. We have never experienced anything like this before in our careers. Kimberly is just one example of many that came through our hospital doors. But I am seeing many positives come out of this dreadful experience. Watching caregivers work together more than ever has been truly

Kimberly Biddle

inspiring, and case scenarios like Ms. Biddle's remind me of why I do what I do.

She had many reasons to give up but did not. And her dedicated hospital caregivers were not about to give up either.

Frank Lucas grew up in the Indianapolis area. He attended Ball State University and received his respiratory therapy training there. He has worked at Franciscan Health Indianapolis for more than twenty-eight years. He is married with two teenage children. Lucas loves spending time with his family as well as time with friends. He enjoys concerts and sports events.

The patient, Kimberly Biddle, granted permission to use her name for this story.

The Original, Shimmering Self

WILLIAM COOKE, MD

"Son, you don't even know. Things are hard. I gotta trade frog [slang for sex] just to eat." Olivia was a brunette female in her early twenties who looked decades older. Sitting next to her boyfriend in my office, she was barely ninety pounds of skin and bones. Probably because of the methamphetamines she used, she was constantly in motion, flailing her arms wildly as she spoke.

In a calm, reassuring voice I said, "I want to do everything I can to help you. One thing we need to talk about is getting you on birth control to keep you from getting pregnant."

She shook her head, "Nah, there's stuff wrong with me, son." Pointing at her boyfriend, she continued, "He's done pimped me out to every man in like three counties, and I ain't never got knocked up or whatever."

I listened without flinching at this confession. She did not need judgment from me. No, she had already shared with me how the whole world seemed to have already cruelly judged her by allowing her to be born into poverty, abuse, and chaos. She did not choose her parents or to have one of them steal her innocence as a child. Since then, her toxic environment had convinced her that all she was good for was sex. The world around her seemed to only value her for sex. Sex meant someone paid attention to her. Sex meant she and her boyfriend could eat that day—unless they spent the money on drugs.

A few months later, I paused outside Olivia's exam-room door. A lot had happened since I last saw her, and I did not want to just rush onto this next patient visit without taking a moment to reflect.

Soon after our last visit, I was called to the hospital to see her. She was sitting on the edge of her hospital bed in obvious discomfort. Between rapid breaths she managed to whisper, "I . . . can't . . . breathe." She was rocking backward and forward grasping at her left side and grimacing.

"Are you in pain?" I asked, as I knelt on the floor in front of her to look her in the eyes.

"Yes," she wheezed, panic written across her face. Every vital sign was critically abnormal, further confirming that something was catastrophically wrong. I had to get her comfortable and stabilize her to further investigate what was wrong and how to help her.

I took her hand, "I need to put you to sleep, intubate you, and put you on a ventilator, ok?"

She squeezed my hand, and looked at me wide eyed, "Any . . . thing . . . just . . . make . . . it . . . stop." She was too agitated to lay down, so I instructed her nurse to give a sedative. Soon, Olivia's breathing began to slow even though she was still clearly scared. Everyone scrambled to get her ready for intubation. As I gently lowered her head down to the stretcher, she looked up into my eyes and seemed to surrender any lingering fight.

I noticed a peacefulness spread across her face. Her youth suddenly shown through all the horror she had experienced in her short life. "Thank you," she whispered. In that moment I saw a simple innocence in the eyes of this crude and sullied woman. Her young, innocent face was unmasked from the shame and toxic stress of her life. As American author Frederick Buechner wrote in *Telling Secrets*, "The original, shimmering self gets buried so deep that most of us end up hardly living out of it at all." For a split second I saw what he was talking about. I was stunned by this revelation and overcome by thoughts of my own daughters as I cared for her. That experience helped me see her even more clearly as a person with intrinsic value deserving of love.

She ended up having a severe infection that had spread from her abdomen into her chest. After weeks of hospitalization with antibiotics, she was finally stable enough to return home. A few weeks later, she returned to my office.

After pausing to remember, I knocked on her exam room door. As I entered the room, she looked up and smiled.

Born and raised in southern Indiana, William Cooke graduated with honors from the Indiana University School of Medicine in 2001 and from the Ball Memorial Family Medicine Residency in 2004. Cooke practices comprehensive family medicine, addiction medicine, and HIV medicine in rural Austin, Indiana. Cooke gained national recognition for his innovative approaches to addressing the unique challenges of serving communities with limited resources, most specifically, the historic 2015 drug-related HIV/hepatitis C epidemic in Scott County, Indiana. Among other awards, he was named the Family Physician of the Year by both the Indiana Academy of Family Physicians and the American Academy of Family Physicians.

Cooke has a book in progress titled, "Canary in the Coal Mine." The book details his experiences as the lone doctor working with the rural southern Indiana town at ground zero of one of the worse healthcare disasters in U.S. history.

We Are All Human

WILLIAM COOKE, MD

It was 2:30 a.m. and the Emergency Room was finally starting to slow down. After working all day, I was most of the way through my moonlighting shift when I grabbed the next chart labeled "Room #7: Headache." I did not like room number seven. It creeped me out. Seriously, why was it isolated from the other rooms? Why was it down a dimly lit corridor? And why does calling it a "corridor" sound creepier than calling it a "hallway"? My next thought was, "I wonder if there's any of that pizza left in the break room," followed by, "Only four and a half more hours until I'm off," then, "Did we even have pizza earlier or was it Chinese? Why can't I remember?" And, finally, "Wait, what was I doing? Right, room number seven. Darn that room. It gives me the creeps."

That was my state of mind as I walked down the dark corridor or hallway, whatever. At least the chart had the word "headache" written at the top and not something like "rectal pain." So, I comforted myself thinking, "How bad could this one be? Maybe, I can even grab a power nap before the next patient."

Entering the room I was a little unsettled to find a very large, muscular, and oddly hairy young man sitting on the exam table. I introduced myself and asked, "What can I do for you?"

He said, "I need help."

I thought, "Maybe, try being a little more specific," but nodded encouragingly for him to continue. He looked away.

"Great," I thought, "It's going to actually be rectal pain."

"It says here you've been having headaches, is that right?" I prodded.

"Yeah, they're pretty bad, doc. And it seems to be, um, getting larger or something."

I took out my pen and began to write and I asked, "The headaches are getting larger?"

"No," he replied, "my head is getting larger." I stopped writing and looked up at him.

"What do you mean," I asked.

"Ever since a dream I had last year, I seem to be growing, especially my head, and it feels like there's something inside it."

My mind started scouring over years of medical training for direction. "Acromegaly"—a rare overproduction of growth hormone—came to mind. Growth hormone would make his head, hands, and feet grow and, since it is often caused by a pituitary tumor, it could also explain his recent onset of headaches. But something did not feel right. Why did he mention his symptoms started after a dream? That seemed out of place. So, I asked him why he mentioned the dream.

He said, "That's too personal," and looked away again. Then, he said in a softer voice, "They're always watching me now."

I asked, "Who?"

"The others."

I felt the hairs on my arms stand up and a chill ran down my spine. More than a little concerned, I glanced over to the door, making sure my exit was clear. I broke the lingering silence, "Tell me more."

Still looking away he said, "Ever since that dream, they've been watching me and lying to my family."

"Why?"

He paused and shifted uncomfortably. "They don't want me to be like them, to finish becoming one of them."

"And what is that?" I asked, trying not to sound as hesitant as I felt. He looked directly at me, studying me with a deadly serious expression. He looked like he wanted to tell me, but something held him back. "It's OK, I'm here to help you," I reassured him.

He looked up, blinked a few times, took a deep breath, and blew it out. He looked at me again and said, "A wolf."

"A what?" my mind screamed. But I continued to hold his gaze and not flinch. I nodded and said, "Why don't they want you to become a wolf?"

He seemed as stunned as I felt by my acceptance of that bombshell. "They're afraid of me and want to make sure I don't complete my transformation."

I responded, "So, you're in the process of changing."

"That's right. It all started with the dream."

I pressed him about the dream. "I think it's important for me to understand what happened last year to be able to help you."

He shook his head. "I don't know, doc. I think I'm just going to go."

"You were scared enough to come here for help. Let me have a chance to help you."

He studied my face again for a moment before giving in to my persistence saying, "OK, last year I was at my house watching TV when I suddenly felt this overwhelming urge to go outside. Once outside, I noticed there was a full moon, and I got dizzy. I fell onto all fours as I started trembling all over. The joints in my arms and legs snapped, my ears started ringing, and my head felt like it was going to explode. The next thing I knew, I was a wolf."

"And this was a dream?" I asked.

"No, it really happened. I think there's something in my head causing all this."

So, something that really happened is usually not considered a dream—unless, maybe, if it involves a beautiful woman. But definitely it would not be a giant, hairy man, and I was not about to point that out to said "giant, hairy man."

Instead, I reassured him that I would do everything I could to help him. I promised him that I would be right back and stepped outside of the room. Alone, walking down that dark corridor, I felt as though I was living a scene from one of those really bad 1980s horror movies. In a moment, he would come bursting out of the door in full werewolf mode to hunt me down. I shook off that thought and headed back to my desk.

I made a call to the on-call psychiatrist. He told me to give the patient the phone number of the behavioral health clinic and discharge him. I said, "Are you sure you want me to let a six-foot-six, 300-pound guy, who thinks that he's a werewolf and that there are people out to get him, just go home?" The psychiatrist asked me what I thought we should do. I told him, "Let me give him an antipsychotic medication and admit him to the psych floor. The psychiatrist told me that if I could get the six-foot-six, 300-pound guy to stay, then he would be happy to take care of him in the morning.

I grabbed a dissolvable antipsychotic and went over to the two security guards stationed in our ER. I teasingly asked, "Do the two of you have any silver bullets?" They looked at each other confused. Maybe, I should have explained what was going on first. Once I did, they agreed to stand outside of the door while I tried to convince the "wolfman" to stay. The three of us headed back to my least favorite room—number seven.

I knocked and entered the room. My patient was still sitting on the exam table, a mountain of a bearded man. Was he hairier now than a few minutes ago? At 3:00 a.m. my tired mind could almost believe his story.

I sat down and paused for a moment. I had no idea how I was going to convince him to stay or how this was going to go. I began by saying, "I'm glad you came here tonight. I know you're scared, and I want to help you. You may be right about there being something in your head causing your headaches and growth. There's a medical condition that does that. We can do some investigating to see if that's what's going on with you. But we need to keep you in the hospital."

He put his hands up and shook his head vigorously. "No way, doc! I need to go."

I said, "If you leave, you're not going to be able to get the answers you came here looking for." He seemed to relax slightly. I continued, "The mind is a powerful thing. There are two possibilities to explain what's going on with you. First, you could be transforming into a wolf, and people may really be after you. The other possibility is that all this has been created by your mind, possibly because of a medical problem that can be fixed. You were scared enough to come here for help, and I understand why. This must be very scary for you."

His eyes lowered: "I am scared. I don't know what's happening to me. I don't even know what's real anymore."

The geek in me felt like we were in some stylized, fantasy sci-fi movie with a funky soundtrack. When would I ever get another opportunity to give Morpheus's pill monologue from *The Matrix*?

"What is real? How do you define 'real'"? I said. "If you're talking about what you can feel, what you can smell, what you can taste and see, then 'real' is simply electrical signals interpreted by your brain."

He nodded.

"So far, so good," I thought. "And I want to help you figure that out," I continued.

He said, "Okay, what do I need to do."

Then, I wondered, do I just keep playing out that scene from *The Matrix*? "This is your last chance. After this there is no turning back. You take the blue pill, the story ends; you wake up in your bed and believe whatever you want to believe. You take the red pill, you stay in Wonderland, and I show you how deep the rabbit hole goes." The camera zooms in on my cool sunglasses. Each lens perfectly reflecting one of my outstretched hands offering the choice of pills.

But I only had one pill, and the damned thing was yellow. And what does Wonderland and rabbit holes have to do with any of this?

I noticed he was staring at me. I said, "I have a pill in my hand that I'd like you to take. It may help you figure out what's real. But there's only one way to find out. Remember, all I'm offering is the truth, nothing more."

I opened my hand revealing the yellow pill. Wow, I really did feel like Morpheus at that moment, minus the cool sunglasses. Well, also minus the cool clothes and the general overall coolness he exuded. Okay, maybe I was nothing like Morpheus and the way I felt resulted from the fact it was now 3:00 a.m. and I was talking to someone who thought he was a werewolf. At least he wasn't experiencing rectal pain.

He began to reach toward me. "This is it," I thought. "He's going to eat me now."

To my utter bewilderment and relief, he ate the pill instead. You know, I always thought it was a little weird how Neo took that pill so willingly with no questions or hesitation. But that Morpheus voodoo stuff really works! Disclaimer: In general, I do not endorse anyone offering a total stranger any pill you've been secretly hiding in your hand or taking such a pill offered to you.

"Now what?" he asked, jolting me out of my thoughts.

"There are two men waiting in the hallway (I hoped that sounded less creepy than them waiting in the corridor)," I answered. "They will help you to your room." I couldn't resist adding Morpheus's final words in that classic scene, "Follow me."

I tell this story in an amusing way, but we helped a man that night who had real potential to harm himself or someone else. We did not just "treat him and street him" as we sometimes say in our business. As far as I know, he is doing much better. It was important for him to be reassured that it is okay to not be okay. It is okay that neither he nor I had all the answers. But in his willingness to be vulnerable and to trust me, he taught me the importance of meeting each other where we are in life. It is about the importance of seeing each other as people first and being willing to connect on a human level, even if the other human may happen to be a werewolf.

Just Because You Are Paranoid, It Does Not Mean They Are Not After You

WILLIAM COOKE, MD

It is easy to slip into viewing a person through a lens tainted with bias. When a healthcare provider has had frequent encounters with a patient, who that person really is can blend into the background of monotony. Occasionally, something will jolt us out of this haze to clearly reveal how different the real world is from the one obstructed by routine. People and life are much more complicated than the split-second judgment calls we often make about them based on previous encounters.

"I don't mean no trouble Dr. Cooke," Jack said. "Like I told that young girl [my nurse] wall-ago, I'm just here for my refills." He was an older man with leathery, wrinkled skin and sunken eyes. He sat in my exam room with his hands on his knees. I asked him about the intrusive thoughts he sometimes has about people being out to get him.

He leaned forward a little, as if to tell me a secret. "I'm a paranoid schizo-phrenic. I never hurt nobody. I just take my meds, drink my beer, and watch my TV."

I went over his medical history, labs, and vital signs with him. No medication changes were needed.

I talk to him about his smoking a little, but he said, "I ain't hurt nobody. But nobody is going to take my cigarettes from me. I just sit and watch TV and leave everybody alone."

A few months later, he showed up in the emergency department. Someone had found him staggering around in front of his house covered in blood from little cuts all over his arms and chest.

His paranoia had apparently not caught up with current history as he was convinced the KGB had somehow implanted tiny beads all over his body. He said that the beads were slowly migrating toward his stomach where they would form a bomb and explode. Therefore, he was trying to cut them out of his body.

At one point he got free from the emergency room staff and made his way to the bathroom with a knife. He managed to continue to cut himself until in the ER staff found him on the floor of the bathroom covered in his own blood.

Thankfully, none of the cuts were very deep but many of them needed to be repaired.

After a short stay at the psychiatric hospital, where he was stabilized, he came back to my office and he told me about the event: "Yeah, I'm a paranoid schizophrenic. I stopped my meds and started having those thoughts, doc. I shouldn't a done that. But, that young boy [the ER doctor] sewed me up real good."

He showed me his arms. All the cuts were healed. Jack leaned toward me a little, gesturing at the exam room door, "Hey, tell that young girl I'm sorry." Apparently, he had tried to hug my nurse and she had objected.

He remained stable for a while as our visits went back to the routine, "I never hurt nobody. I just take my meds, drink my beer, and watch my TV."

A few months later, Jack was found outside his apartment, covered in his own blood again, with a knife a few feet away. The situation seemed obvious. His call to 911 for help also seemed consistent with his history of paranoid delusions: "I need help! That young boy just stabbed me to death!"

But this time Jack was so critically ill that he was not expected to pull through. When I went to see him, he had already been pronounced brain dead. But he was being kept on life support until his organs could be harvested for donation.

During this time, the police discovered the shocking truth. It turned out that while he was sitting on his couch watching television, a man jumped through Jack's front window with a knife and repeatedly stabbed him. I could not believe it. However, that truth allowed me to stop seeing him through the stories about him and to see him as a real person.

I visited him before they took him off life support to say good-bye and to process what he taught me. People who are hypochondriacs still get sick, people who have chronic chest pain still have heart attacks, people who frequent the emergency departments still have real medical emergencies, and just because you are paranoid, it does not mean they are not after you.

Death Can Be Good

WILLIAM COOKE, MD

I saw her, a dark silhouette against the setting sun, light shining through the window behind her. Why was she alone? My patient, Mr. Steele, was her husband, and I knew the love she had shared with him had endured the sum of a common man's life. How would I be able to tell her she would lose him tonight? He had already faded into that shadowland between life and death, just beyond the prevailing light of her love.

Their visits to my office were always a highlight of my busy day. I would sit and listen and ask questions between the routine practice of going over their medical issues and reviewing their treatment plans. He sometimes told me stories of when he served in World War II. One day he lost his usual jovial persona, grew deadly serious, and looked down. I felt the presence of some unseen weight his soul carried. He looked up and through his eyes I could see some terrible blend of fear and regret.

His bottom lip quivered slightly as he spoke: "Soldiers don't tend to freeze up the first time they shoot someone. I didn't. No, your training just kicks in, and the damned thing's done before you even had time to consider it." He paused and I waited in awed silence: "It's that next time you have to shoot someone that gets you. Not sure how many good men got shot because they hesitated. You see, every time you take aim after that first time, you remember what happened to that other human being when you pulled the trigger." His finger pulled the trigger of the invisible gun he pointed in my direction. A chill ran through me as he struck my heart as sure as if he had really shot me.

I thought of that moment as I approached Mr. Steele's wife. Confronting death is the hardest part of my job. Although not comparable to the physical violence seen in war, the act of telling someone their loved one is dead still feels violent. Mr. Steele was right—you do not think about it the first time. You just follow your training and you do it. There is no memory of that mother's mournful wails, that son repeatedly punching the wall until his knuckles bled, or that wife whose countenance seemed to shift to sheer terror as she looked around the room confused and asked, "What am I supposed to do now?"

This was all buzzing around my mind as she looked up. I suddenly found myself gazing into the eyes Mr. Steele had lost himself in as a young man and had never recovered. In that moment I could see that she already knew. Past the sadness in her eyes I could see a quiet confidence and what seemed like joy. She must have seen my bewilderment, as a subtle smile gently touched her wrinkled lips.

Her hand, knotted with years, reached out for mine. I wondered if the twists in her fingers matched his as if molded over time into a perfect fit. As our hands touched, I lowered my eyes looking for comfort between the cracks in the floor. I stood there as a professional man in my late thirties feeling like a child. I labored under the burden of my duty as I heard her weathered voice, "Child."

I instinctively looked up pitifully. My mouth opened and then closed without saying any words.

"Yes, child?" was her reply in such a warm and loving voice, I felt as if she was comforting me.

"I'm sorry," I stupidly uttered dropping my eyes again. But she understood. She took my other hand and I looked back up. Tears filled both of our eyes and for some inexplicable reason I embraced her. As we turned to walk to her husband's room together, she told me, "We had a good life together." She smiled, and continued, "A good life yields a good death, and sometimes death can be good."

Mindfulness

SARAH COLE, DO

Before I became a doctor, I was a punctual person. I was the person who arrived five to ten minutes early for social engagements and fifteen to twenty minutes early for business meetings. As a medical student I watched the clock and my preceptors as they fell farther and farther behind in clinic or as they apologetically called family members at the end of the day to explain why they would again be late for dinner. I convinced myself that I would be different. I would be the one family doctor to balance compassion and comprehensiveness with such efficiency that my patients would never wait past their appointment times. I would be the one family doctor who could make it home in time every night to cook a from-scratch meal for my family

It did not take long in practice for reality to disabuse me of this notion. It did, however, take much longer for me to accept that if I wanted to provide any semblance of compassion and concern in the exam room with my patients, then being "on time" now meant running fewer than twenty minutes behind schedule in the clinic or arriving only fifteen minutes late for a social event.

I fretted over inconveniencing other patients by running late. I experienced maternal guilt about coming home to my children just as they were getting ready for bed. My mother, a nurse, attempted to soothe my frustration over my new, unwanted chronic tardiness. She calmly repeated, "A doctor's time is not her own. We all know you're late because you were helping someone, not because you were nibbling chocolate bonbons while reading magazines." (She's recently updated this to say, "not because you were nibbling chocolate bonbons while scrolling Facebook.") But I still struggled.

It was finally one of my patients who taught me to relinquish this frustration in a most humorous way. Ms. Kay was a delightful woman in her seventies with a history of moderate chronic obstructive pulmonary disease and cirrhosis. On a cold February day she waited patiently in an exam room forty-five minutes past her appointment time as I strove to catch up from an influx of cough, cold, and flu visits that had been worked into my schedule. In somewhat of a tizzy, I finally breezed hurriedly into the room, briefly shook her hand, dropped breathlessly into the seat in front of her, and apologized for being late.

Ms. Kay waved a hand dismissively as she said, "Dr. C., at my age, there are two places I do not worry about being late—the doctor's office and the beauty parlor. It just doesn't seem to come out right if we rush things."

I paused and looked at her as her words caught up to me, and I laughed. "No, ma'am," I replied. "I certainly wouldn't want to be in that chair when my hair stylist was just trying to catch up." She smiled at me knowingly. And suddenly it seemed a lot less important to be "on time" that day. I took a deep breath and refocused on her. "Now, Ms. Kay, what can I do for you today?"

Ms. Kay has since passed away, peacefully, surrounded by her family, but I have relayed her words to a few of my other patients, people who seem wise and jolly like her. I have relayed them to more of my medical students and residents as we remind ourselves to be present in a healthcare world that can distract us. But most often, I replay those words in my head on the days when I'm tardy, and I think of Ms. Kay teaching me to slow down and just be with my patients. Those words still make me smile.

Sarah Cole's hometown is Saint Louis, Missouri. She is a graduate of Truman State University in Kirksville, Missouri. She remained in Kirksville to attend A. T. Still University/ Kirksville College of Osteopathic Medicine. Founded in 1892 by A. T Still, it was the first institution of osteopathic education in the world. Cole practices in Saint Louis, where she is the program director of Mercy Family Medicine Residency.

"When I close the door to the exam room and it's just the patient and me, with all the bureaucracy safely barricaded outside, the power of human connection becomes palpable."

Danielle Ofri, MD

Published in the *New York Times*, July 13, 2016

Miracles Do Happen

SUMMER WILHITE, MD

I have always known that I wanted to be a doctor. What I did not know, however, was how long the days would be, both literally and figuratively. When I have a particularly difficult day, I like to remember this one patient because she is a miracle. My faith is very important to me, and this story helps me to know that God continues to work.

It was the first time I had seen this patient, a forty-six-year-old female with obesity, chronic back pain, depression, and a history of nonmetastatic malignant melanoma.

She came in because of a painful breast. Her right breast had been sensitive over the past few months but had worsened suddenly over the past two weeks. She did a self-breast exam and felt a "bump." The pain was so significant that she was unable to sleep. Her family history was significant for breast cancer in maternal and paternal grandmothers.

On physical exam her right breast had a hard mass from 4 o'clock to 8 o'clock that extended into the underarm area, and the breast was very tender to palpation. I told her I was very concerned about breast cancer, and she said she knew; she thought it was breast cancer, too.

I ordered a diagnostic mammogram and eight days later she went for the mammogram. I received a phone call immediately following the mammogram from the technologist. She told me that the radiologist, Dr. Jameson, had read the mammogram and personally examined the patient. She told me, "He finds no palpable abnormality of the right breast and no evidence of malignancy on the mammogram."

The mammogram was normal! The only recommendation was to continue yearly routine mammograms. I was stunned. I knew that God had healed this woman. Sometime later she came back for another appointment. We talked about the mass. She told me that on the day of the mammogram she woke up and the mass was gone. She said that a lot of people were praying for her, and she believed God had healed her. I agreed with her, and it was such an amazing confirmation of God's love and healing power.

It helps me to know that I am not working alone, and that the Ultimate Healer is working through me and with me. Miracles do happen.

Summer Wilhite received a bachelor of science degree from the University of Southern Indiana and her medical degree from University of Louisville School of Medicine. She completed a family-medicine residency at Franciscan Health Indianapolis. Wilhite has a special interest in women's health, preventive care, pediatrics, and weight-loss management. In her spare time she enjoys exercising, decorating, and spending time with her family. She practices in Indianapolis.

Crossing a Bridge Too Far

RICHARD D. FELDMAN, MD

Very early in my practice I leaned a very valuable lesson in patient communication. Physicians are faced with the responsibility to inform patients and their families of very bad news. Much of the time it concerns a diagnosis of a serious or life-threatening diagnosis of cancer.

Doctors learn in medical school and residency training that such news should never be extended to patients over the phone or, today, in an electronic form, for example, in a messaging function with patients in the electronic medical record. This unpleasant task should always be done face to face. And, if possible, with other family members present because confronted with the shock of a serious diagnosis, many patients may remember little of the details especially after they hear the word "cancer."

There is also an ethical consideration, which has changed over the years from the mid-twentieth century era of paternalism in medicine: In contemporary medical practice, doctors do not withhold information from patients, especially as it relates to serious or terminal illness. For example, it is not uncommon for families to request that the physician not inform an elderly parent or grandparent of a terminal illness in an effort to spare the patient from emotional distress. I have always refused such requests unless the patient is significantly demented or otherwise of very limited mental capacity and would not understand the implications of the discussion. Patients have the absolute right to know.

But what should be the timing of extending bad news to patients once it appears likely there is a serious diagnosis?

When I first went into practice I had an elderly patient, Henry Burkhart, in the hospital with significant gastrointestinal symptoms. Preliminary scanning manifested what looked like a huge primary liver tumor. I was told by radiology it was certainly cancerous. A subsequent arteriogram showed a mass of arteries surrounding and feeding this "tumor." All we needed was to perform a needle biopsy of the mass to get tissue for microscopic examination to confirm the diagnosis, which was already virtually certain.

On rounds the next morning I informed Henry that it looked like he had liver cancer, but that we needed to do the biopsy merely to confirm the diagnosis. We sat together in his hospital room. He had tears in his eyes, worried about his wife's future without him. He thought he had no alternative but to place her in "an old folk's home." He was devastated, and being close to this patient, I was devastated as well.

That afternoon the interventional radiologist performed the needle biopsy, and after multiple attempts he called me to let me know of his quandary: All he could get back was bloody fluid. He could not explain the results as he was certain the patient had a solid liver tumor. The radiologist ordered a postbiopsy liver ultrasound and the "tumor" had vanished! A follow-up ultrasound sometime later confirmed that the problem was indeed gone. The mass apparently was a very large "world's record" (as he referred to it) liver cyst mimicking the appearance of a malignant hepatoma. Crazy!

I returned to Henry with the good news. He was so relieved and thankful. To him, it was a miracle of sorts. He could go on with his life and look after the well-being of his elderly wife. It never occurred to him to be angry with me for prematurely giving him a death sentence until I was certain of the diagnosis. He died several years later of a heart condition.

Like most other physicians I now never give patients serious or life-threatening diagnoses until I am undeniably certain with irrefutable evidence in hand. Until this time, serious or life-threatening conditions might be included among other possible diagnoses, but never the singular diagnosis. Breast abnormalities found on mammograms or chest nodules seen on chest x-rays or CTs are other applicable situations frequently encountered. This is the lesson I learned long ago.

Not uncommonly, just when physicians think they know the likely diagnosis, patients prove us wrong. Sometimes that's a very fortunate occurrence.

The Death of a Child

COLTON JUNOD, MD

It was a night shift in January. The emergency department was slowing down as the hour grew later. An eager premedical student at the time, I was "scribing" for the doctor on duty. Most of the patients had been discharged, which meant the doctor could devote some downtime to searching the Internet for a tractor he wanted for his farm. I used this downtime to ask the doctor some questions that had come up earlier in the shift.

"What are the indications for giving epinephrine for an allergic reaction?" I asked. I cannot recall what prompted me to ask this question. We must have seen a patient with an allergic rash earlier in the shift. The doctor responded with an explanation of the pathophysiology of anaphylactic allergic reactions.

The emergency department remained calm and quiet for the next couple hours. Nurses took this time to catch up on charting and doing crossword puzzles. It seemed to be an ordinary nightshift. Suddenly, the tones of the 911 dispatch scanner began to echo throughout the emergency department. The piercing sound of these beeps always caused my heart to begin to race as it indicated someone needed help.

"I need police, fire, and EMS to respond to a male child with a rash and trouble breathing," said the dispatcher.

Immediately, I turned to the doctor and said "epinephrine" in a proud voice as it related back to our previous conversation about anaphylaxis treatment. He nodded his head in agreement.

"Someone get the paramedic on the phone so we can figure out dosage and give epinephrine if needed!" exclaimed the physician. The paramedic and physician talked through the epinephrine dosage over the phone.

Several minutes later, the paramedic called back saying the child was very sick, and they were enroute to our hospital. This paramedic known to be a very seasoned paramedic, so we all took his words seriously and began to prepare.

Over the next few minutes the emergency department started to come to life. The night shift staff in the hospital was a very tight-knit family. When something bad was going down, everyone worked together and anticipated everyone's next move. The staff was highly reduced at night, so they all really relied on each other to work as a well-oiled machine.

Respiratory therapy, lab, nursing supervisor, and ER staff were standing ready to jump into action when the ambulance arrived. We were prepared for the worst.

The ambulance arrived and medics rolled the gurney into the trauma room with the child's parents following closely behind. It was immediately clear that this was not a case of anaphylaxis. The toddler was lying there limply with a petechial rash and mottled extremities and had a very serious infection. The doctor and nurses quickly jumped into action to stabilize the young patient. The child laid there cooing and crying tiredly. A sound I will never forget.

After watching the treatment team work on the child for a few minutes, I began to feel emotional. I walked down the hall to the supply closet and shed a few tears before quickly regaining my composure to assist wherever needed.

I noticed the family was outside of the room staring inside wondering what was going on. They knew the situation was critical, but I thought I might be able to explain step-by-step what was happening and attempt to answer their questions. I did this for a few minutes and sensed their appreciation.

The doctor came out of the room and explained to the family that their child was very ill and needed to be transferred to a large hospital with specialty pediatric care. The pediatric intensive care team arranged to pick up the child from our hospital. After their arrival, they saw how critical the child was, performed intubation, and quickly departed for their hospital.

Before the family departed, our nursing supervisor gave them a handheld "guardian angel," a small comforting keepsake, and some thoughtful words. This simple act of kindness is something I will remember for the rest of my life.

After their departure the ER staff was emotionally and physically exhausted. The physician reassured everyone that the teamwork was world class and that we did everything we could for the child.

We received word the next morning that the child had passed away en route to the next hospital.

A couple days later, all staff members that were involved in the case went to a "debriefing session" where we could talk as a group about our feelings and thoughts about the case with the hospital chaplain. It was here that I realized it is okay to be emotional about a patient case.

When I first went to the supply closet to shed a few tears, I felt guilty. I worried that I would be spotted by a colleague and viewed as "weak" or "sensitive." I had viewed doctors and nurses as stoic with tightly held emotions and thought I needed to force myself into that mold as well. However, in the case debriefing, I learned than many people struggled after the case. I was not alone. Many had thoughts of their own children or wondered if they could have done something medically different for the dying child. Luckily, my coworkers and I had each other to lean on and with whom to talk through the event.

I am now a medical student and think about this case often. As I reflect, I realize how much this patient caused me to grow as a medical professional. We are not robots that move from patient to patient thinking solely of diagnosis and treatment protocols. We are humans. We are humans who receive the privilege to be entrusted with the lives of those we serve.

At the time of writing this story, Colton Junod was a medical student at the Indiana University School of Medicine in the Rural Education Program at the Terre Haute campus. He is originally from Vincennes, Indiana, and graduated from Butler University in 2018. He aspires to be a rural-Indiana physician.

John Loves Clara

SUSAN HARTMAN, MD

Over the span of twenty-five years, it is amazing to look back and realize all the interconnections within a family-medicine practice and the lessons that patients can teach. When I graduated from residency in the late 1980s, there were very few hospital-owned medical groups and no private practitioners recruiting new partners in the location where I chose to put up my shingle. A fellow graduate and I had to navigate finding a location, getting a bank loan, buying furniture, deciding what insurance contracts to accept, writing office policies, and hiring our first staff.

The aspect in which we did not struggle was finding patients. I was fortunate enough to bring about 400 patients with me from our residency. One small local hospital bought out a retiring practitioner and sent us boxes of patient charts, and another of our former residency-trained doctors closed her practice to focus on her family. She divided her patients between another group of colleagues who had been out of residency one year and my practice.

It was through that generous referral that I first met Clara and John Jacobs. They were both in good health for being in their late sixties. John had recently retired from his machinist job, and Clara, who never worked outside the home, spent her days in the company of her children and grandchildren. John had a very dry sense of humor, one that took me quite a while to be able to ascertain when he was serious and when he was kidding. Clara was a sweetie; she was kind, very outgoing, and forever smiling with a good word for all. She was always dressed immaculately with her hair done (every Saturday so it would look nice for church). You never saw one without the other because Clara never learned to drive a car and John would not have it any other way. The only time they were apart was for "that female exam" where Clara said, "Johnny has no business seeing down there." Mind you, they have four children, so I know they were close enough to make that happen at some point.

They were still madly in love. Clara and John were childhood sweethearts and got married just before John shipped out for a tour of duty in the U.S. Army. I loved the way they looked at one another and teased each other playfully. It was only later in the game when navigating through some family health crises that I saw what real love meant for them.

Once Clara and John felt that this young "kid" was okay, I was introduced to the adult Jacobs children, their spouses, and then grandchildren as they came along. Clara always called me "Kid" in conversation, then would correct herself and say, "Oh, sorry, I mean doctor." I always smiled at her embarrassment and assured her that I was fine either way, and that I certainly was not offended.

As our relationship grew, she would ask about my family, and I was happy to share a few details. For her, family and faith were the only top priorities that existed until May rolled around for the Indianapolis 500 and then in August for the Indiana State Fair. Some things you just do not miss, no matter what. She would come by the office in her black-and-white-checkered outfit for her blood-pressure check every spring, and I knew where she was headed. She had a knee replacement one summer after suffering with so much knee pain that it had dimmed her ever-present smile a bit. Clara managed to convince her surgeon, postop week two, that she needed a scooter. He asked why, as a walker would be more appropriate. She responded, "to go to the fair, of course!" John just smiled and she went to the fair with a scooter!

I was once told by a professor of medicine that I should not send patients birthday cards, make extra hospital visits when I was not the attending physician, and never, never, ever go to funerals or send sympathy cards. His reasoning for all this was to limit liability by not giving the impression of "guilt" to a family who might be litigious. This professor never apparently had a family-medicine practice because all those things seemed so natural to do when a family trusts you with their most precious possessions—their family and themselves. The Jacobses got their share of graduation cards and unfortunately sympathy cards and funeral home visits, not solely by me but by my staff as well. We were all family.

For the Jacobses, I was there when five grandchildren were born and saw the pride and happiness on Clara's face as I placed each one back in her loving arms after I had examined them in the hospital and pronounced them perfect. She also loved it when, after the first office visit for each one, I would carry the infant around the office to show off that beautiful new life to my staff. I did this for almost all my babies, but I'd never let her know that. She was certainly a favorite, but so were all my "kids."

I was also there when a sixth grandchild was born prematurely in early summer, struggled mightily, and later succumbed to an intestinal inflammation after a few short days. I have a huge heart for kids and having to deliver the news that this beautiful baby boy was not going to make it just about killed me. I planned what I was going to say and how I was going to break the news to the extended family now gathered in the waiting room, but when I walked in the room so stoically and controlled, they instinctively knew, said it was okay, and comforted me as much as I was trying to comfort them. Several years later, I asked Clara about that day, and she said that she knew what was coming by the look on my face. She said I was always honest with them and prepared them well, so she knew when I walked in the room that what I was going to say was not good news. She wanted to spare me the difficult task of telling them. The funeral home was quiet and subdued for this child because there are no words when an infant dies. My staff and I attended the visitation. This strong Christian family was shaken but not lost.

Not long after the infant's death, John came in alone which was a "red flag" for me. It was his routine appointment time, but it was not for him. He was worried about Clara, now in her late seventies. He said she was not right. I asked him for details. He said she missed a hair appointment, then could not go to church because her hair was not fixed right. What may have seemed trivial or a bit funny to an outsider was a clue for me that she was likely depressed. When you know your patients well, you pick up on small events that can mean something more serious. Even when she had her knee surgery, every day in the hospital she wore make up and had her hair fixed as nicely as it could be when spending most of the day in bed. John said that he tried to get her to come with him for the appointment, but she said no. I asked if I could call her, and he started to tear up; he was surprised that I would offer but thankful for my gesture.

I would like to say that it was a magic phone call and that she responded quickly, but it was several months before she was back to the old Clara—joking, smiling, hair perfect, and calling me "Kid." And just in time for the state fair, too! Her daughter made sure that they had elephant ears and visited the dairy barn, just for me. She knew that my dad judged the 4-H ice cream contest, and the dairy barn was my favorite stop at the fair.

There were two divorces and four great-grandchildren born in the span of the next five years. Through these joys, celebrations, disappointments, and sorrows, the Jacobs clan persevered and kept the routine. Every Christmas there were goodies for my staff and a card with the entire clan pictured on the front; every Easter the office was presented with a homemade butter cream

Easter egg and a Resurrection card. I was humbled by the privilege to care for this multigenerational family.

In their early eighties, Clara and John were both troubled by chronic aging ailments—arthritis, a bit of hypertension, some mild heart disease, and hearing loss. Both were compliant with medical regimens, fussed about their weight gain (but loved to eat), and continued to keep regular appointments with me in the office. One afternoon Clara came back to see me by herself. She was using a walker now and quite bent over due to some lumbar spinal degenerative disease. She wanted to talk to me alone and left John in the waiting room with her daughter. I helped her into the exam room.

Clara told me that John was having some issues dressing himself and did not seem to remember what she had told him. She thought he was teasing her, but it was getting to be more than she could handle. She looked angry. She wanted me to talk to him and get him to shape up because he was getting hard to love with his current behaviors. Just like when John came alone after the death of their grandson, I knew this was more than just teasing out of control.

After a few visits, specialty consultations, and lab testing, John was diagnosed with early dementia. He knew something was wrong when he could not keep the checkbook but was afraid to disappoint her, so he tried to make her laugh to cover up his mistakes. She nearly slugged him in the office when he related that story to me, but I saw that glimmer in his eye and her smile creep back on to her beautiful face. It was then that I knew they would be okay and handle whatever came next together. The Jacobses were a tight-knit, supportive family who braved through tragedy and rejoiced in celebrations. It is a cliché that "love conquers all," but I was true in this case. John's dementia would be just one more adjustment. And one more change: A grandson was now assigned driving duties to make sure Clara got to the fair!

A few years later, Clara pulled me aside in the hallway and asked if I would promise her one thing. She was clearly worried but more relaxed than prior to John's diagnosis. She said, "If I die before Johnny, please make sure he has on a clean shirt for my funeral!" We both laughed, but I knew she was serious.

I left my practice after almost twenty-five years due to some health issues that prevented me from fully practicing my profession. Clara was one of the first patients who I met when we opened the doors and one of the last patients to come to say good-bye. She was crying, I was crying. We hugged. She thanked me for taking such good care of her family and said "Kid, we've sure been through some tough times together for the past twenty-five years, but it was a fun ride. I hope you learned a lot from us."

I said, "I sure did!" I learned loads about love, devotion, and family.

I'm happy to report at this writing, John and Clara have just recently celebrated their seventy-fifth wedding anniversary. Clara is still living independently in their home with family assistance, and John is in memory care. We keep in touch.

Susan Hartman serves as the medical director of Quality for Franciscan Physician Network in Central Indiana, a division of Franciscan Alliance. A family physician, Hartman transitioned to a full-time quality position after more than twenty years in both private and employed practice arrangements. She is a graduate of the Indiana University School of Medicine and the Franciscan Health Indianapolis Family Medicine Residency, where she continues to teach medical students and residents. Hartman completed a master's in health quality and safety management at Thomas Jefferson College of Population Health.

"Out of your vulnerabilities will come your strength."

Sigmund Freud, MD

To Err Is Human but Arrogance Is Unacceptable

ZACHRY L. WATERSON, DO

The residents were in didactics and were being instructed on professionalism and interpersonal communication. They were viewing a remarkable movie titled *The Doctor*, starring William Hurt. The movie is about an arrogant physician who becomes ill himself and faces the realities of entering a complex health-care system as a frightened patient rather than a confident doctor. It is a powerful and moving story.

At the close of the didactic session, I shared with the residents a personal story about a breach of professional character, which I committed a few years ago. Although this is certainly one of the most embarrassing and shameful moments in my career, I felt the need to share this story with them. Learning always seems to be solidified when students can relate the topic to life stories and events. After sharing my story with the residents, several came to me and encouraged me to share my story with others. They informed me they were emotionally touched by my story and my willingness to share my own failures so they might not make the same mistake. So, I thought I would share my story with you.

It starts years ago when I was a resident with a patient, John, an imposing man standing some six-feet three-inches tall and about 240 pounds. He had snow-white hair and beard and always wore military-issue dungarees. He was a Vietnam War veteran and was in the Special Forces for more than thirty years before retiring. Even in his late sixties, I would have not wanted to tangle with him. John had multiple chronic medical problems, but most were well controlled.

John was the type of patient who, no matter the reason he was scheduled for an appointment, could monopolize the visit. It could get very irritating. He would like to tell stories about his combat experience and military conquests. I found those stories to be very interesting at first, but as I progressed through my residency and the number of patients I was expected to see increased, the stories got old fast! I would find myself trying to quickly move through the office visits with him, minimizing the interaction. I did not want to schedule him back for follow ups. He became the patient all physicians begin to dread. You know the patient when you see them on your schedule you begin to hyperventilate, panic, and think, "Great, now my day is ruined." At last my residency was complete, and John would be turned over to a new intern to manage, or so I thought.

I was now in private practice and John found me. He transferred to my new practice location, and again, at first, it was not a problem. Starting out, I was not as busy and was able to devote time to listen to John chatter away, always having to redirect him to why he was in the office. It got to a point that I did not need to schedule follow-up appointments, as John was in the office every six weeks or so if he needed to be or not. I began to think he just wanted someone to talk to, or perhaps he was just lonely. I began to "tolerate" John but as my practice grew and my patient demands increased, I simply did not have time for John and his stories.

I began to be rather curt with John, but that did not deter him. I went from curt to downright rude, again to no avail. I tried every technique that I could remember being taught in residency on managing difficult patients, but nothing seemed to work. I just endured what I thought was torture. I could not for the life of me figure out why John continued to seek care from me. I certainly would not have wanted a doctor like me. The next chapter in my life had come, and I left private practice for a career in academic medicine. Hooray. No more John. Not so fast.

Within weeks of starting my new career, there was John on my schedule the first day of my new clinic! How could that be? How did he find me? Not sure myself, I entered the room and the stories started to fly. But this visit was different. John's voice, always a little squeaky and high pitched, was now hoarse. This seemed to have happened in just a few months. I sent him for some imaging and sure enough he had a tumor in his neck. He was terrified as his uncle, who was also a heavy smoker like John, had laryngeal cancer. John was convinced this was what he had, too.

I sent him to otolaryngology, and they took over management. I did not see John for several months but continued to receive notes from otolaryngology, oncology, and other specialists. Several more months went by and no sign of John. Then one day out of the blue, John is on my schedule. He did not need to see me. He just wanted to come in and tell me all about the last six months. He did not have laryngeal cancer, as it turned out; he had a relatively treatable thyroid cancer. He seemed to be in good spirits and thus began the every six week visits. Sigh!

It was about three months later that he came into the office again. This time it was different. He was hoarse again and also had trouble swallowing. I immediately sent him back to otolaryngology. This time the prognosis was not so good. He had developed a second head and neck cancer and this time, unfortunately, it was extremely aggressive and had metastasized. Otolaryngology, oncology, and radiation oncology were all seeing him. He quickly began to deteriorate, and it was recommended he consider hospice. John, always the fighter, finally agreed. I referred him to the hospice facility and turned over his care to the hospice physician.

Over the next several weeks, I did not hear anything from John. I had received a few orders for home healthcare and some miscellaneous orders that required my signature. A few days later, extremely busy with administrative issues and running behind due to meetings, I went to my afternoon clinic already irritated to find John on my schedule. I exploded! Why is he here? What does he want from me? I don't have time for this! I continued to rant and rave in front of residents and nurses. I was outraged that our office staff would schedule him. Then my nurse poked me in the chest and said with a very stern voice, "Shut up and go see your patient!"

I entered the exam room with an attitude and was met by two young men who I had never met before; they introduced themselves as John's sons. I was surprised. I did not know John had any children; it dawned on me that I had never asked. I turned my head to sit down and then acquired my first look at John in several months. I did not recognize the patient I knew before as John. He was emaciated, cachectic, and pale, almost transparent. He was unable to speak and had a feeding tube in place through his abdomen into his stomach. I immediately began to feel quite embarrassed and ashamed of my behavior. I asked his sons if there was anything I could do or if there was a reason for the visit? They simply replied, "He has a letter for you and wanted to see you one last time."

At that moment, I never felt less of human being in my life. I could not believe the way I had treated him, and the way I had carried on in the workstation in front of my residents and nursing staff. I was ashamed of myself and humiliated. I did not deserve to be his physician. At that moment, I did not deserve to be a physician at all.

I could not even look John in the eyes. He took my pen out of my hand and wrote on a piece of paper the following: "It's okay, Doc. I know that I was a pain in the butt as a patient, but you always listened. You always cared. You always made time for me. I just wanted to see you one more time and say good-bye." I could no longer hold back the tears, and I broke down at that point. Every time I relive this story, I get choked up. I will not share with you what he wrote in the letter he gave me, but every time I think I am having a bad day I pull that letter out of my desk and read it.

Why do I share this story, you might ask? In this era of electronic medical records, managed care, private and federal patient satisfaction surveys, and extreme physician burnout, I want to remind physicians through my story to never lose sight of why we became physicians. Do not ever lose your empathy and compassion for your patients. I share this story because, as I told the residents, I want physicians to understand the ultimate trust and faith our patients place in us. I want physicians to understand that patients are frequently under great stress as well and are often not at their best when seeing us.

I tell this story because of what it taught me, what John taught me—to err is human, to be arrogant is unacceptable. John died three days after seeing me. I hope he knows how much he taught me and knows he made me a better physician.

Zachry Waterson grew up in Syracuse, Indiana, on Lake Wawasee. He attended Manchester College in North Manchester, Indiana. He graduated from the University of Health Sciences College of Osteopathic Medicine in Kansas City, Missouri, in 1999. Waterson completed his family-medicine residency training at the Fort Wayne Medical Education Program, serving as chief resident his third year. He joined the residency faculty in 2003 and after leaving private practice joined the residency full time becoming the program director in 2010. He and his wife, Pam, have two daughters. He is an avid waterfowl hunter and fisherman.

Positive Living

JOSEPH SCHERGER, MD, MPH

A gentleman in his mid-eighties came to me to establish care. His mental health was very fragile, and his problem seemed to be a combination of mental-health conditions rather than a specific disorder. He had mild cognitive impairment, some depression, some obsessive-compulsive disorder, and some paranoia. If he went off his antidepressant he decompensated.

Through all this he stayed well by living by one saying, "AMTD: Attitude Makes All the Difference." He practiced that and was friendly to everyone.

He stayed positive and loved his monthly visits with me just to talk. He would also ask if I used AMTD with other patients, my students, and my residents. I could honestly say I did.

I thank him for his gift to me of positive living.

Joseph Scherger is a family physician at the Eisenhower Health Center in La Quinta, California. He is also a core faculty with the Eisenhower Health Family Medicine Residency Program. He is the author of two books, 40 Years in Family Medicine *and* Lean and Fit: A Doctor's Journey to Healthy Nutrition and Greater Wellness. *Originally from Delphos, Ohio, Scherger graduated from the University of Dayton in 1971. He graduated from the UCLA School of Medicine in 1975. He completed a Family Medicine Residency and a master's in public health at the University of Washington in 1978.*

Lessons on Fatherhood

MIN QIAO, MD

In my third year of medical school, I took care of a young boy who was hospitalized for a cystic fibrosis exacerbation. He was admitted overnight, and when I met him in the early morning, he was still asleep, a tiny figure under the covers. He looked like a toddler although he was already seven years old. I looked around the room for an adult to speak with to complete my history so that I could be a dutiful little student. I found behind the curtains surrounding his bed his father, who was also asleep. Despite my attempts, he was in deep slumber and did not stir. I went on to do my best with my physical exam with the boy still asleep.

I would never get a chance to get that patient history that I was after, but after some chart sleuthing, I found out that this boy, Ian, had been in and out of the hospital. A "CF tune-up" as we liked to call it. Cystic fibrosis is a disease that cripples the lungs from being able to properly clear secretions. Thus, bacteria and infections are drawn to these patients like moths to a flame. Out of necessity, children with cystic fibrosis are admitted to the hospital regularly for IV antibiotics.

Later that day, I went to check up on Ian and found him bouncing on his bed, Twizzlers in one hand and a bag of Lays potato chips in the other. Normally, I would have at least tried to encourage him to slow down on the junk food, but CF patients have so much trouble absorbing nutrients that we are desperate for them to eat anything and everything. It is also why every time they eat, they must take enzyme pills to help them absorb and digest the food that they ingested.

Instead I asked, "Did you make sure to take your medicine with these?"

Ian smiles back at me with a toothy grin "No," with a little chuckle.

"Well, you know you have to take your medicine every time you eat, or else you'll have a belly ache and really bad poos!" I said with a smile back.

Ian sits down on his bed. "Ok, fine," he said still smiling. "Who are you?"

I introduced myself and mentioned that I had met him early this morning but that he was asleep. We talked for a bit; I asked him how he was feeling, and after a while I asked if his dad was coming back.

Still chewing on his Twizzlers, Ian said "He needed to take a shower. He's coming back." Before I could inquire more details, Ian hopped to his feet and looked at me eagerly and asked, "Hey! will you take me for a walk? The nurse lady said she would, but she never came back. Please?" This was a boy who knew how to get what he wanted. I could not refuse him.

Since children with CF are so prone to infections while in the hospital, they are often restricted to their rooms. If they were to leave, they have to be gowned, gloved, and masked to prevent any chance of catching one of the perilous diseases down the hall. It makes the hospital stay quite mind numbing, especially for eager and playful children like Ian.

Over the next couple of weeks, I would get to see Ian every morning, monitoring him for any signs of regression. In the afternoons, whenever I needed a break from the busywork, I would sneak back to check on him. He would greet me with his toothy grin and a mischievous twinkle in his eye. Each time, he would have a request for me. Some days, we went on tricycle rides around the floor. Other times, we walked through the nurse's station as he tried to charm another popsicle out of them. Always with his distinctive smile, he would deliver his favorite line, "C'mon! Please?"

One time, he managed to convince me to bring him a giant ice cream sundae from the cafeteria. As we sat there, chocolate fudge covering our faces and ice cream dripping down our hands, I asked him about his family. I asked him about what kinds of things he liked to do with his dad, where is mom was, and who else lived at home with him. I knew that he had a less than ideal home life because there had been several social work notes in his file, and because, what kind of seven-year-old child stays in the hospital alone for weeks without a single visitor? From what I could tell, Ian was extremely fond of his dad and loved making fried chicken with him in the summers. He did not speak much about his mom or anyone else.

When it finally came time for his discharge, I found myself sad that I would never get to see what would become of Ian. Per my usual routine, I prerounded on him early in the morning. This time, however, he was already awake. Ian leaped from his bed as I walked in, yelling, "My Daddy's coming today! My Daddy's coming!"

I could not help but mirror his excitement and said, "Oh my goodness! Are you so excited to go home?"

He could not register my question in his exuberance. "Can you help me call my Dad? He's coming today!" he said.

"Of course. We can do that in the afternoon."

That afternoon, as promised, I greeted Ian in his room. For the first time, he did not greet me back with his signature smile. "What's up, little man?" I asked.

"The phone in my room isn't working," he replied. "I tried to call my dad and it wasn't working."

"Okay, well, let's find you another phone then," I said.

We proceeded to the closest nurse's station, and he tried his father's number again. "The number you have dialed is not in use" was heard in the phone's receiver.

His brows furrowed looking at the phone, and then he turned to me. "You try," he said.

"Okay!" I said with optimism. As I dialed the number on the keypad, I could feel my heart sinking with each deliberate press of a button. Once again the call failed to go through. "I'm sorry bud. Maybe we can try again later," I said. He was crestfallen.

"How about some ice cream?" It was the only thing I could think to say.

I stayed with him for the next hour, trying my best to distract him and perhaps even more myself from the anger rising inside me.

A little while later, Ian was fast asleep in his bed, crashing from his sugar high. I passed his nurse in the hallway and she said that she had luck with his father in the past and volunteered to try to reach him. When she was finally able to get in contact with his father, she told me that his father had some car troubles and would not be able to pick him up today. He could not provide further details about when he would be available.

We tried to be gentle in waking Ian up as if somehow, it would break the news easier. He sat up and listened intently as his nurse relayed this information.

When she was finished, he shook his head, confused, and said, "My dad doesn't have a car! You're lying."

We were silent, staring back at those bright blue eyes. Finally, his nurse broke the silence saying, "Well, how about we try again tomorrow. It's already too late for you to leave the hospital anyway. We'll try again tomorrow."

What was with Ian's father? It was not completely clear. But we did know that both parents were involved with drugs and the mother was completely absent. Ian's father had been recently battling his addiction, but we felt he was doing his best to be there for his son. Was he in the middle of a relapse? Were there other issues going on? I will never know for sure, but life for this family was certainly chaotic and disjointed.

Feeling defeated, I walked back to the workroom to finish up my notes. I opened the most recent lab results we had gotten back and saw that Ian's had come back too. They were perfect—all perfectly normal. A perfect little boy. I could not help but wonder how long he could stay that way.

Min Qiao was born Shanghai, China. As a newborn she had a congenital bowel obstruction requiring emergency surgery. Understanding the impact that physicians have on their patients and her family's immense gratitude toward the physicians who saved her life, she knew from a young age that she wanted to be a healer. Qiao immigrated to Indiana as a child and now considers herself a midwesterner. She attended the Indiana University School of Medicine and is now a neurology resident at Washington University in Saint Louis.

Letting Go

ALLISON CRONE, MD

I spent January of my third year of medical school on inpatient internal medicine wards. The hours were long and the days busy. I often arrived at the hospital before sunrise and left after sunset, living in a sort of perpetual twilight. It was on one of these cold January days that Jim arrived at the hospital, accompanied by his wife Susan. His symptoms and the chest x-ray taken in the emergency room pointed to pneumonia, and a quick glance at his chart revealed that he had been hospitalized three other times in the past year, also for pneumonia.

Jim was in his early seventies and had been diagnosed with Parkinson's disease about a decade prior. In the past two years, he had developed a steadily progressive dementia. Together, his symptoms had left him bedridden with little ability to communicate. His family, particularly his wife, had been committed to his care for years, and the strain in Susan's face was evident as she remained faithfully by his bedside.

I learned about Jim through Susan's eyes. She told me about when they met, freshman year of college in a business class. They were married a few years later. She told me with pride about their three sons and showed me pictures of their grandchildren. How Jim had loved to sit with those children, how he would laugh—deep belly laughs—at the things they would say. He loved to fish and do crossword puzzles and take walks through the tree-lined streets of their neighborhood.

Susan paused: "Well, he *used* to love those things. Before."

Their life was split into a before and an after, the symptoms of his disease drawing a line between the two eras. Before, carefree days spent sipping coffee and cradling grandchildren and strolling leisurely hand in hand on the first sunny day of spring. After, a difficult path of doctor's offices, medications, a slow and progressive loss of control of body and mind. It was clear that this path had been long and winding, the terrain steep, and the footing uncertain.

The pneumonia turned out to be due to aspiration, as it had been in his prior hospitalizations. Due to his illnesses, Jim was no longer able to protect his airway when he swallowed. Later that day, our medical team met with Susan to share this news.

My attending physician began: "Susan, we have found the cause of Jim's pneumonia. It's like the last time he was hospitalized; he is not able to swallow properly, so small bits of food and drink are moving into his windpipe and down to his lungs, leading to infection."

Susan nodded. She had heard this before.

More gently, the attending continued, "It may be time to start thinking about our options. I know these repeated hospitalizations are difficult for both of you. We can think about placing a feeding tube to decrease the risk of these aspiration events. We can also think about shifting our focus a bit, from curative medicine to making him comfortable."

"Are you talking about . . . hospice?" The word hung heavy in the room. Susan looked searchingly from one face to the other, and then to her husband, tears in her eyes.

"I am," my attending confirmed. "I know this is a lot to process, but there is a great deal that can be done to make him more comfortable and to maximize the quality of the time he has left."

"No," Susan said firmly, wiping a tear away with some frustration. "I can't, we can't just give up. I think we should do the feeding tube."

I gazed at Jim, lying asleep in the bed. Since he arrived, he had spoken little, his words muffled, his mind muddled by dementia, and his muscles held captive by Parkinson's. Because of his severe dementia, the decision of what to do ultimately fell to Susan. I felt a stab of frustration at the fate of this poor man, by all accounts a kind man, a good father and husband. Were we doing him justice by prolonging his life at all costs?

The next day, I came to check on Jim and Susan. I entered the room to find Susan holding her hand to Jim's face, looking at him tenderly. He shifted his hand toward her, a minute movement, and she grasped it in her own.

She met my eyes: "I think he wants to eat."

I began to reiterate why he was not able to have food—his difficulty swallowing, his recurrent pneumonia—but she stopped me.

"I know, I know. He isn't able to eat much anymore, but it seems to be one of the few activities that still makes him happy." She heaved a sigh: "To place a feeding tube would be to take that away from him."

She sat on the small couch beside the bed, tears in her eyes. I sat beside her and held her hand. She said the words quietly: "I think maybe I should talk to someone from hospice."

Jim and Susan left the hospital a few days later. In the end, Susan opted to pursue hospice for her husband and decided against the feeding tube. Jim was eating his regular meals, despite the risks, and his mood seemed to improve. There had been a change in focus to providing the best possible quality of life for Jim in his final days, even if that meant that he would ultimately have fewer days. Although this was a difficult decision for Susan, she felt confident that it was the best decision for Jim and that it was what he would want.

In the hospital, you see many kinds of love. Sometimes love means holding on for dear life, weathering the storm together. Other times, love is the quiet, steady act of simply being with another person. And sometimes, love means having the courage to let go.

Allison Crone was a medical student at the Indiana University School of Medicine when she wrote this story. She was born in Indianapolis, Indiana, and attended IU for her undergraduate studies. While in medical school, she became fascinated with medical imaging and plans to be a radiologist. She enjoys hiking, swimming, yoga, and values spending time with family and friends.

Helping a Patient through a Rough Time

RICHARD D. FELDMAN, MD

As the residency director, I received this letter of appreciation years ago from a patient who was being cared for by a family medicine resident:

I was referred by my counselor at the hospital's behavioral health center. She recommended that I see a doctor as my resting pulse rate was high, and I had a lot of other symptoms. Dr. Reynolds took my case. When I first saw her, I was totally exhausted and depressed. I literally had not slept in days. I had tremors, fainting spells, weight loss, and itched all over.

Five other physicians had told me I was suffering from postpartum depression. I had a C-section, endometriosis was discovered, and I became infected. I spent three weeks in the hospital when my son was five weeks old. For some reason I was not recovering.

Dr. Reynolds was very professional and reassuring. She examined me and suggested a possible overactive thyroid, soon confirmed by tests. Her straightforward manner convinced me to stick with the program she mapped out. She was firm, she established trust, and she gave me much needed hope. One by one, Dr. Reynolds treated all my symptoms and patiently followed up with me through what I am sure was a very frustrating process. I called her too often, questioned everything, was overly concerned, reluctant to take medication, and I cried a lot.

She was very honest with me and she really listened to my concerns. I have never met such a considerate doctor or one who was concerned for my total health. She said we'd stick through this until I felt better and had no more symptoms. It took two years, a thyroidectomy, and many appointments and long phone calls, but I finally feel better.

I cannot thank her enough. The quality of my life is significantly improved.

Dr. Reynolds has restored by faith in doctors by treating me with dignity and respect when I was at my worst. Through her guidance and orchestrating of my medical needs, I have regained my health. I imagine the day will come when I don't marvel at that. I have assumed responsibility now for my own health and happiness.

Many, many thanks to Dr. Reynolds, she is a wonderful doctor.

In all my professional years, this is the one letter that most profoundly demonstrated to me the power of a positive doctor-patient relationship.

It confirmed for me the importance of physician mindfulness and communication that can occur, especially in family medicine and other primary-care specialties when patients are cared for over time with comprehensive, continuous, concerned, compassionate, and personalized care. The letter demonstrates the best professional and personal attributes of a physician, true to the philosophical underpinnings and values of family medicine.

The specialty of family medicine is also committed to patient advocacy and coordination of care while navigating the patient through the healthcare system. Family physicians have always been trusted advisers and compassionate counselors. They are driven by the need to make people whole in mind, body, and spirit; they treat people, not merely diseases. I have always been very proud to be a family doctor, as my father before me, and like my youngest son following in my footsteps.

Fostering an environment of trust and mutual respect, just as expressed by this patient is essential. The letter is a perfect example of continuous healing relationships over time and patient-centered care.

Certainly, the patient in this story benefited from this relationship with better health and well-being. But I assert that this doctor benefited from this patient interaction in many ways as well. Triumphs in the practice of medicine are exceedingly important professionally and personally for the physician. Helping a patient to achieve or regain health reinforces passion for the profession and reminds doctors why they chose a medical career. All physicians need these triumphs that come through doctoring and patient relationships.

This patient letter reminds me that what we do as physicians is meaningful and important, and so often makes a positive difference in the people who entrust their lives to us. Providing medical care to patients is both a privilege and profound responsibility. It confirms for me that physicians can do so much good for patients, and that nothing in medicine feels better than to know that one has truly helped a fellow human being.

It's about gratification and fulfillment through the power of human connection.

Stefan

REBECCA P. FELDMAN, MD

Despite the more than three decades that have passed, there is an indelible memory etched in my brain of the first time I met Stefan. It was just another day in the office in the first handful of years I had been working as a family physician, or so I thought. In walked a portly, balding scientist in his sixties, a new patient for me, there for a yearly physical. His eyes were a twinkling azure blue, and he wore a broad grin on his face. Did I detect a cleft lip concealed under the white mustache? His right hand was extended for a warm handshake, but there was no mistaking the fact that his fingers were fused into two main digits plus a thumb on both hands. An Eastern European accent was apparent at the first hello.

When I introduced myself as Doctor Feldman, Stefan asked, "Are you Jewish?" I replied, "Not by heritage but by marriage. Are you?" Stefan said, "By heritage I am Jewish, but I left that behind long ago." He immediately reminded me of a younger, larger version of my beloved father-in-law, Max Feldman, whose family immigrated from Eastern Europe when he was ten. What a first visit! The two of us just clicked and I began to learn bits of his history, gleaning more of the story over the decades to follow as I continued to see him as a patient and our friendship grew.

Stefan was born in Poland to a mother with lupus who died giving birth to him. His father and his father's two maiden sisters were left to raise this smart and handsome little blonde boy with major birth defects, but they never let those disabilities get in the way of a normal upbringing. When Stefan was twelve years old his father died of tuberculous; it was just Stefan and his aunts from then on. Stefan loved to ice skate and when he was fifteen he first set eyes on the beautiful raven-haired Helena skating on the pond near his house. It was love at first sight for them both! Round and round they twirled together on the ice, and from that day forward, they were inseparable. They finished high school and college during Hitler's rise to power in Germany. Stefan and Helena married and Stefan began his PhD studies in pharmaceutical chemistry. Imagine becoming a chemist with claw-like hands, but that was his dream. On September 1, 1939, Germany invaded Poland, triggering the start of World War II.

Stefan's aunts and Helena's parents knew they were in grave danger, as they were all Jewish. They hatched a bold plan to buy false identification papers, assume Catholic identities, and flee to Warsaw, where they would hide in plain sight as Christians. They were able to get only two sets of papers; the aunts opted to stay behind. Stefan, Helena, and her parents traveled separately as couples, and the journeys were arduous. They all carried cyanide in their pockets in case they were captured. At one checkpoint, German soldiers believed that the Aryian-appearing Stefan was Christian but accused the dark-haired Helena of being a Jew. Finally, Stefan convinced them that he would *never* marry a dirty Jew.

They all made it to Warsaw and were able to find tenement apartments near each other and just next door to the walls of the Warsaw Ghetto. The apartments were accessed by ladders that they would pull up at night for security. Food was scarce. They learned their catechisms and regularly attended Catholic church. Stefan and Helena and her parents all got jobs in the same factory, but they never acknowledged to anyone that they were related. If one of them had been discovered to be a Jew, the entire family would have been taken to the public square and executed by gunfire. Stefan worked by day and continued to study for his doctorate at night. Tragic news reached them that his beloved aunts were murdered by the Gestapo as they attempted to hide in their outhouse. Meanwhile, thousands of Jews were being deported to concentration camps by cattle cars from the Warsaw Ghetto right over the wall next to their apartments. Somehow the family members all managed to survive to see the Warsaw Ghetto uprising and finally the end of the war.

After World War II Poland was still a frightful place under the reign of Soviet Communism. Stefan was allowed to take the exam for his PhD in pharmaceutical chemistry at the famed University of Warsaw; most transcripts were lost during the war so they took his word that he had completed his studies. He passed and became a professor at that university. Stefan and Helena had their only child, a lovely daughter named Sonia. Stefan rose to the rank of chancellor of the University of Warsaw, which came with a livable salary and a personal driver. Sonia later told me that her friends liked to play at her apartment because they always had food in the refrigerator. Of course, the family continued to raise their daughter as a Catholic.

Stefan hated Communist Poland. He and Helena longed to move to America and raise Sonia in freedom. However, Sonia was already a university student (in pharmaceutical chemistry, of course) when the opportunity arose.

The family was allowed to take only $50 and some clothes with them and flew to Rome for six months, where an agency (probably Jewish) worked on placing Stefan in a job in the United States. That was enough time for Sonia to fall in love with her current husband, Mario. Ironically, Sonia only lived in the United States for a year before marrying Mario and moving to Rome. Stefan and Helena eventually moved to Indianapolis, where they bought their dream house in a small quiet neighborhood and Stefan worked as a chemist. Freedom at last! They were so proud to become U.S. citizens in their late fifties. Aside from their daughter, freedom was their most prized possession.

This story was told to me in bits and pieces over the decades. As I got to know Stefan, my husband and I were lucky enough to be invited to dinner at their home. Helena was the consummate cook, so elegant and entertaining. We reciprocated and our three sons got to know them as well. They became like family over the years. Stefan and Helena would travel to Rome to see Sonia, Mario, and their two children, and Sonia and the children spent most summers in Indianapolis. But tragedy struck when Helena was diagnosed with renal cancer. I met Sonia and Mario for the very first time at Helena's hospital bedside in Indianapolis. They were able to take Helena and Stefan back to Rome, where Helena passed away and is buried. Stefan's shining light was gone. Sonia and Mario begged him to remain in Rome permanently, but he said he was too old to learn another language (he already was fluent in Polish, German, Russian, and English). He had an aversion to Europe because of the war. So, he returned to Indianapolis.

Stefan almost lost his way without Helena. My family continued to see him frequently and I took him to lunch at least once a month. Sonia spent a month every fall and spring in Indianapolis with her father. We got to know Sonia well during those visits and met her daughter and son when they would occasionally visit as well. As Stefan approached his ninetieth birthday, suffering from congestive heart failure, he finally relented and moved to Rome. Waving good-bye to him at his beloved home in Indianapolis, I knew I would never see him again. Six months later, surrounded by his family, Stefan died and was finally reunited with his Helena.

What did I learn from being Stefan's family doctor? So many things. That you never know what the next patient will bring to your life. That a little boy with birth defects can marry the girl of his dreams, survive the Holocaust, become a scientist, produce a family, and finally find freedom from oppression. But the most amazing thing I learned came only two years ago, long after Helena and Stefan were gone. We were in Rome visiting Sonia and Mario and their children and grandchildren, as had become our custom every year or two. Sonia and Mario took us for our first visit to the World War II Jewish Ghetto in Rome. As we were walking though, I remarked to Sonia that her children must be so proud of Stefan and Helena for surviving the Holocaust. Sonia stopped, gave me a surprised look, and said, "But my children have no idea that Stefan and Helena were Jewish or what they went through during the war, and they must never know!" I was shocked. I had met her children, now adults, many times and had no idea that Stefan's and Helena's history had been kept a secret from them. Sonia was raised a Catholic and as a child, for the family's safety, was never told anything about her parents' prior names or lives. Sonia finally learned that her parents were Jewish and had survived the Holocaust as they were immigrating to the United States, but she sensed the pain caused by dredging up the past, so she never discussed it with them. And to this day, she has no interest in learning the details of the story. Sonia did give me permission to write this as long as the names were changed and no identifying dates were used. But she will never read it.

Stefan taught me what a privileged place family physicians hold in the lives of their patients; how our patients entrust us with so much more than just caring for their health. We know their histories, hopes and dreams, and family secrets.

Rebecca P. Feldman was born in Washington, DC, where her father worked at the Pentagon for Nelson Rockefeller. Her family moved to Middletown, Ohio, when she was four. Feldman graduated from Denison University in 1975 and the Indiana University School of Medicine in 1981. She attended the Franciscan Health Indianapolis Family Medicine Residency and practiced both family medicine and occupational health at several institutions. She retired from Eli Lilly and Company in 2005.

"Even after having learned from some of the most brilliant and kindest doctors, I can undoubtedly say that the greatest teachers I have had are my patients."

John Choi, MD

Bilan

NANCY J. BAKER, MD

As I scanned my morning clinic schedule, I saw among many familiar names, one I did not recognize. At 10:15 a.m. I was scheduled for a twenty minute, two-month well child visit with a new patient named Bilan. Before seeing the child, I scanned the electronic health record to see if there were records of her mother's maternity and delivery care and/or her newborn hospital record.

Seeing none, I knocked on the exam room door, entered, introduced myself, and was greeted warmly by the Somali interpreter. Before me sat a young mother. On her lap she held a curly dark-haired newborn wrapped in a colorful infant blanket. After telling the mother I was pleased to see her and her daughter, I asked, "What can I do for you today?" To my amazement, Bilan's mother answered, "I don't think my baby can see."

Stunned, I turned to the interpreter and asked her to ask, "Can you tell me more?" Bilan's mother reached into her bag and pulled out a stack of papers that she told me were from the out-of-state hospital where Bilan had been delivered, at term, two months ago. I quickly scanned the infant's newborn discharge summary, which listed several diagnoses, including the absence of the band of nerves that joined the two sides of Bilan's brain, blindness, the possible inability to produce several important brain hormones, excess fluid in her brain, and a seizure disorder.

Knowing little about these congenital conditions, I reassured the mom that I was pleased to assume primary care for Bilan, but I would need to spend time reviewing her records in detail and consult with several of my subspecialty colleagues regarding Bilan's need for further imaging and bloodwork. First and foremost, however, I told her that I would arrange for her daughter to be seen by a pediatric eye specialist. She seemed relieved and pleased to report that her daughter was nursing well and gaining weight.

Over the next seven years, I had the pleasure of caring for Bilan as she underwent a variety of tests and procedures. These included the placement of a shunt to drain the excess fluid in her brain, surgery to relax her tendons, muscle injections, brace fittings for her legs, eye exams, and physical therapy. Equally satisfying for me was caring for Bilan's mother through her two subsequent uncomplicated pregnancies.

I looked forward to my office visits with this new immigrant family who would arrive in my office with Bilan in her wheelchair, an infant sister, and a toddler sister who would always attempt to climb on my lap. As they got older, each little girl wore a customary hajib. My initial worries that Bilan's mother might become overwhelmed with her oldest daughter's physical and mental disabilities proved unfounded. The care and affection among this family was extraordinary. We continued to work with an interpreter at every visit, yet Bilan would always look directly at me, smile, and greet me enthusiastically when I entered the exam room. I was never sure if she could really see me or not.

When I retired from practice, I was surprised when Bilan and her mother made a special visit on my last day in clinic to say "Good-bye." As both approached me in the corridor, I was touched by the colorful balloons and flowers Bilan held in her lap. Her mother smiled, whispered in Bilan's ear, and then lifted the wheelchair footrests. To my amazement, Bilan scooted herself forward, slowly stood with assistance, and then walked hesitantly toward me to give me a hug. "Thank you," she said, "for everything." As I struggled to hold back tears, I thought to myself, it is you who I should be thanking. I am inspired by the patience and stamina I've witnessed in this young family as they've faced one obstacle after another.

Nancy J. Baker practiced and taught full-spectrum family medicine for more than three decades. For the majority of her career she has been residency faculty, first at Saint Paul Ramsey Medical Center (now Regions Hospital, Saint Paul, Minnesota), and then at Smiley's Clinic, which is affiliated with the University of Minnesota Medical Center, Minneapolis. Since 2013 Baker has been a hospice medical provider at Our Lady of Peace Home in Saint Paul. In addition, she is a core faculty member with the Rural and Metropolitan Physician Associate Program at the University of Minnesota Medical School.

House Calls

NANCY J. BAKER, MD

"Doc, thank you for coming," said the tall, wizened farmer. "Please come in. I see you've brought your assistant. Here, have a seat little lady."

As a five-year-old, I had no idea what my father did when he made a house call. As one of two general practitioners in our small rural Illinois community, he would often be called out in the night to attend a sick child or elder. What was unusual about this cold winter's night was that he had brought me with him. I rested my head on the patterned Formica table and gazed upward at the cracked plaster ceiling. I heard soft murmurings in the room adjacent and was just about asleep when Dad approached with his large black doctor's bag. He reached inside and withdrew a small glass vial labeled with his neat penmanship. He emptied several pills from the bottle into a small envelope, gave it to the farmer, and explained how often each should be administered.

Shortly thereafter, we walked back to the car. As he reached for the door handle, he looked over his shoulder, waved to our anxious host, and gently admonished, "Please call me in the morning if she's not better."

Thirty-five years later, I turned to Mike, the family medicine resident seated beside me in the front seat of my car and asked, "Is this your first home visit? Let's talk about what might happen." It was mid-December and we were en route to an apartment on Saint Paul's east side. Three weeks earlier, one of Mike's maternity patients had had a caesarian section to deliver her seventh child.

"I'd like to check her incision, weigh the baby, ask about breastfeeding, and see how the other children are faring," said Mike. As I pulled up to the curb, we spied three small faces pressed to the glass of a first-floor apartment window.

Shortly thereafter, I watched these curious children crowd around Mike begging him to examine them as well. "Me first. . . . No, me next. . . . Please, can I see that?" This young doctor moved them gently back as he lifted Marvin, the tiny newborn, into his arms. He listened to the infant's heart and lungs, palpated the small belly, and attempted to shine a bright light into the child's tightly closed eyes.

"You have a good-looking son," Mike remarked.

The serene new mother replied, "All my children are good looking." We walked into the back room to check her abdominal incision only to discover that she had no bed upon which to recline. She and her husband slept in sleeping bags in the center of the floor. Surrounding, were small piles of clean clothes that she had neatly stacked.

As we turned to leave, reminding Mike's patient to bring Marvin to clinic in three weeks' time for his first set of shots, one sibling after another cried out, "I want a shot," "I want a shot," "Me too, I want a shot." "Please, may I have a shot too?"

I have done many home visits during my two-decade career as a family physician. I have visited frail elders, including a woman with new onset of a heart arrhythmia, another with a gangrenous leg, a pregnant teen with persistent vomiting, a patient dying of cancer, a young woman eight-months pregnant on bedrest due to premature rupture of her membranes, a three-day-old newborn in an emergency shelter going through cocaine withdrawal, and a young woman, two weeks postop from spine surgery, who felt "too sick to come to clinic" to name but a few.

For me, this is just one aspect of primary care at its best, and it's tremendously rewarding for me to experience. I get to see my patients and their families in what is often their most comfortable of surroundings. Though I am usually unaccompanied on these house calls, I find the experience quite like that I had at the tender age of five when I went with my father on house calls. I am welcomed eagerly into each patient's home, I am often offered something to eat or to drink, and I am always thanked for the visit. I, too, carry a black doctor's bag. It contains a few medical instruments as well as equipment to draw blood. Missing, however, are those small vials from which my father dispensed medication with such care. Regardless, I offer my experience, my insight and counsel, and conclude most visits with the same simple advice he offered, "Please call me if you're not better in the morning."

This essay was originally published in January 2006 in Minnesota Medicine. *It has been edited slightly and is reprinted here with the editor's permission.*

Attitude

NANCY J. BAKER, MD

The call came at 3:00 am. "Nancy, I have a fourteen-year-old here in labor. Her membranes have ruptured and she's eight centimeters dilated. Fetal heart tones look good."

"Fine, I'll be there in ten minutes." As I drive through the black night, I am apprehensive. Will everything go alright? After twenty-five years of delivering babies, I still feel some discomfort. Fourteen. What was I doing at age fourteen?

In class, I remember looking up from my notebook to see an erect penis on film. Amazing. From the corner of my eye, I saw others fidget and quickly look down as if taking notes. Mrs. Nelms was nonplussed as she narrated text describing how an egg is fertilized. Conception. I had no idea. I preferred writing reports about the nation's presidents, writing poems about such things as vegetable steamers that looked like spaceships, and learning geometry.

As I rush into labor and delivery, the health-unit coordinator says, "No hurry. She's just started to push. You have time to change your clothes." I put on scrubs, wash my hands, knock on the door, and walk in to see Katie hard at work. Her nurse is opening the instrument pack on the nearby table. The resident physician on call is putting on her gown and gloves.

Katie's mother, her sister, her best friend, and her aunt stand by the bedside. One moment they count in unison, "1...2...3...4...5..., push Katie, push. Breathe quickly and push again. Come on baby, come on. You can do it." I hear the fetal heart-rate monitor beeping at 140 to 160 beats per minute. The contraction ends and they laugh, "We can see the baby's hair."

Katie looks tired but smiles as they lay a wet washcloth across her brow. "How much longer will it take?" she asks.

"Not long," says the resident. "Would you like a mirror to see the baby's head?"

She nods, "yes," looks, and is amazed. She had no idea.

I step back and consider my role in the age-old ritual of birthing. Seven women surround this young mother who is laboring. As Katie's breathing becomes more rapid, as her anguish intensifies, her coaches and attendants seem to sway and chant in concert. The rhythm of our counting and the chorus of our voices becomes a kind of spiritual. We slowly move inward, closing the circle as if to protect, yet hasten the birth process.

Between contractions, Katie's lids flutter, and she moans softly. Momentarily, we are silent, waiting. As the baby moves closer, it feels as if we should shout or pray. The resident physician gently touches Katie's skin as it stretches around the infant's head. Slowly, the brow, the nose and ears appear, and the head turns to the right. As the shoulders move downward, then up, a small cry can be heard amidst the gasps and panting. "It's a girl!"

Grandma cuts the cord. The tiny, wet, and wrinkled babe is suctioned, dried, and wrapped in a warm blanket. I chuckle to see her tightly closed eyes and defiant, protuberant lower lip. Katie's best friend cries out, "Oh Katie, has this baby girl got attitude!"

I walk from the room, complete the delivery summary, change out of scrubs, and return to my car in the early morning light. I am joyful, but also apprehensive. After twenty-five years of delivering babies, I still wonder if everything will go alright.

This essay was originally published in February 2005 in Minnesota Medicine. *It has been edited slightly and is reprinted here with the editor's permission.*

Tender Callings

NANCY J. BAKER, MD

It was -10 degrees Fahrenheit and I noted that my seventy-year-old patient with an inoperable intestinal tumor, complicated by massive fluid in his abdomen, was due to see me at 2:00 p.m. in clinic. Knowing his overall frailty and fearing him vulnerable to a fall, I called his care provider and advised them not to come as scheduled. I said I would make a home visit later that same afternoon.

My patient's apartment is only a few blocks from clinic and overlooks the majestic Mississippi River, a few miles below Lock and Dam Number 1. We had a cup of tea and after discussing his clinical course thus far, I did a rather cursory physical exam and advised him that we should "stay the course" and proceed with hospice care.

When I stood to leave, I noted two pictures on his living room wall. One appeared to be a portrait of a nineteenth-century cleric. The second, a pen-and-ink drawing of a disheveled man, seated, with his leg draped over the arm of a stuffed chair. I asked about the first and was told, "That's Gerard Manley Hopkins, my favorite poet. See the framed 'Windover' poem I have above the bed." I asked if the disheveled man was Seamus Heaney. "Indeed. He and I went to the same grammar school in Ireland, although I was two years older than he. Heaney agrees with me that Hopkins's prose is difficult to decipher but his poetry is extraordinary."

Briefly, I shared my passion for poetry, and told my patient that I had been doing a series of podcasts using poems to talk about the experience of illness and the nature of the doctor-patient relationship. He asked eagerly for the web address and promised to listen so that we could discuss the poems at my next visit.

Over the next two months I made visits to see my patient and his caregiver every one to two weeks. After we discussed medical issues related to his anticipated death and the troublesome dying process, our conversation would take on a lively tone as we discussed Hopkins's poems as well as those we read together by Dannie Abse, W. H. Auden, William Carlos Williams, Emily Dickenson, Wendell Berry, and Mary Oliver.

It was after such a visit last that I found myself penning a poem for him that used some of the clever alliteration and vibrant imagery employed by

Hopkins in his famous "Kingfisher" and "Windover" poems. The next week I gave him a copy of the poem below. It seemed fitting that I convey to him my profound admiration, as well as give him permission to die. I will be forever grateful to this dear man for his friendship, for having introduced me to Hopkins, and for helping me understand the person within the person, suffering from a life-threatening illness, and awaiting imminent death.

". . . for that I came."
(in homage to Gerard Manley Hopkins)
Oh soft spoken, tender hearted
man of God and son,
you are a fisher of men for the King.
You admonish the dragons to fly away
as you embrace the chevalier.

Your lovely limbs and eyes keep grace
while you confess your fear.
You stake the pains and search your soul
wondering why, how
when will this wasting wait end?

Brute beauty and valour meet my eye
though you dread self-reflection.
I know these moments only
(not those of yesteryear)
and dare to hope for peace.

Your lived life in God's eye
shines bright, yes gold-vermillion.
I am the better blessed by you. I bow.
My tongue flings out this heartfelt prayer,
Go gladly home go now Godspeed.

This essay and poem were originally published in the October 2008 issue of Minnesota Medicine. *It has been edited slightly and is reprinted here with the editor's permission.*

Did I Miss Something?

GRACE LEE WALKER, MD

An elderly gentleman, Mr. Kilgore, came in for a checkup. Everything looked good for his age, and there was nothing new that needed to be addressed. I asked if he had any questions or concerns. He said he had appointment at the Bureau of Motor Vehicles to renew his driver's license and wondered if he needed to take a driving test. He had good vision, was alert and engaged, and seemed healthy, so I told him he would do fine. A few days later I got a call from a police officer. My patient had committed suicide with a self-inflicted gunshot wound. I asked the officer if he failed the tests necessary to renew his driver's license. The officer said no. Everything was in order. His house was clean; his wallet and dentures were on the kitchen counter. And, he had a newly issued driver's license.

I had no idea he was a suicide risk. This made no sense. He did not seem depressed. Did I miss something? I felt very unsettled and sad.

Another patient, Mr. McCloskey, was an octogenarian with a chronic blood disorder and was legally blind from macular degeneration. He also had a tremor and could not hold his hand steady. He had a big Cadillac and a companion, Yvonne, who drove him to the office. Mr. McCloskey was always impeccably dressed in a white shirt, tie, and coat. He carried a special "straight edge" that he used to guide his writing as he wrote out his check to pay the bill. He needed frequent transfusions, and he could always tell when his hemoglobin dropped down too low; he could call, and we would arrange for a couple units of blood.

I made a house call once because he thought he messed up his pills, and he could not recognize one pill from another. His ranch-style home was well kept. The way he moved about, one would not know that he was legally blind. He had a system. He utilized rubber bands around the prescription bottles to identify them. There was either one, two, or three loops around the bottle depending on the specific medicine. He had three bottles in the kitchen and one in the front room. The rubber bands broke and he could not read the labels; Yvonne was busy. I helped him sort out his prescription bottles. He was grateful.

One day a police officer called. Mr McCloskey had died. He had checked into a motel dressed in his white shirt, tie, and coat. He laid in the bathtub, tied a plastic bag tightly around his head and neck, and shot himself. There was a suicide note. He wrote that he was tired, he hated to do this to Yvonne, and he apologized for making a mess at the hotel.

I had no idea he was a suicide risk. He did not seem depressed. What did I miss? Again, I felt very unsettled and very sad for my patient.

Yet another patient, Mr. Costin was a ninety-nine-year-old retired law-yer who had been living in a retirement community since he was eighty. He voluntarily gave up driving around age ninety. He used to be an Indiana State University basketball booster and made all the home games, both men's and women's. He had a lady friend at the apartment complex and spent a lot of time with her, going out to Walmart, attending educational programs, and social events. He was the only person I know who bought Facebook stock at the initial offering and laughed all the way to the bank.

Imagine my surprise when on an early December Sunday afternoon his daughter called me and said, "Daddy says he's had it. He refuses to shower and stopped going to physical therapy. He says he's ready to die and wants to go to the hospital." I offered to make a house call; his daughter met me at the front door.

Mr. Costin was seated in his living room, dressed and groomed. He rec-ognized me and greeted me by name. He was calm and quiet, his usual self. I asked him what he needed, and he said he was ready to die: "It's no fun to live anymore; my kidneys are failing; my potassium is too high; I'm falling; I can't see, so I don't go out shopping anymore. The nights are so long. I can't stand it anymore."

"Are you in pain?" I inquired.

"No."

"Are you sad?"

"No."

"Are you angry?"

"No."

"Are you afraid?"

"No," he responded matter-of-factly. No, he had no plans to hurt himself. He had been a "Do Not Resuscitate" patient for many years. We had executed all the appropriate end-of-life and Living Will documents, and there was a sign on his refrigerator door stating he was a "no code."

"It's just not fun anymore, and I am afraid of falling; I've fallen three times. I can't do anything. I don't want to be in pain."

Mr. Costin and I discussed that although there was an inpatient hospice unit at the local hospital, he was not appropriate for admission. There was no imminent issue that warranted going to the hospital. Although elderly, he was not in pain, he did not require nor did he want any IV fluids, and he was still in good shape. He had lost his confidence and his will to live. Mr. Costin said he was not afraid of dying and just wanted to be comfortable. I recommended hospice services and he agreed. He was open to having someone stay with him, at least during the nights, so that there would be someone there when he needed to get up to go to the bathroom. Hospice staff could also help him with his bathing and personal hygiene. He would stay on his current medications.

For months after that afternoon meeting, the Wabash Valley Hospice continued its care for Mr. Costin, providing around-the-clock companions. He was able to go to the dining room with his walker. He was curious and interested in life again.

I was most concerned that I was going to lose this gentleman. I thought he was going to will himself to die. I learned that he just lost confidence in himself. With family support and community resources, we can sometimes bring light back into our patient's lives.

The previous two suicides made me very sad. It felt like somebody robbed me of a family member. I wondered what courage it would take to pull a trigger on oneself and make sure it worked. Both suicides were carefully planned and duly executed. They were not poor, they were not sick, and they did not appear in any way depressed. They were such violent deaths. To this day, I am afraid of firearms of any kind. There was no way I could have anticipated those outcomes. I did not know what they were thinking, and they did not choose to share with me. That was the way it was.

Mr. Costin chose to share his sentiments with me. He told me how he felt, and we tried to find a way to address them. I accept now that Mr. Costin was old and did not have all that long to live. I did not used to think or feel that way. As a young physician, I thought I could fix everything and make sure people lived. It never occurred to me to ask patients or their families what they preferred, but I do now. I felt so bad after these suicides that I had to talk to a counselor/ethicist to see if I needed to undo any wrongs that I may have unknowingly committed. In reflection, it was a growing process and I needed to keep learning and progressing in life and profession.

I do not know why I have not had any more such encounters for the last twenty years. I am a better clinician than I was twenty-five years ago. I am a calmer and more accepting person, but I think I will always be shaken by a patient committing any form of suicide. These are experiences that touch my core like it was yesterday. As I grow old with my patients, I worry about them.

Still a work in progress.

Grace Lee Walker is a graduate of the Indiana University School of Medicine and the Franciscan Health Indianapolis Family Medicine Residency. She has been a loyal, longtime member of the voluntary residency faculty since her graduation and has also taught IU medical students rotating through her office. Walker in private practice in Terre Haute, Indiana.

A Good Death

ALLISON FARINA, MD

"Hi Mr. Williams," I said, "I got a message that you wanted to talk to me."

"Yes, doctor. I was thinking about our conversation at my last visit. Do you know something that I don't know?"

"Well, Mr. Williams, I know that you have bad COPD, and that isn't going to get any better. It may one day take your life. I want you to be prepared for when this time comes. I want you to have someone you trust available to tell the doctors your wishes when you are too sick to do so."

Mr. Williams continued to follow-up with me for regularly scheduled appointments for his diabetes and COPD. He faithfully mailed me his blood-sugar logs every six to eight weeks, being sure to also let me know his blood pressure, pulse, and if he missed a reading for any reason. Sometimes he came with his lady friend to his appointments, and sometimes he came alone. We talked about death once more after he had to start CPR and call the ambulance for a friend that collapsed outside in their yard. But overall, things were status quo.

Over a year from our conversation about his end-of-life care wishes, he started to have more frequent COPD exacerbations. I noticed his name showing up in my in-basket more often for hospital admissions. I always skimmed through the chart and, if available, I would stop by to see him in the hospital. Then things took a turn. After he went home, his name popped up again for admission, and then two weeks later he was back again in the emergency room. And a couple of times he was admitted to the Intensive Care Unit. He was intubated with a breathing tube and subsequently extubated. He recovered and went home.

I knew that things were getting worse, and I felt helpless. I was finishing notes one night and he popped up on my inpatient list as being in the ER. He was intubated again. I looked at his labs—they were not good. His kidneys were failing and nephrology was consulted.

I knew then that he would not survive this admission. He would be my first patient to pass away that I got to know and take care for a couple of years. As a young physician, I tried to start preparing myself for his death. My pager went off—I had a patient in labor.

I checked his chart during the day while on labor and delivery. He survived the night and was admitted to the ICU again on the ventilator. His Health Care Representative made the decision to not pursue dialysis. Palliative care was consulted, and he was made a "Do Not Resuscitate." The decision was made to extubate, to keep Mr. Williams comfortable, and to let him pass away.

Meanwhile my patient delivered her baby, a boy. I checked Mr. William's chart again. He had passed away during the delivery. I did not know what to do. I felt disappointed that I was not at his side. I felt the need for closure. I made the long walk to the ICU from labor and delivery, but by the time I got to his room his body had already been taken to the morgue. I tried to ask the nurses standing in the nurses' station about his death. They gave me a confused look.

I finally was able to ask, "Did he pass peacefully?"

"Yes, he did."

I had to settle for this as my closure. I said my usual prayer that I started saying as an intern, "Dear Lord, you gained an angel today. Please be with his family and friends during this time." I went home and tried to sleep. I realized the irony of my day with the circle of life. I felt sad, confused, happy, and exhausted about everything that happened that day.

It was not until weeks to months later that I started to accept the impact that Mr. Williams had on my career. At the time of our conversations, I was only a second-year resident. I am sure I fumbled through parts of that conversation, but Mr. Williams did not mind. I would dare say that I was one of the first to seriously talk to him about his eventual death. He listened and was prepared. His desires and wishes for his care at the end of life were honored.

Life on this earth is finite, but as a family physician, I can help guide my patients on the hard decisions to make. It is not easy, and I will likely fumble through the conversation on end-of-life care many more times, but I will continue to have these conversations. I want my patients to be informed and empowered to make the best decisions for themselves so that we, as their healthcare providers, can do our best to help them have a "good death."

Allison Farina grew up in southern Illinois near Saint Louis. She completed undergraduate and medical school education at the University of Missouri, Kansas City's six-year combined BA/MD degree program. Farina completed the Franciscan Health Indianapolis Family Medicine Residency, and she is currently working there as an associate director for the residency program.

A Cruel Virus

TAYLA M. NIDEY, RN

March 15, 2020. A date forever etched in my brain. The fear of COVID-19 reaching our community had become a life-altering reality. I had the honor of caring for an amazing individual who would later be remembered for her kind heart, as well as her bravery. She was the first of many to be hospitalized on my unit due to this catastrophic virus. Emily Whalen was ninety-one years old and spent her final two days reassuring everyone within her presence that everything was going to be okay.

Our first day together was spent planning her transition to comfort measures that were to take place the following day in accordance with her wishes. Emily, unlike many others to follow, had the opportunity to plan her final good-byes with her family as the lack of oxygen had not yet caused a significant change in her cognitive state.

Later that evening, I taught her children how to safely don and doff their protective wear, some needing assistance with the ties due to trembling hands. One child was excluded due also to being infected with COVID-19. The children visited the patient in pairs, passing off a phone sealed in a biohazard bag that was utilized to FaceTime the absent child. The next day, final good-byes would be said over the speaker of my Vocera (electronic nursing communication device) as the patient drifted into a peaceful state of unconsciousness. I wish with every fiber of my being that every proceeding death caused by the coronavirus would be as peaceful as this one.

However, the cruel, harsh reality to follow was that COVID-19, more times than not, would come unbiasedly. It would not give time for families to say good-bye or to be able to accept death on their terms. Perhaps the most gut-wrenching truth about COVID-19 was that it would later bring in spouses, sick with the virus as well. Young adult children would be forced to cope with the grief of losing one parent as they would try to keep up with the progress of the other. Some lost both parents within days of each other. Husbands and wives, separated only by the closed doors of their rooms and the length of a corridor, were forced to discuss their loved one's final wishes as they themselves fought for every breath.

I find it unjust to leave this unfair amount of grief the coronavirus has left in its wake unacknowledged. Though as relentless as this unfathom-

Emily Whalen

able disease has proven itself to be, health-care workers have shown an even stronger sense of resilience. Treatments against COVID-19 have advanced significantly since my first encounter with the virus on March 15 thanks to the efforts of healthcare teams across the globe. These advances have resulted in higher hopes of recovery for many patients and their families.

I continue to work proudly alongside my brothers and sisters in this fight to hopefully help prevent more families from enduring the tragedies that have plagued so many before them. United, we will overcome COVID-19 just as our mentors did when faced with previous pandemics such as the Spanish flu, tuberculosis, and Ebola.

Our compassion will not faulter.

Tayla Nidey is a single mother of an energetic five-year-old girl who has a passion for fashion and dinosaurs. She grew up in Vincennes, Indiana, where she was the captain of the varsity soccer team. While attending nursing school at Ivy Tech she worked part time as a bread merchandiser for a bakery and as a student-nurse at Indiana University Health. Upon graduating in May 2019, Nidey accepted a critical care position with Franciscan Health Indianapolis on the Medical Progressive Care Unit.

Emily Whalen's daughter, Mary McQueen, gave her permission to use her mother's name for this essay.

A Mentor and Friend

RICHARD D. FELDMAN, MD

This is not a story typical of what is contained in this book. This is not an account about how a doctor was touched by a patient in the normal course of his or her practice. This is a story of how an individual profoundly influenced my life *before* he became my patient. And I was only his doctor in a certain sense. I was not his primary doctor but became involved in his care from afar, consulting in his care with his wife, Elenita, in the last years of his life.

I had the great fortune to become a student of Doctor Joseph Epes Brown during his short tenure at Indiana University, Bloomington, before he left to begin his many years as a professor at the University of Montana. He was a renowned scholar and a pioneer in Native American studies. When Joseph was a graduate student in the late 1940s, he lived for a time with the well-known holy man of the Oglala Sioux, Black Elk. Black Elk is the subject of the epic book, *Black Elk Speaks*, by John Neihardt written in 1932. It remains one of the most important and enduring books regarding Plains Indian religion and thought. If you have not read this beautiful book, you should. Together with Black Elk, Joseph wrote the book *The Sacred Pipe*, and others of his own relating to his experiences with the old Lakota medicine man.

Studying with Joseph was an experience that would have a profound and lasting influence on my life in exceptional ways. That was fifty years ago, and I am proud to say I was his friend until he died, and I remain a friend of his family today.

My relationship with Joseph began my junior year in college when I registered for a class in American Indian religion. The course merely sounded interesting. Little did I realize at the time how much the subject would capture my imagination. I studied with him over the next two years and, with his encouragement, completed a special project studying and crafting sacred plains ceremonial pipes using the traditional red catlinite for the stone bowls, ash wood for the stems, and incorporating other traditional materials.

Through the years I continued my study of Native American religion, art, and culture and kept in touch with him occasionally. Regrettably, that contact was mostly in the form of Christmas cards with little notes that we would exchange each year. This was a time when I could have learned so much more from him, but medical school, residency, career, and family took my time and focus. I wish I could relive those years again, this time with better balance. One thing that Joseph taught his students was the concept of "center." I remember that sense of centeredness and know that it must be renewed from time to time; it is so easy to lose.

I did visit him in 1976 on his ranch near Missoula, Montana. I was driving from Indianapolis, where I was attending medical school, to Seattle for two months of training. Some years before he expressed an interest in obtaining one of my catlinite ceremonial pipes. I remembered his request and made a pipe especially for him as a gift. It had an inverted T-shaped bowl and flat ash wood stem with a catlinite section on the end fitted with a small wooden mouthpiece. I wrapped it into a deerskin bundle with a short note expressing my appreciation for the things he had taught me, as those teachings helped me see and appreciate the world more fully. He seemed so pleased when I handed it to him. He burned sacred sage under the bundle before he opened it. Examining the pipe, he remarked that it was most elegant. It was a perfect moment and one that I will always remember.

Years later, I met a student from the University of Montana. I mentioned to him the story of presenting the pipe to Joseph, and he related to me that he had seen the pipe in his office at the university. Joseph told him that a former student from Indiana had made it for him. I feel good that it was proudly displayed, and that we shared the pipe together.

After I presented the pipe to Joseph that morning in Montana, we had breakfast of toast and coffee in the kitchen. We chatted about his life in Montana, the intervening years, and his days in Indiana. I remember he once told me that he never felt comfortable in the Midwest woodlands, that he felt closed-in, and that he wished to return to live and teach in the wide-open country of the West. I asked him that morning something I had always wondered about: Of all the places in the world, how did he come to IU to teach Native American religion? He looked at me from the corner of his eye and hesitated. I realized I had happened upon a subject that he considered private. He responded that since I had been so gracious to present him with the pipe, he would tell me the story:

> I was in Sweden with my wife and young children. My position there was ending soon, and I had made application to various institutions for a teaching position. I was feeling desperate. It was late, and I had not received any responses. I remembered a song that Black Elk had once taught me. It was to be used only if I was really in trouble and needed help. At the moment

Joseph Brown (right) with Black Elk

I finished the song, a letter dropped through the slot in the door. It was a letter of acceptance from Indiana University.

So, Joseph Brown came to teach, and I was fortunate enough to become part of it.

At the end of my visit, Joseph felt compelled to give me a gift in return. He noticed my new car that I was driving across country, an orange Camaro. He expressed concern it was probably a very fast car and that I should be very

Professor Brown

careful. He took a feather off the shelf in his library, fitted it with a buckskin thong, and presented it to me. He told me if I kept it close, it would always protect me. I placed the feather in a parfleche case with sage and sweetgrass and have it near me to this day. Looking back from that time, I consider myself to be very fortunate in life. Just before I pulled away, Joseph leaned in the car window, shook my hand, and said I would always be welcome.

I tried to visit him again during another trip out West in 1980, but unfortunately, he was away buying horses. But in June in 1993 I returned to the Brown ranch with my wife, Becky, and our three small boys. Before we arrived, Elenita asked if I knew that he was ill. "No, I had no idea," I responded. I had not heard from him for some time. She said he had developed Alzheimer's. She wanted to warn me and to anticipate his condition when we all met.

When we arrived, we were warmly greeted by Joseph, Elenita, and their grown daughters and son. As I talked with Joseph, I was again impressed with his intense, thoughtful, and spiritual presence which I remembered so well from my college days. But I also noticed something about him that I never saw when I was younger: Part of that presence was his beautiful penetrating deep blue eyes that seemed to look through to one's soul.

I recall that Joseph invited Black Elk's son Ben Black Elk to Bloomington to speak to our American Indian religion class. He was a likeable old man full of stories. He talked of many things in his life including his famous father and of the days when Joseph had lived with their family on the Pine Ridge Agency in South Dakota. I had an opportunity during a school break to visit him and his son, Henry, in the little family cabin near Manderson, South Dakota. From my discussion, it was clear to me in what high regard the Black Elk family held Brown.

When Joseph talked with Ben in class, he would address him as *"Ate"* (father in Sioux). It was the Sioux way of expressing respect and his sense of relationship with an older man. When I said good-bye to Joseph at the conclusion of my visit with him at the ranch, I addressed him as *Ate*. It was meant to express my respect, but I did it as much to satisfy something within me. Joseph looked at me without changing expressions, but I think he knew what was in my heart.

In 1987 Joseph was nominated for the Distinguished Teacher Award at the University of Montana. He requested that I write a letter in his support. This is most of that letter:

> There have been several people at various stages in my life who had great effect on my development as a person and physician. These are individuals who helped create for me a world view and a sense of meaning and values. Certainly, there was my father who was also a family physician and a couple of other medical mentors. And there was another, Dr Joseph Brown, a professor of Native American religious studies at Indiana University. The late 60's and early 70's was a wonderful time of discovery and re-definition of values for my generation. For some of us, finding the wisdom of the American Indian was an important part of that experience. . . .
> Indeed, my life was forever changed because of my contact with him.
>
> As a college student, I remember the spellbound feeling that I had as he spoke about the mystic and spiritual aspects of the Plains Indian. Through the relating of his experiences in spoken and written words, he introduced his students to a beautiful religion, to the holy men of the Oglala Sioux, and to the different reality of visions and personal power gathered from the elements of nature and the surrounding world. Soon I was fascinated not only about the subject matter but with this scholarly professor as well. For Dr. Brown also manifested in a way the same mystic and spiritual presence as did his teacher, the old Sioux medicine man, Black Elk, of whom he so

frequently spoke. Because of this presence and his ability to bring to life that which was so deeply internalized within his being, I came to appreciate and understand on a deeper, inner level the spiritual essence of Plains Indian religion.

Over the two-year period I studied with Dr. Brown, I had the opportunity to come to know him more than the typical student. . . . I intently pursued my special study of the Plains Indian ceremonial pipe with his encouragement. . . . I remember the feeling sitting alone with him in his office as he showed me the pipe Black Elk had given him, comparing it to the ones I had carved and discussing the project. I so much revered and respected him that I seemed to always feel a certain nervousness, callowness, or even foolishness in his presence. I had trouble putting my thoughts together, and I talked too fast. . . . I was simply in awe of him.

Many years have passed since I sat in a classroom with Dr. Brown. Looking back on it now, I understand that profound effect he had on my life. Besides family and career, my ongoing study of Plains Indian religion, culture, and Native American art are my most pervasive and compelling interests. It has added passion, depth, and beauty to my life and led me down amazing paths. I am often asked how I became interested in Native American studies and my thoughts always return to Joseph Epes Brown. I find it impossible to separate the subject from the teacher, for in my mind they are one in the same.

After finishing my undergraduate work at Indiana University, my focus changed from the social sciences and the humanities to medical school. In my career in academic family medicine, I hope that I inspire my students as Dr. Brown inspired me. This is the greatest compliment I can give him, for one of the most important attributes a teacher can possess is the ability to inspire others who wish to learn. Dr. Brown introduced many of us to the beauty of another world view and of a different reality. He challenged us to learn more and to try to understand something so different from our everyday lives. I thank him for enriching my life.

I should add that my care of patients has also been influenced by Joseph. I believe my fascination with people from other cultures, backgrounds, and worldviews is, in part, due to his introduction to me of Native American religion, culture, and thought. It opened the door of appreciation to our world's diversity seen every day in the practice of medicine. I enjoy talking with patients about the uniqueness of their lives and experiences.

Joseph's mindfulness of presence is something I try to emulate in patient care. When one spoke with Joseph, he was fully engaged in the conversation. He listened attentively, immersed in the story being told. He was never in a

The author (left) with Brown

hurry to respond and was carefully thoughtful in his responses. Being a good listener and fully present with patients are essential to good medical care and building therapeutic relationships with patients.

During that 1993 visit to the Brown ranch, it was obvious that Joseph was in the throes of Alzheimer's, which was robbing him of his intellect. What a cruel disease, especially for someone like Joseph. At the beginning of the visit I feared that he did not remember me, but soon Elenita and I both had no doubt that he did. Elenita and I talked about his condition during that visit and periodically for months afterward. She had questions, and I offered by advice as a physician and friend. An Alzheimer medication had just been introduced, and I told her it was worth a try. We continued our discussions after his local physician placed Joseph on the medication that I had suggested.

We discussed any side effects he was experiencing, dose adjustments, his other medications, and possible progress he may have achieved. But, alas, ultimately the medication had no real effect. Joseph died in 2000. I am honored that his son, Sasha, uses the pipe I presented to Joseph as his personal ceremonial pipe to this day.

I was honored that Elenita consulted with me as a physician in his care. She expressed her appreciation for my desire to help him; and she understood how important it was to me to do so.

I was privileged to speak at his memorial celebration in Montana.

Joseph Brown's family approved using his name for this essay.

"Unquestionably, my experiences as a patient changed my behavior as a physician. Although I had always thought of myself as a capable, caring internist and hematologist, my medical education had not prepared [me] to care for patients as well as did the added experience of having myself been a patient. How might it have been otherwise? It is hardly practical to require that every physician have a serious illness as part of the process of preparing to care for patients. . . . It may prove helpful, however, to listen carefully to physicians who have been patients."

Herbert S. Waxman, MD, *Annals of Internal Medicine*, 1997

When the Doctor Becomes the Patient

SHIRLEY M. MUELLER, MD

When I found out that I had something in common with Luciano Pavarotti, the legendary tenor, it was not that we both sang well. Instead, each of us was diagnosed with pancreatic cancer. The opera star had a major operation to remove it. I refused surgery. Pavarotti died. I am alive.

As a practicing neurologist for twenty-four years, I never expected to be on the other side of the reflex hammer. Still, when my tests showed a pancreatic mass, I assumed that I had an expiration date. Ninety percent of those diagnosed with the malignancy die within six months. Randy Pausch, the author of *The Last Lecture*, is one example.

My problem began when belly pain started awakening me at night. An abdominal CAT scan showed a pancreatic tumor. I was sure the more sensitive MRI would disprove it. My doctor, a professional acquaintance for years, apparently thought this, too. We chatted casually waiting for the radiologist's interpretation to be faxed to his office.

Then something totally unexpected happened. Instead of coming into the room with the report, the nurse slipped it under the door. My doctor looked startled. I was too. Had she read the contents and felt uncomfortable about handing it directly to the doctor?

Still my internist showed no emotion when he read the document. What puzzled me though was that he kept reading it over and over without uttering a sound. The silence spoke for itself. The MRI report was long, but the pertinent sentence was succinct: "There is a pancreatic mass, 3.4 x 3.3 cm."

Because of my medical training, I knew how serious this was. Though I had read reports like this for my patients, I never expected to see it for me. I was frightened and apparently my physician was too. He did not seem to know how to handle a grave prognosis for a professional acquaintance.

My internist's office made an appointment for me to have a biopsy within a few days. The surgeon was my fourth choice as the first three specialists were not available quickly. Though this physician was a default, it gave me consolation that he went to the same medical school that my husband and I also attended.

A common motto among surgeons is "When in doubt, take it out." He did want to take it out, and immediately. He explained that I could lose my spleen if the operation went badly. What frightened me the most though was his bravado attitude, a kind of know-it-all demeanor. To me, this meant that he was overconfident, a quality I always disliked and associated with poor performance. In my experience, those in my profession with real expertise do not have to act arrogant.

I looked up the mortality for the kind of surgery. It is 14 percent. In my opinion, it might be higher for this doctor because I was not sure he did many of this specific operation. The rule of thumb is that unless a physician does twenty-five or more a year of one kind of procedure, he is not sufficiently skilled to achieve a low mortality rate. I decided not to decide.

On Monday morning I called the Sloan Kettering Medical Center. Research on the Internet indicated it is one of the two best pancreatic cancer hospitals in the nation. The admitting person said there was a cancelation for Tuesday morning. My husband and I booked the next flight to New York City, sparing no expense. We were on time for my 11:00 a.m. appointment, though the doctor did not see us until 5:00 p.m. This made me reflect that while I kept patients waiting too, it was virtually never more than two hours. I wondered what my doctor's tardiness meant in terms of her time management and if this apparent inability flowed over into her quality of patient care.

The physician finally saw me briefly and said I needed another test. By 6:00 p.m., when all the other patients had left, I was drinking buckets of water to hydrate myself for yet another CAT scan. This procedure consisted of more pictures with greater resolution than the one in Indianapolis. Thereby, the test could be read with added clarity.

The young radiologist talked with me right after the test. He seemed both confident and competent after interpreting so many of the same kind of procedure I was hoping to learn I had the less malignant kind of tumor, one that would provide three to five years rather than three to six months of life. Instead, the radiologist told my husband and me something I was unprepared for. He said that my previous reading was a mistake. What was interpreted as a mass was not. He believed the real culprit was a stomach ulcer found in earlier tests.

I was stunned. It was just as wrenching to adjust to life as to death. I reflected, "How much worse was my ulcer because I had been incorrectly diagnosed with pancreatic cancer?"

My husband and I made our way out of the tomb-like building that had been bustling earlier in the day. It was at the end of rush hour, about 7:30 at night. Strangers were on their way home. They, of course, paid no attention to us. They had no way of knowing that I was like Lazarus, a woman who had just been given life and did not yet know what to do with it, except for one thing. I make a vow to be kinder to everyone, especially patients in life-threatening situations.

Shirley M. Mueller grew up in Waukon, Iowa, and attended Clarke College in Dubuque, Iowa, and the University of Iowa Medical School. She subsequently rotated through pediatric and neurology residencies and additionally took a cardiovascular fellowship. She is board certified in pediatrics as well as neurology and psychiatry. She was in the private practice of neurology for twenty-four years, seventeen in Indianapolis. Mueller's current profession is writing about and giving lectures regarding the neuroscience of the behavior of art collectors. Her book, Inside the Head of a Collector: Neuropsychological Forces at Play, *was published in 2019.*

Entrusted Care

KRISTIN WOOD, MD

The past ten years in practice have given me such an appreciation for each of my patients. They all have a story to tell and something to teach me. When I think about a patient who has taught me so much, the first patient that comes to mind is Will. My story about Will could begin all the way back to when he and my grandmother were good friends in the 1940s, but instead of going back that far, here is how Will has impacted me personally and professionally.

In 2008 I first saw Will in my role as a physician at his daughter's funeral. I hugged him and his wife with tears in my eyes and guilt in my heart; I was the one who found the cancer that killed their adult daughter. Will entrusted me with the care of his daughter. She came to me for anemia and through a thorough work up, it was determined she had a gastrointestinal carcinoma that led to her passing less than a year later.

Will first saw me when I was a baby in our church's nursery. He was a high school friend of my grandma, and they attended the same church through their high school and adult lives, which included watching each of their grandchildren grow up.

After the death of their daughter, Will and his wife chose to come to me for their medical care. She was nearly bent in half with terrible scoliosis, and I watched Will display his love for his wife by taking wonderful care of her and documenting every detail of her care for me to review. A year or so later, I attended and spoke at his wife's funeral after she passed away peacefully in hospice due to the restrictive and painful nature of her scoliosis.

Will continues to be my patient and has brought his new wife to be my patient as well. I continue to be blessed by our patient-physician relationship. He is now an amazing eighty-six-year-old and continues to split wood and be one of the most active octogenarians I know.

My time caring for Will has shown me so many things. Finding a cancer in loved ones, which shortens their life does not have to leave me feeling guilty for the pain and suffering of the patient and the family. Instead, it gives the family the chance to cherish those last few months. Sacrificial love and care of a loved one, though time consuming, is incredibly rewarding and speaks volumes of God's love to their family and friends.

And, finally, patients really do trust me! Even when they remember you as a toddler charging through the church hallways or as a teenager who probably talked too much during church services, they have always and continue to believe in me and trust my counsel as a physician. I feel humbled and honored but most of all rewarded.

Kristin Wood enjoys practicing Family Medicine with Franciscan Physician Network in Mooresville, Indiana, along with teaching young doctors at the Franciscan Health Indianapolis Family Medicine Residency. She cherishes her time taking care of patients of all ages and walks of life, along with delivering babies. Wood graduated from the Indiana University School of Medicine and finished her training at Ball Memorial Family Medicine Residency.

The Little Things

NANCY J. NAM, DO

Grace was a fifty-seven-year-old Asian woman who never drank and had no history of chronic infections or IV-drug use. Her blood was drawn every three months by her family doctor because she had been diagnosed with prediabetes. Grace decided to be proactive, so she cleaned up her diet and started exercising regularly. She also had a history of hypertension, but with her recent weight loss and lifestyle changes she was able to maintain a normal blood pressure. Soon after, she underwent a routine colonoscopy and mammogram with no abnormalities detected on both exams. Grace was in the clear. She anticipated that she would have many years of healthy life ahead of her.

Unexpectedly, Grace started to have a sharp pain in her abdomen. Was it a complication from the colonoscopy? Did she have a perforation of her bowel? She was scheduled for an MRI. The pain became unbearable, and she was rushed to the emergency room. The MRI was performed, and finally the reason behind her pain was revealed. It was liver cancer, a six-inch tumor, advanced-stage, and inoperable, which had most likely already spread to her lungs.

A month had passed since the diagnosis and Grace was placed on a first-line anticancer medication. Following the treatment, she broke out in hives and skin peeled off her hands and feet. She was completely intolerant of the medication. The second-line drug chosen carried promise. It was a newer immunotherapy, so there was hope. Two weeks later, tumor-marker levels on blood tests decreased in half! Had a miracle happened?

Unfortunately, a week later tumor-marker levels were back to where they had started. As weeks past, her tumor markers continuously rose, and her condition rapidly deteriorated; her oncologist recommended a third-line medication. Her family members were immensely relieved that another option was still available. However, Grace wanted to focus on pain management and spending her remaining time with family. Her family tried to persuade her to at least try the therapy, but she stoically stood behind her final decision. Approximately six months following her diagnosis, Grace drew her last breath in a hospital room in the palliative care unit surrounded by family.

Grace was my mother. I lost my greatest supporter during my first year in medical school. This whirlwind of an experience taught me there are limitations in medicine, and many times treatments we currently have are only supportive and not curative. The reason I chose to pursue medicine was because I was amazed to learn how one surgery or taking a single medication could drastically improve a person's life. As student doctors, we dedicate a lot of time learning algorithms to accurately diagnose and treat our patients. When I become a clinician, similar to how a family member might feel, I am certain that I will constantly ask myself if I missed the earlier "red flags."

Clinicians are trained to see patterns. However, this is the very reason why an atypical presentation of a medical condition could also be missed. On the other hand, this is also why research is conducted and treatment protocols are constantly becoming more individualized.

Despite the outcome, I also witnessed how the little things matter in patient care. Details such as when the physicians and nurses said *advanced*-cancer instead of *late-stage* cancer, or when we were offered a cup of tea while my mom was undergoing her infusion therapy. In the end, my mom's fight against cancer taught me to approach medicine with an open mind, to be detail-oriented, and to offer kindness and encouragement. Although we strive to provide the best care and wish for miracles, medicine is not only about curing the disease. Perhaps what I perceived to be a limitation was in fact very much a part of medicine. For in addition to medical care that cures, good care can also be facilitating the transition to death and making the process as comfortable and painless as possible.

In a sense, one of my first patients as a medical student was my mother, and that sad yet cherished experience will carry with me for my entire career; perhaps more important, for the rest of my life.

Originally from downtown Chicago, Nancy J. Nam moved to Indianapolis to attend Marian University College of Osteopathic Medicine. She is pursuing a career in primary care and hopes to emphasize the importance of preventative medicine. She enjoys a range of interests, including building an eclectic collection of teas.

Forgiveness

TAMERA VANDEGRIFF, MD

This story begins in September 2013. My patient Bobby came to the office on a Friday evening as the last patient of the day. Bobby was a retired maintenance employee from the hospital where I worked. He has been my patient for many years, and he called late in the afternoon complaining of right-upper abdominal pain. I readily agreed to see him at the end of my already full schedule.

Upon entering the exam room, I could tell Bobby was uncomfortable but not in distress. My exam indicated that he had some right-upper abdominal tenderness but no signs of an acute surgical abdomen. His vitals were all stable and he did not have a fever. However, Bobby could be quite impatient and insisted we needed an ultrasound that night. After working in the hospital for so long, he knew just enough about medicine to be his own advocate. So, reluctantly, I called the ultrasound department and luckily the technician was still there. The ultrasound was done and read immediately. The results were called to me at home that evening by the technician—no gallstones, no fluid around the gallbladder, and no gallbladder wall thickening. I called Bobby that evening to give him the good news. I offered to order further gall bladder imaging, but Bobby had decided he would try a course of a proton pump inhibitor (an anti-acid medication) first and let me know if it was not getting better. When the report from the ultrasound arrived on Monday, I quickly initialed it and placed it in Bobby's chart without a second glance.

Fast forward to April 2014. It is again Friday afternoon and again I am seeing Bobby late in the day. Now he is having severe abdominal pain in the right-upper abdomen and into the right flank. He is clearly in distress. He had one episode of vomiting earlier in the day. Earlier this week he was in an outside emergency room for nausea and vomiting, but they gave him IV fluids and antiemetics and sent him home. On exam he has right-sided abdominal pain with multiple signs on exam of a possible acute surgical abdomen. He does not wish to return to the emergency room, but I am able to obtain an immediate CT scan of his abdomen. This time when the radiologist himself calls my heart sinks as he reports, "three gallstones and a 15cm renal mass invading the inferior vena cava." I stammered, "I don't understand he had an ultrasound six months ago with no report of a renal mass." His exact words were, "If they didn't see this six months ago, they were blind." With trembling hands, I quickly flipped Bobby's chart open to the first report. There on the second page of the report it stated: "3 cm solid renal mass suggestive of renal cell carcinoma." At that moment, I wanted to curl up and disappear, but I knew that I could not do that.

I called Bobby with the bad news of the gallstones and the tumor. I had already arranged for a urologist and general surgeon to meet him at the tertiary care center. He was admitted and given IV fluids and pain control and his surgery was planned for Monday. I called our risk management team as well as my hospital's chief medical officer, Doctor Carter, and explained the situation and my mistake. I told all of them that I wanted Bobby to know of my error and I wanted him to know of it from me. I knew that we would have to act quickly as the error would be uncovered very quickly by his surgeons.

Late Saturday morning, I met Doctor Carter at the tertiary care center. Together we approached Bobby's room and I felt my knees might buckle and I could barely breathe. I went into Bobby's room first and asked his permission to bring in my chief medical officer. He was quite shocked to see me, and I could tell he knew something was wrong. Once Doctor Carter was in the room, I told Bobby I had made an error, a very careless error, in taking care of him. I told him about initialing the first report without really reading it, and that on the second page it listed under the findings: "3 cm renal mass concerning for renal cell carcinoma." I told him how very sorry I was for my carelessness, and I waited for the worst.

His response was shocking and overwhelming and filled with grace. He looked me in the eye and told me that, yes, I had made a mistake, but to err is human. He told me that he believed God would see him through this cancer, and he would put his life and treatment in His hands. And then he said, "I forgive you." The most powerful three words in the English language. Doctor Carter asked if he would pray with us, and Bobby gave his consent. We said a prayer, and we both thanked Bobby for his bravery, his faith, his grace, and his mercy.

I left that hospital room that day with a new understanding of what it truly means to forgive. I am happy to say that Bobby is more than five years cancer-free and that his family remain my patients.

Tamera Vandegriff graduated from the Indiana University School of Medicine in 2002 and completed her Family Medicine Residency in 2005 at Saint Francis hospital in Indianapolis. She has since been practicing with Saint Vincent Medical Group in Frankfort, Indiana, and is now the regional medical director. She is happily married to her husband Alex and they have two sons, Coltyn and Wyatt.

"If we see the miracle of a single flower clearly our whole life would change."

Buddha

Flowers

RICHARD BEARDSLEY, MD

When I think about a patient that I learned the most from the answer is easy, Karl Theilig. I met Karl in the 1980s on a Sunday morning shrouded in fog so thick that I could hardly drive. While creeping along the road at about ten miles per hour, out of the corner of my eye I caught a glance that intrigued me.

I was passing an old house that had its entire yard covered with flowers. I turned off the road and walked up to see a shadowy figure barely discernible through the fog. I could hear his wife from inside the house playing hymns on the organ. Hearing that and seeing the vague apparition of the man working in the garden made me think that I had somehow arrived at place that I never expected to gain entrance. He asked if he could help me, and I said that I was just amazed to see his yard full of gorgeous flowers. Immediately, I felt that I had found a real friend. He was busy weeding his garden, was barefoot and shirtless wearing only cut-off jeans and chewing on an unlit cigar.

He stopped work and we sat down and talked about his garden, and I told him that I was developing a big interest in gardening. At that time, he was in his seventies, and I was in my thirties. After a nice discussion, I drove on. His house was on a route that I passed frequently, and after that day I would always slow down passing his house to gaze at his flowers. I soon started stopping in for conversation.

Over time as we became better acquainted, we developed a relationship that involved informally trading medical advice for samples of his perennials. I certainly got the better end of that deal. Eventually he formally became a patient of mine, seeing him in my office. I was continually amazed at his physical strength and endurance as he worked endlessly in his garden. His grounds did not have a single blade of grass, just his flowers that he endlessly hoed, weeded, and harvested.

Eventually, I would stop at his house after a long day and sit at his card table with folding chairs under a shade tree and chat, occasionally having a beer with him. His card table was always covered with gorgeous bouquets stuffed into milk jugs that his neighbors would drop off and buy the flowers for a trivial fee. Each one could have sold for a hundred dollars at a florist.

Painting of Karl Theilig

On these visits I learned of his very difficult early life, severely lacking food in his home in Germany between the world wars As a young child he learned the art of gardening. Eventually, he was sponsored to immigrate to the United States and first lived in southern Indianapolis with a group of German gardeners in similar positions. With hard work, he was eventually able to move to his house where he lived until his death.

He became a skilled gardener and eventually oversaw landscaping and maintenance for the governor's mansion. He became a good friend of a governor who would often call Karl to come to his house and slip into the garage behind the mansion to talk privately with him. The governor just needed to blow off steam away from the press and the public eye with someone he trusted and who would listen.

I had similar experiences with Karl when I needed to get something off my chest as well. I remember stopping after a particularly difficult office day and he asked me what was wrong. After I reviewed it with him, he said, "That's awful, my patients [the flowers] never talk back to me that way." Eventually, my family got to know Karl and would visit him with me. He became like a grandparent to my children.

Meeting Karl early in my career, I was able to watch him gracefully age well into his nineties, remaining in excellent health and taking very few medications. He had horrible osteoarthritis in his hands, but never complained. He would eat a few raisins soaked in gin every day, which he had been told (not by me) was the best treatment for arthritis.

My fascination with Karl and his vitality were key in kindling my interest in geriatrics and when the first geriatric boards were offered in the United States, I took them, and this became the primary focus of my four-decade career. I often used examples of him when teaching geriatrics to family-medicine residents.

To this day the perennials that he gave me over the years have survived, and I look forward to spring when they magically reappear like Persephone arising from the earth after a long winter. Karl would always meticulously clean off his shovels and turn over the compost at the end of a long day, even when he had no more energy left. Just today, I walked into my garden shed and saw the thick dirt stuck to my shovels. I knew Karl would not approve of that so, I stopped and took each shovel and meticulously washed them off until they were clean by Karl's standards.

After that I turned over the compost, too.

Editor's note: Many on the northeast side of Indianapolis will recall the much-beloved Karl Theilig, who sold perennial flowers from his garden at his home, a grey-painted wooden Victorian house on East Kessler Boulevard. My wife, Becky, and I lived at the time just down the street on Kessler and would go over periodically to buy flowers for our garden from this special man. Shortly before he died, he brought us a gift of hibiscus plants. We still have them in our garden. We think of him often.

Richard Beardsley is a third-generation family physician who practiced at Franciscan Health Indianapolis for thirty-six years and was also a revered faculty member in the institution's family medicine residency. He grew up in Frankfort, Indiana, and attended DePauw University and the Indiana University School of Medicine. Beardsley completed a family medicine residency at Franciscan Health and is board certified in both family medicine and geriatrics. Now in retirement, Beardsley's activities include Global Health Brigades to Amazonia in Ecuador, painting classes, gardening, and art history classes at Butler University.

Karl's daughter, Helen, gave the editor permission to identify him by his name.

Baring My Soul

WILLIAM M. GILKISON, MD

Doctors are human and have the same emotions and reactions as everyone else. They have as many opinions and biases as nonphysicians. But when it comes to patients, physicians are bound by their professional ethics to not allow their decision making to be influenced by personal biases regarding their patients. Despite their patients' behavior and personality, their belligerence or obstinance, or their arrogance or passive-aggressiveness, the doctor must remain controlled and imperturbable. We are expected to treat every patient with the same level of compassion, understanding, and concern and not be offended if they swear at us or call us names. In short, we are to be nonjudgmental, impartial, and professional.

Human nature being as it is, and because we all have limits to our tolerance, we do not always like where a situation has placed us. We just do not like the person we are treating—his or her personality is unlikable, their demands are unreasonable, or their attitude is objectionable. But because of professional ethics, we must suppress our feelings and carry on. Any doctor will tell you they had favorite patients who they could talk to easily, who were pleasant and courteous, and were appreciative of the time and effort expressed on their behalf. Those were the folks you were always happy to see. They did not stress your medical knowledge or make you feel uncomfortable.

But on the other hand, there are the patients whose visits are a challenge. Those you knew were going to take a long time and require you to dig deep into your knowledge bank to find solutions for them. The folks who kept you awake at night wondering how to better deal with them. Those when you saw their name on your schedule caused you to sweat and your pulse to race. They are the folks who made you wonder why they chose you as their physician and if they felt uneasy with you as well. In short, they were people you did not like. People who, despite your feelings toward them, still must see your very best professional demeanor. It was difficult but necessary. Treating the patient, the same as you would anyone else; being patient with them; answering all their questions; spending the time needed to know them better; and letting them know you're there to tend to their physical and psychological problems were imperative.

One obvious example of this attitude was the elderly lady who came to me asking to be a new patient. She had made a "get-acquainted" appointment to meet me and to discuss her problems. It was our opportunity to learn about each other. I must have been very busy or in a bad mood that day because I brusquely informed her that I did not want her as my patient. I had never done that before, nor have I done it since. I based my decision on two things: the way she looked and her demeanor. I just did not like the way she looked and acted. Talk about judgmental! I made the decision that this lady was going to be a problem I did not want to take on! I told her "no." It was just wrong! I am sure she left my office in tears, thinking I was mean and hateful. She was right; I behaved badly. I have regretted that incident ever since.

Putting aside personal feelings and displaying nonjudgmental and accepting attitudes are difficult things to do, especially if one has strong feelings of what is considered right or wrong. Providing proper patient care necessitates that you do not allow yourself to be influenced by any dislike for the patient or by personal biases for any reason. You may not approve, for example, of the patient's lifestyle or social behavior, but negative reactions toward the patient should not be exhibited. The patient must not know of your disapproval. Those feelings must be subjugated in favor of acceptance of the patient so effective medical solutions can be sought through a therapeutic relationship. Patients must feel that you are there to treat their problem at that moment. Rapport must be established and maintained.

As a family doctor, I was rarely confronted by belligerent, inebriated, profane, or sociopathic patients like emergency room physicians experience every day. My patients were people I had cared for for many years, so we knew each other and got along well. I may have had some with whom I had differences or there was a lack of fondness, but I did my very best to treat them the same as all the others.

I learned throughout my career that a successful, effective physician is one who can instill trust and confidence in the patient, suppress biases and negative feelings, and live up to the patient's image of a physician. The doctor-patient relationship must be a strong bond. It must never be weakened by prejudice or hatred. The physician is the one who must alter his or her feelings to comply with patient needs and is the one in the position to do so. Being a good physician demands it.

William M. Gilkison is a retired family physician with forty years of practice experience in Indianapolis, Indiana. He is a 1969 graduate of the Indiana University

School of Medicine and completed a family-medicine residency at the University of Colorado School of Medicine in Denver. For twenty-three of his forty years he was a solo practitioner. Obstetrics, pediatrics, geriatrics, and general-internal medicine were his areas of interest. Gilkison retired in 2013 and now resides in a suburb of Phoenix, Arizona.

Stillbirth: A Tragedy of Life

WILLIAM M. GILKISON, MD

The death of a loved one is always a sad, tragic occurrence in one's life. Of course, one of life's major stresses is the death of a spouse. But I think the death of a child is far worse. Life is just beginning for them; they are innocent and trusting and love unconditionally. The death of a child is devastating, unquestionably, but so is the death of a baby during pregnancy. What a horrible situation. Young parents who have tried to conceive, sometimes for years, have finally gotten pregnant and are very excited to have a baby in their lives. They have set up a nursery; purchased a crib, changing table, diapers, clothing; had baby showers; and are eagerly anticipating the arrival of the addition to their family.

Then the unthinkable happens. Ominous symptoms occur that harken the warning of a situation every mother dreads—vaginal bleeding, uterine pain, fluid leakage, the loss of fetal movement, and, worst of all, the absence of a fetal heartbeat. Tragically, something has happened that has caused the baby to die in the womb. Is there a worse imaginable tragedy that can happen to expectant parents?

In my twelve-and-a-half years of practicing obstetrics, I had two pregnancies that ended in stillbirth. Both were first-time pregnancies that were progressing normally and suddenly went bad. Both mothers suddenly noticed the absence of fetal movement and fetal demise was confirmed by the absence of the baby's heartbeat. I ordered tests to look for causes but was unable to discover a reason why. In far too many instances that is the case.

Physicians feel sorry and sad for the parents, grandparents, and all close family and friends who are grieving. I tried my best to empathize and sympathize with them and provide support when I felt they needed it. But I discovered that the feelings I had for these two families were inadequate when compared to the emotions I felt when my own son and daughter-in-law experienced a stillbirth at thirty-five weeks during their first pregnancy. I understood, then, the amount of love and understanding they needed. I thought I was being supportive and helpful to the patients, but a stillbirth is much more emotionally devastating than I ever realized. As a parent and grandparent my heart ached for my son and daughter-in-law who lost a baby, they were so excited to welcome. My heart broke seeing that little baby lying there lifeless. And I cried and cried and cried. I hurt for the baby, my children, and my wife.

Parents who have a stillbirth need time to grieve. They need time to hold the baby, name it, bathe or clothe it, take pictures, take part in any religious ceremonies consistent with the family's beliefs, and save keepsakes. In their home, they will continually be exposed to reminders of their loss and may need grief counseling in a stillbirth support program. These aspects of still-birth may not be really appreciated until one personally experiences the loss. When one is not directly affected by this tragedy, one may not realize how great the need is for support.

Fortunately, both of my patients and my daughter-in-law went on to have healthy live births. Had I previously known how emotionally charged stillbirth is, my approach to my two patients would have been different and far more empathetic. Stillbirth is a most poignant tragedy of life. It is one of those times I need to use all my abilities to understand and be as supportive as possible.

The Other Woman

WILLIAM M. GILKISON, MD

Family medicine is a unique specialty. Where else can one see patients so diverse that even the most ardent skeptic will not suffer boredom? Behind every exam-room door could be a person with multiple-organ system disorders or psychological disruptions that challenge our intellect and resolve. We family docs are positioned to know our patients well. We know their children and their spouses and develop an awareness of how their family functions and relates to one another. No ophthalmologist, radiologist, anesthesiologist, or dermatologist will ever understand this dynamic and will probably never encounter what I recently experienced. I met "the other woman."

I was shocked when I learned the saleslady at local store was that woman. As I was paying for my purchase, she casually mentioned that years ago I had been the family physician for her husband and three stepdaughters. "Oh, really?" I said. When she told me the girls' names, I instantly recalled the painful scenario the man in this saga initiated by divorcing his wife.

He left her and the three young girls behind. The girls were at the age when his leaving left a huge void in their lives, and understanding his reasons were beyond their maturity. What followed were months of counseling, numerous pharmacological agents, many tears, and lots of time for the ex-wife to come to a degree of acceptance of the situation. It now also stirred a lot of antagonism in me. How could he do what he did to his wife and three daughters so callously and selfishly? At the time, I was naively unaware that "the other woman" existed because his denial of an affair made it appear he was merely restless and wanted out of the responsibilities and restrictions of marriage and fatherhood.

Well, that was certainly not the case, as I came to learn. Now, many years later, the salesclerk who I had encountered so frequently in this store, while just making small talk, brought all this emotion back to mind. I could not help but think to myself, "This is the other woman!" She had been the reason the man left! Proudly displayed on her desk was a picture of the two of them in a cozy pose. She said they had been married for years, and that his ex-wife and the girls had come to accept her and the disruptive choice the man had made years ago. And believe it or not, they were all friends. I was really surprised and more than a little disturbed. I had just met the reason he abandoned his family.

I vividly remembered how hurt and blindsided his ex-wife felt, how it upset the girls' lives and later relationships, and how it fractured their family unit. The other woman was real. She was standing right there in front of me, smiling as if all was happy and joyous, and because of the passage of time, the ex-wife was able to cope with the huge loss and get over the pain it caused. I smiled back and behaved cordially but could not dismiss from my mind the upheaval that had occurred back then. It had been a very difficult time for his ex-wife and girls. However, it sounded like now, from the other woman's perspective, all was forgiven, and harmony had been restored. I would have love to get the ex-wife's opinion on that.

Retirement has taken me away from daily occurrences such as this. To say I miss dealing with frustrating scenarios like this would be incorrect. Obviously, these situations too often have bad outcomes, and, in the end, someone gets hurt. The physician has feelings, too, and despite his or her best efforts to remain impartial and nonjudgmental, cannot help but have feelings toward one or the other of the involved parties. It is simply human nature, driven by our values. One is not being honest with oneself to deny those feelings.

Life is stress filled and the dissolution of marriage and family is one of the more challenging situations presented to family doctors. Seldom do they feel they have impacted these problems with their patients as successfully as they would like. Unfaithfulness and adultery deeply hurt the offended individual, and trust in the offender is very difficult to regain, if it ever is.

Family medicine is not a boring, repetitive discipline. It is filled with all the physical and emotional stresses family life presents, but through patience, compassion, and persistence, the family physician can make a difference in their patients' lives. The results may take years to reveal, but ordeals like the other woman trauma will come to resolution with time and with acceptance. However, it will never be erased from one's consciousness. I know it will not be from mine as this recent encounter displays.

I'm glad to learn the situation righted itself, but it required sacrifice and the dismissal of feelings by the ex-wife and her daughters. The other woman prevailed this time. She has three stepdaughters and something the ex-wife lost, her husband.

Rejection

WILLIAM M. GILKISON, MD

Physicians are programmed to expect people to "do what they say." We give an order and without question it is carried out. The doctor says, "Nurse, get me a hemostat," or "Give Mr. Smith 4 mg of morphine." We say it, and it gets done. We are not accustomed to being challenged or told "no!" Often, because of these expectations, we become overly demanding or expect everyone to jump at our command, even at home. More than once, my wife responded to my request with, "Don't get bossy; you're not at the office now, so, no!"

Similarly, when I started practice, I expected everyone would like me and would want me to be their doctor. Prior to that time, in my residency training and during my military service, patients were randomly assigned to the ward where I was the responsible physician. They had no choice who was to be their doctor. They were stuck with me. However, as far as I know, no patient ever requested to be transferred from me to another doctor.

During my first months in practice, I was very fortunate to receive numerous patients who had chosen me at the recommendation of their recently retired family physician. Every patient was a new patient, and I felt blessed that so many new families were coming my way. One such family was the six-member, Italian-Catholic Marconi family—mom, dad, and four kids under sixteen years old. How perfect! Just what a new, energetic family doctor wants. A young, healthy family who would be my patients forever.

I saw Mrs. Marconi and a couple of the children a few times and did my best to present a caring and concerned demeanor and a competent presence. She seemed happy with my care and never mentioned any problems. Then, suddenly, the unthinkable happened, at least in my mind.

I received a written request from Mrs. Marconi to have the family's medical records sent to another doctor! What? Another doctor? Why? I was very upset. I could not understand what I had done to warrant this. Had I offended her, the kids, or misdiagnosed something? This had never happened to me. I could not get over it; my ego took a beating and I felt personally insulted, so I called her.

That was a difficult phone call for me, not to make, but to accept the outcome. Mrs. Marconi was very calm, polite, and courteous, but was very noncommittal. She gave no reason other than just wanting to change. I repeatedly asked if I had said or done something to offend her, but, again, she was noncommittal and passive in her responses. I apologized for any misbehavior and, naively, pleaded with her to reconsider her decision, to no avail.

That records request and phone call were stark awakenings I finally accepted. No matter how friendly I was, how capable I was, or how professionally I behaved, I did not connect with her. I was being rejected. She had chosen someone else, not me. I was disturbed to think that maybe, for some reason, she did not like me. I had never faced that before and now that I was in private practice, it was important to me for patients to like and respect me. That leads to good patient rapport and success in treating patients. It took me several weeks to accept that rejection and to realize I cannot please or be liked by everyone.

Now, more than forty-five years later, I remember that incident very distinctly. It left a big impression on me. It was the first time I faced professional rejection and moving on from it was difficult. Personal or professional rejection is a big part of human interaction. What emerges as a result is determined by how one deals with the situation. This scenario taught me not to brood over rejection, but to accept it and not be offended by it. I have come to realize that every person differs from every other and may view situations and interactions differently. I cannot please everybody, and I cannot make people like me. I do the best I can in the way I do it, and not everyone will agree with my manner. That's a fact of life that I must understand and accept.

One cannot win every time and learning to accept rejection or loss is very important for coping with life's ups and downs; it is essential for a happy, successful life and career. I thought everyone would be happy with me as their doctor, but I learned otherwise. I'm glad this happened early in my career because similar rejections occurred over my forty years in practice and dealing with them became much easier.

I found self-acceptance.

He Was Not Supposed to Live

WILLIAM M. GILKISON, MD

I delivered a baby who was not supposed to live. He was too small. He was too premature. He did not have a heartbeat during the late stages of labor. I thought he was already dead when he was delivered. But he beat the odds and defied the expected norms. He survived and is alive and well more than forty years later.

It is such an amazing narrative; it is a story of the great strides pediatricians have made in the care of low-birthweight infants. How the important specialty, neonatology, has emerged, grown, and changed the quality of outcomes for premature infants. How the parents of these infants can feel more reassured of the survival of their "premies."

This story takes place in the late 1970s when I acquired a new obstetrics patient referred by another patient. This was Mrs. Parry's first pregnancy. She was in her early twenties and in good health except for asthma. According to her medical history, she was a severe asthmatic and had flareups with wheezing and shortness of breath quite frequently. Now she was my patient and experiencing active episodes of asthma.

In the 1970s asthma treatment was not as sophisticated or as effective as it is today. And because she was in the first trimester, the first three months of pregnancy, I had to be very careful what I prescribed. Accordingly, I was limited in what I could use to treat her. Inhaled corticosteroids were not developed yet, so in addition to theophylline and albuterol, oral corticosteroids were used a lot. Theophylline, a bronchodilator, was not considered safe to prescribe in early pregnancy, and albuterol, an epinephrine-like drug, can affect blood pressure and heartrate, so I recommended using it only in an emergency. I was left, then, to prescribe an oral corticosteroid, prednisone, to control her asthma. It worked reasonably well, but I was cautious in using it.

A full-term pregnancy is forty weeks. Somewhere around twenty-eight weeks Mrs. Parry's asthma went crazy. Her pregnancy seemed to be going well up to that point, but her asthma was severe enough to require hospitalization. Intravenous steroids quickly improved her condition, and she was able to return home on oral prednisone.

A few days after returning home, the unthinkable happened. For some unknown reason, her membranes ruptured, and she began leaking amniotic fluid. When this happens, labor usually starts spontaneously, but if it does not the doctor is obligated to induce labor within twenty-four hours. Ruptured membranes expose the infant to infection from outside because the protective barrier between the infant and the outside world is no longer intact. Mrs. Parry's labor started on its own. If her membranes had not ruptured, I would have given her medications to stop premature labor, but that was not an option.

So, I had a young woman with severe asthma having her first baby, and her "water broke" twelve weeks early. She was in labor, and all I could do is keep her comfortable and wait. A twenty-eight-week baby is going to be very small and in the 1970s had a slim chance of surviving.

Labor progressed quickly. We moved Mrs. Parry to the delivery room for delivery of we-did-not-know-what. Fetal monitoring of the baby's heartrate was done using an external device strapped to Mrs. Parry's lower abdomen. The nurse monitoring her labor reported that she could not detect the infant's heartbeat right before delivery, so it appeared I was preparing to deliver a stillborn baby.

Mrs. Parry easily delivered a one-pound, nine-ounce baby boy who appeared lifeless. He was floppy, not breathing, cyanotic, and I could not detect a heartbeat. I placed him on the infant warmer next to the delivery table and went back to caring for Mrs. Parry. The delivery room nurse, as is always done, vigorously wiped the baby dry, cleaned him of blood and vernix caseosa (the white, cheesy material on a newborn's skin), and noticed he was breathing. When I heard this, I immediately inserted a tube into his windpipe and breathed air into his lungs. His heartbeat returned, his color improved, and he moved his tiny, tiny arms and legs.

The baby was immediately turned over to the expert care of our neonatologist. Through many months of diligent care, he survived. He was on a ventilator to assist his breathing until he could breathe on his own and was fed intravenously until he was able to take oral feedings. Infants weighing less than two pounds had a very poor chance of surviving, and if they did, often had neurological problems from lack of oxygen to the brain during labor or delivery. This young man had no such complication.

Mrs. Parry recovered from her labor and delivery and went on to have two more children, neither of whom was premature. The young man in my story is now a healthy forty-year-old whose only effects from his premature birth are his small stature (but both parents were below average height) and a raspy voice from injury to his vocal cords from long-term intubation. About fifteen years ago the hospital women's auxiliary sponsored a neonatal reunion. All infants who had spent significant time in the neonatal intensive care unit and their parents were invited to a special luncheon with the neonatologist and nursing staff who cared for them. It was well-attended, and my one-pound, nine-ounce young man was one of the prominent success stories.

I think the thing that prevented this newborn from dying was the intravenous cortisone his mother received for her asthma. Very premature infants commonly have hyaline membrane disease, a condition of their premature lungs that lack enough development to be effective. Treatment with beta celestone, a cortisone preparation, will promote maturity of the lungs in preemies. Women who go into premature labor are given beta celestone as soon as possible after the onset of labor. The drug passes from the mother's bloodstream into the infant through the placenta. This treatment has been shown to improve lung maturity and dramatically reduces the frequency of hyaline membrane disease in those instances and lessens the breathing problems. Had Mrs. Parry not received IV corticosteroids, her baby might have been stillborn.

Thanks to that event, an attentive delivery room nurse, and an expert and highly professional neonatologist, this boy's life was saved. My role was accidental, but I am proud to have been involved.

Looking back on this case, I am reminded of the astonishing advances we made in medical care over the decades that I practiced, including the care of premature newborn babies. As physicians, we are compelled to do everything possible to sustain life.

Editor's note: At the turn of the twentieth century, the infant mortality rate was more than 16 percent. Today, it is just a small fraction of 1 percent. I recall that Doctor John Hurty, the Indiana Commissioner of Health in the very early part of the last century, authored and published a book on healthy pregnancy and childcare that was given to each Hoosier expectant mother. In the book he remarked that he hoped that the mother would see her newborn survive into adulthood. Imagine that. There was no expectation that a child born would necessarily survive to be an adult. How far we have come in public health and healthcare.

I can appreciate the gratification that Doctor Gilkison felt from this episode in his very long career. What a triumph. The changes and improvements in medical care he witnessed are amazing and should not be taken for granted.

"Never forget that it is not a pneumonia, but a pneumonic man who is your patient. Not a typhoid fever, but a typhoid man."

Sir William Withey Gull, MD, physician to the Prince of Wales and Physician-in-Ordinary to Queen Victoria.

Your Name Is What?

PHILIP M. COONS, MD

Little did I know when I began a psychiatric intake on Susan that the repercussions of that interview would color my professional career and propel me into little-known psychiatric realms that I had never imagined. The psychiatric evaluation began with what I thought was a cut-and-dried panic disorder. I was a second-year psychiatric resident in 1974, and I was just beginning an outpatient clinic rotation. Not far into the interview, I discovered that Susan had amnesia that could not be easily explained by an organic etiology.

After completing three hours of evaluation and staffing my patient with a seasoned psychiatrist supervisor, I still could not determine the cause of her amnesia. As I pondered what to do next, I finally decided to request psychological testing. What followed was a seven-hour evaluation performed by a psychology intern under the tutelage of an experienced psychologist. Several weeks later their response to my amnesia question was, "We can't answer your question." They had administered numerous psychological tests in their quest to determine the cause of Susan's amnesia. These tests included the usual outpatient clinic test battery plus a host of specialized memory tests.

While the testing was being completed, I sent for previous psychiatric records and arranged for a collateral interview with a friend, as her family was not available. The interview never happened. At about week five, I received a brief psychiatric report from a local research clinic. The psychiatric diagnosis was multiple personality disorder or MPD (MPD is now known as dissociative identity disorder or DID due to its name change in our diagnostic classification system in 1992). Unfortunately, the report was far too brief. There was no elaboration of symptoms and no history. It was only one paragraph long.

Just after my seventh session with Susan, I was finally able to confirm a diagnosis of multiple personality disorder. After our session was over, Susan went to the waiting room to sit until her ride arrived. Shortly thereafter, I went to the waiting room to check my mailbox. I found a handwritten note from "June." It was in a completely different handwriting from Susan's normal script. Since my next hour was free, I invited June back to my office. What confronted me was astounding; June was quite different from Susan. She had a different voice, different mannerisms, and different attitude toward me. What had been a shy, retiring young woman had suddenly turned into a sophistical urbane lady. How could this be happening?

I remember quite clearly my first reaction to seeing Susan dissociate. The hair on the back of my neck and arms quite literally stood up. I shivered with this sudden piloerection. Once I had regained my composure, I thought that I had just actually seen a patient with MPD, and it would probably be the sole case that I would see in my career. Little did I know at the time. I cannot clearly recall Susan's reactions to me, but in similar patients that I have treated, many report that for the first time they have felt accepted and understood since their complaints are not dismissed as pure fabrication.

I was reasonably certain of my diagnosis since I had attended a presentation of a case of MPD at Purdue University, where I had taken a psychiatry elective during my senior year of medical school. I had been led to believe that MPD was a rare psychiatric condition and that I would probably never see such as case.

My next step was to search the literature on MPD, and I found surprisingly little. The second edition of the *Diagnostic and Statistical Manual of Mental Disorders* (DSM-II) merely listed the diagnosis of multiple personality without listing symptoms or diagnostic criteria. This was the psychiatric diagnostician's Bible and it was of little help. Next, I consulted Friedman and Kaplan's huge *Comprehensive Textbook of Psychiatry*. It also offered little help.

Finally, I delved into psychiatric journals. We did not have computerized search engines back in 1974. I had to do a laborious year-by-year search of the bound volumes of *Index Medicus*. I turned up surprisingly little, maybe twenty articles, mostly case reports. There was one good review article, but it was from 1944. Fortunately, I did find a 1971 article on the principles of psychiatric treatment of MPD that contained a wealth of practical treatment recommendations. It became my "Bible" on the treatment of MPD for the next several years. If only I had come across Ellenberger's 1970 *The Discovery of the Unconscious,* I would have been far ahead of the game, but I did not find that book for another several years. Ellenberger's book on the history of dynamic psychiatry would have opened a world of nineteenth and early twentieth century French and American literature on multiple personality by such notable authors as Alfred Binet, Pierre Janet, and Morton Prince. Over the course of several years I located about 125 pre-1972 articles, mainly through combing through the bibliographies of articles that I had obtained through interlibrary loan. Most of these were gleaned from other journal articles' bibliographies and were not from the *Index Medicus*.

My psychiatric supervisors could give me little help since none of them had ever seen, much less treated, someone with MPD. They were, of course, interested in my case and helped me to stay on the straight and narrow path of conducting psychodynamic psychotherapy.

So where to go next in my quest to learn more about the psychiatric treatment of MPD? Little did I know, but a psychiatric renaissance in the diagnosis and treatment of MPD was about to take place and I was to board on the ground floor of this rapidly rising elevator. As luck would have it, Cornelia Wilbur, MD, the psychiatrist in the 1973 nonfiction book *Sybil*, gave a Psychiatry Grand Rounds in our department at the Indiana University School of Medicine. After she attended lunch with the psychiatry residents. I sat next to her with my patient's chart and presented my case. Her most helpful advice was to listen to the patient and let her tell her story.

I learned much while treating Susan. I learned that MPD patients do not usually present with flagrant dissociation and obvious displays of their personality states. They almost invariably were abused physically or sexually during childhood. Amnesia for childhood abuse and other personality states is common. Depression, posttraumatic stress disorder, and substance abuse are extremely common as co-occurring psychiatric disorders. Probably one of the most interesting facets of treatment in MPD patients is that their transference behavior and attitude toward the therapist varies with different personality states and the therapist's countertransference (personal reaction to a patient) also varies according to what personality state is present. The clinician's feelings are often a subtle clue to the diagnosis, if the therapist is a good listener and self-observer.

Over the next two years Susan became a regular long-term patient of my mine who I staffed with two seasoned psychiatric supervisors. For nine months Susan moved out of state, but she returned to therapy upon her return to Indiana. I continued to treat her when I joined the IU School of Medicine Psychiatry Department, but she moved away again. Several years later I saw her briefly again, but she did not continue treatment. At that time, she was still dissociating into various personality states, but she had matured and seemed not to be troubled as much by her symptoms.

As a young staff psychiatrist in our psychiatry department, I became very busy. Around 1977 the American Psychiatric Association sponsored a panel on MPD at its annual spring meeting. Wilbur and Ralph Allison, a psychiatrist from California, were cofacilitators. Since I could not attend, I enlisted the help of my boss, Patricia Sharpley, MD, who attended and brought me copious notes.

Iver Small, MD, our assistant hospital superintendent, encouraged me to begin corresponding with experts in the field of dissociation. I began corresponding with Allison, who asked me to join him and other psychiatrists who had treated MPD patients at a workshop on MPD at the next American Psychiatric Association in 1978. At that time, it appeared that a doctor who had seen one case of MPD was deemed qualified as an expert on the treatment of this supposedly rare condition. My qualifications were based on the old medical school adage, "See one, do one, teach one." We learned several years later that MPD is not a rare psychiatric disorder but is probably as common as schizophrenia (1 percent of the general population).

Thus began my professional career in researching and presenting papers on dissociation, primarily involving cases of MPD. Over the next decade I continued to present at APA workshops on MPD. In 1984 I began giving papers at the newly formed International Society for the Study of Multiple Personality and Dissociation (today the International Society for the Study of Trauma and Dissociation).

As a budding academic psychiatrist, I knew that I must begin publishing articles in psychiatric journals, so I chose to write a review article on MPD. As a young naive academic, I had no idea that review articles were usually invited submissions. I struggled mightily with my first paper and even took a course on academic writing given by a librarian at our medical school library. After several painful rejections, my article was finally published in 1980 as the lead article in the *Journal of Clinical Psychiatry*.

My first research project on MPD involved doing electroencephalographic, or brainwave studies, on two patients with MPD. I acted as a "normal" simulating comparison patient. This paper was published in 1982 in the *Archives of General Psychiatry*. Our results showed that there was nothing inherently different from the brains of MPD patients and normal people.

Unfortunately, money for research on dissociation was not available because of disbelief in the condition by high-ranking psychiatrists on research-funding review committees. These psychiatrists did not believe that MPD existed and their efforts to discredit the field of dissociation hampered the production of research on dissociation for years to come.

I eventually established a Dissociative Disorders Clinic at the Larue D. Carter Hospital outpatient clinic and over time saw about 450 patients with various types of dissociative disorder, including dissociative identity disorder, dissociative amnesia, dissociative fugue, and depersonalization disorder. I was able to publish many professional journal articles, book chapters, and letters to the editor resulting from research involving these patients. Most involved dissociation. My expertise in the field of dissociation eventually contributed to my participation in the development of the dissociative disorders section of both the *International Classification of Diseases* (tenth edition) and the *Diagnostic and Statistical Manual of Mental Disorders* (third edition revised and the fourth edition).

My promotion to full professor of psychiatry in 1994 was based upon my research, professional publications, service, and teaching. In 1995 I retired from Larue Carter but continued part time with the Department of Psychiatry and did forensic psychiatry.

My second career in forensic psychiatry occurred by happenstance. Since I was recognized as an expert in treating dissociative identity disorder, I was asked to act as an expert witness in court cases involving DID in the early 1980s. Unfortunately, this work involved malpractice cases involving poorly trained clinicians who violated therapeutic boundaries with their patients. They became friends with their patients, ceased to be nonjudgmental, overly advocated for their patients, and some even developed sexual relationships with them.

I have often wondered why some clinicians who treat DID become embroiled in malpractice lawsuits. I think the explanation varies from case to case. With some clinicians, it is the result of inadequate training in the treatment of DID and PTSD. In others, the malpractice results from wanting to nurture the patient back to health. And in still others, it is the result of an unscrupulous clinician taking advantage of the patient.

By the 1990s I found myself doing court-ordered evaluations on a variety of criminal defendants to determine their competency to stand trail and sanity at the time of the crime. Of the random court-ordered exams that were assigned to me, I found that 7 percent had some type of dissociative disorder. By the end of my second career in forensic psychiatry, I had testified in 113 criminal and civil court cases. Of course, the number of cases evaluated far exceeded the number of court cases because it is only the minority of cases that end up in trial.

I happily retired in 2012 after a thirty-seven-year career in psychiatry. Looking back over my professional career, I find it astounding how one patient could change and ultimately direct my career trajectory. I am incredibly thankful for all that my patents of all diagnoses have taught me. It all began in 1974 when Wilbur echoed the words of the great physician, William Osler, MD: "Listen to your patient. He is telling you the diagnosis."

Philip M. Coons is a graduate of Wabash College and the Indiana University School of Medicine. He completed residency training in general psychiatry at IU Hospitals in 1975. Currently he is professor emeritus of psychiatry at the IU School of Medicine. Coons is past president and fellow of the International Society for the Study of Trauma and Dissociation and has received both of their prestigious Morton Prince and Cornelia Wilbur awards. He is also past president of the Indiana Psychiatric Society and Distinguished Life Fellow in the American Psychiatric Association.

When a Patient Reminds You of Someone You Know

RICHARD D. FELDMAN, MD

Have you ever met someone who really reminds you of someone else you know well? It could be the sound of his or her voice, mannerisms, or facial and other physical characteristics. There is a natural human tendency to redirect your feelings for this individual, either positive or negative, to the new person just encountered. It's called "transference." It's probably close to the conditioned response we learn about in Psychology 101.

One almost anticipates that the the new person will share similar interests, talents, shortcomings, beliefs, actions, or personality traits with the previously known person. My wife and I recently met a young man that looked like the twin of one of my nephews. Everything about him appeared exactly like him, even down to his voice. There was the initial natural expectation that he would be exactly like my nephew in every way.

In the medical relationship, transference refers to a patient's feelings toward the doctor or other health professional through the process explained above. It can certainly affect the doctor-patient relationship either positively or negatively regardless of the actual actions, attitudes, and personality of the physician.

Another phenomenon is referred to as "countertransference." In this case, the situation is the opposite: the redirection to the patient of the doctor's feelings for a person already known because the patient reminds the physician of that person. Again, it could be positive or negative. It might be a person from the physician's personal life or even another patient. We have all experienced the phenomenon of transference in our lives.

I particularly remember two patients that involved countertransference. Both experiences were fortunately very positive.

Otto was an elderly patient originally from Germany who immigrated to America sometime between the two world wars. His English was excellent, but he still had a moderate German accent. There was something about his facial features and his accent that absolutely reminded me of my grandfather, who immigrated to America in 1907. Otto was a comparable size to my Grandpa Harry and had a similar walk. There was a certain toughness about him, typical of that generation that came to America and built a life here. I remember one day he told me a story that as a teenage boy he swam across the Reine River to escape the Allied forces. For the life of me, I cannot remember what he was doing to necessitate an escape!

I instantly felt a warmth toward this old man, and it lasted until the day he passed away. I always loved to talk to him about the "Old Country" and asked him questions about his life experiences. He was much like my grandfather in many ways. It was like talking to my Grandpa Harry again, and I enjoyed it.

He had some serious health conditions over the years I cared for him, but we worked through them together. I always enjoyed seeing him in my office and during his hospital stays. I took a special interest in him, and I think a major reason I did so was because it was like having my grandfather back again. He was one of my special patients, and when he died, I emotionally felt like my grandfather had died again. I never told him of his similarities to Grandma Harry, but I imagine if they had had the opportunity to meet, they would have liked each other and enjoyed each other's stories about their former younger lives so far away.

I entered medical school to become a psychiatrist, and before switching to family-medicine residency training I spent a year in the Indiana University School of Medicine psychiatry residency. One of my first hospitalized psychiatric patients was Erica, a young woman with wavy auburn hair. She was schizophrenic and was hearing not-so-nice voices. They told her to do things that she felt was wrong and that she was a terrible person. She was far from terrible and was a sweet, engaging, intelligent, and talented person. She was also an excellent artist and while hospitalized focused on creating abstract sculptures. I am not big on abstract art, but I liked her work.

When I looked at her, she greatly reminded me of a very close college friend, Debbie, who is best described like a sister to me and we keep in contact to this day. Erica did not particularly share any personal attributes with Debbie other than a pleasant demeaner and an artistic flare, although in different ways. Erica was an artist, while Debbie a musician with a July Collins-like voice. But there was something striking about her appearance and her presence that wonderfully smacked of Debbie.

Again, I became very close to this patient. She was special and I spent extra time with her daily in the hospital talking her through some difficult times. Unfortunately, despite various attempts with multiple medications, she was not making much progress with her thought disorder. I was clearly aware what was going on with my countertransference, and it undoubtedly was a big factor in my approach with her. I had such a warm feeling for Erica. I wanted her to get better and for her emotional pain to end.

When I left the rotation, she gave me a hug and presented me with one of her sculptures. She thanked me for all my time and help. I told her she would do well and to hang in there. I never saw her again and have no idea what happened to her. Somehow, I believe she is doing well with the advances we have made in psychiatric medications since I cared for her more than forty years ago. Beside, like Debbie, she possessed strength of character and had depth of personality on her side.

The relationship between doctors and patients are sometimes not entirely straightforward and can be influenced by emotional entanglements involving persons not involved in the therapeutic relationship. I am fortunate mine were positive ones.

The Unremarkably Remarkable

MASHA PUZANOV, MD

Early in my fourth year of medical school, I rotated as a subintern on the hospitalist team at our academic, quaternary-care hospital. There I saw the most complex, advanced, and rare pathologies of my medical-school career. They were, as we called them, the "zebras," the challenging-to-diagnose cases—a student's dream. But the case I remember most was no zebra. It was ordinary, even mundane to some. Perhaps the unremarkable reaction to the case made it, to me, tragically remarkable.

Ms. Landers had just been transferred from the Intensive Care Unit to my team. Such a transfer meant that the patient no longer required the highest acuity level of care. Patients transferred in this manner were deemed to be clinically stable. In Ms. Landers's case, stable was a generous term.

"Ms. Landers is a fifty-five-year-old patient with alcoholic hepatitis and is in acute liver failure," my attending physician said as our team stood outside the patient's room. The attending turned to the medical students, "Who wants to follow Ms. Landers?" I caught a quick glimpse of the patient. Right away I could tell she appeared very ill.

"I will," I volunteered. I sensed this case would be instructional on a level beyond pathology and textbooks.

When we entered the room, the first thing I noticed when I laid eyes on Ms. Landers was her skin. It looked as though her whole face and body had been applied with a bronze coat of paint. "Jaundice," I thought. I had never seen such clear picture of jaundice until that moment. A yellow hue also replaced the whites of her eyes. Jaundice was an indication the patient was suffering from liver damage. Her eyes were wandering about the room as she tried to make sense of where she was. Her eyes caught mine for a moment. She was intermittently moaning and was clearly in pain and discomfort.

"Ms. Landers," I said, and she looked at me. "Do you know where you are?"

"Hospital" she replied. We often asked these questions to gauge a patient's mental status.

"Do you know the date?" She stared blankly. "Do you know what day it is today, Ms. Landers?" I repeated. No answer, just moaning.

We continued our examination. She was a large woman I later learned by looking at her hospital chart, but somehow in that hospital bed she seemed much smaller. Catheters were coming out of various parts of her body, including a urinary catheter and urinary bag with amber colored urine filling up its contents. After a brief physical exam, we left the room. My attending turned to me, "This is likely end-stage. Her labs are awful, and her prognosis is grim. We'll consult palliative."

When our team was done rounding, I looked up my new patient in the hospital record. Ms. Landers had a long battle with alcohol abuse and had been in and out of rehab programs for years. She had decided to enroll in another cessation treatment program but had instead ended up in the hospital for liver failure. She was not presently married but had a son my age. I read over her hospital course in the ICU and then turned to the vitals and labs. Indeed, the picture was grim. She was septic with low blood pressure. Her electrolytes were off. She had kidney failure and grossly elevated markers of liver failure. Her organ systems were beginning to shut down.

I saw Ms. Landers the following morning on my own. She was alone and looked scared. She was still confused and this time could not maintain eye contact with me. Her eyes were fixed straight ahead, as if trying hard to focus, to overcome the level of pain and discomfort she must have been suffering. She was moaning even louder than the day before. I looked at her catheters. Her urinary bag had brown liquid, and her catheters were slowly filling with an equally brown viscous fluid. Pain medication hung as a drip by her bedside.

"Why isn't anyone with her?" I thought. "Why is this dying woman alone?" I put my hand on Ms. Landers's shoulder. I did not know what to do. What words to say? And would she even comprehend them? "You don't know me, and I hardly know you, but I am here," the gesture was meant to convey.

Days passed like this, and she was getting worse. She was growing more confused and did not know where she was. And worse still, I found her alone each morning. My daily ritual remained the same: I would put my hand on the patient's shoulder, pause, and hope that some of her suffering would be lifted, even if just for a moment. During these pauses, I would I think back to another patient our team saw the week prior. A woman of similar age with the same diagnosis and the same prognosis. That patient died surrounded by family who slept by her side, a stark contrast to my lonely patient.

One late afternoon after passing by Ms. Landers's room, I saw she had a visitor. I walked in and introduced myself. I learned she was a friend of the family. She had been coming to see the patient in the evenings. "I am here because she has no one else. I've had family and friends die from similar causes.

Drugs, alcohol. I've been here before, I can handle it," she said matter-of-factly. She spoke in a tone in which I could detect the slightest hint of sorrow. She continued, "Her son is good, and he loves her. But their relationship is complicated. I told him I'd come here."

The following day a goals-of-care discussion was held with the patient's son. The hospitalist, palliative-care physician, and I made our way to Ms. Landers's room. The son had already arrived. He was tall and strong in stature, but I saw a young man whose large frame was merely a shell for a gentle, understanding, and mournful soul. "Our relationship hasn't always been the best, but she is my mother and I care deeply for her," he said, appearing to hold back tears. We explained the medical prognosis and the options that remained for his mother. He decided to proceed with comfort care only. We left the room to discuss the medical plan outside the doorway. Minutes later, her son left the room wiping a face full of tears.

Soon a new attending physician took over the hospitalist team. During morning rounds the students would give a brief overview of their patients' hospital course to catch the attending up to speed. When we walked into Ms. Landers's room, she was no longer moaning. She was sleeping and appeared more comfortable with her higher dose of pain medication. Still, she was alone. She was dying alone.

In that moment I felt sick and wanted to run out of the room. If I stayed in the room, I thought, I surely would break down in tears. I opened my mouth and stalled for what seemed like minutes. "Oh, yes I remember reading about this patient," the attending said. "Inpatient hospice. Nothing for us to do." And we left.

Nothing to do, and yet I was not satisfied. The great tragedy of dying alone, slowly on a deathbed, seemed commonplace to those around me. My attendings marched onward, the nurses tended to their new patients, and the rest of the world housed in the hospital walls moved on. Except me. I think of well-known deathbed scenes in fiction where no patient dies alone. Even Ivan Ilych died in his home in the company of family. Countless nonfiction books are written about patients surrounded by loved ones. The best possible day at end-of-life care does not include a lonely, solitary existence.

But it is not so difficult to imagine that many people might die slowly, over days and weeks, in solitude. In Japanese there is a word for this phenomenon, *kodokushi*, or lonely death. The elderly Japanese, increasingly socially isolated, die alone as they age. An old family friend died in this manner, alone in her apartment, and no one knew for days. But just because it is fathomable to imagine a lonely parting does not make it any easier to accept.

One ordinary morning I arrived at my desk in the hospital and refreshed my patient list. Ms. Landers was no longer there. She died overnight. I paused and felt an overwhelming sense of sorrow for a lonely woman I hardly knew.

During rounds my attending, as if by habit, stopped in front of Ms. Landers's old room and looked to me to present. "She died overnight," I said. "Oh," the attending shrugged, "I didn't even notice," and quickly moved on to the next patient.

When I drove home that evening, I wept. I wept for a woman whose story I had never known. I wept for a woman whose death had barely gone acknowledged. I wept for a woman who must have envisioned a different ending. I hugged my partner deeply that night. "My worst fear is not dying," I confessed. "My worst fear is dying alone."

Masha Puzanov received a degree in economics and Spanish from Indiana University, Bloomington. After a brief stint as a corporate financier, she attended the IU School of Medicine, during which time she wrote this essay. She is currently pursuing a residency in psychiatry.

Unexpected Kindness

KRISTIN WILLFOND, MD, MPH

It was Christmas Eve, and I was miserable. As an intern it was my lot to work the Christmas holiday shift. This is my favorite time of year, and my family was at my house eagerly awaiting my arrival. I came in to work my twelve-hour shift and was greeted with a long list of current patients, new admissions, and, overall, a lot to do.

Normally, I'm an upbeat person. I now recognize that I was probably experiencing some burnout, which contributed to my holiday pity party. One of my admissions changed that.

Marianne as a middle-aged woman who had come in with abdominal pain and ended up having her gall bladder taken out. I went to see her after her surgery, and despite the recent anesthesia, she was very kind and wanted to know when she could go home. When I explained that she would likely be here until tomorrow, she was visibly upset. She told me that her husband was dying at a different hospital and requested to go home sooner so she could be with him and her children. I told her I would do my best, and I would check on her after I spoke with the surgeons.

When I returned, I was greeted by the addition of Marianne's family; everyone was wondering what my decision was. I told her if she could eat comfortably, we could send her home with close physician follow-up. She had such an engaging vivacious personality, her nurse and I stayed in her room for much longer than necessary, chatting away. She mentioned that she was looking for a new primary-care doctor, and I gave her my contact information. The evening she left, I saw Marianne's nurse and we discussed her care. We could not believe that someone going through such personal hardship could be so kindhearted. The nurse told me that Marianne had filled out a card thanking us for her care. Marianne had specifically mentioned me and said she was happy to have found her new doctor.

I did see Marianne once in my clinic. Her husband had since passed away, and she was managing as best she could. We mostly sat and talked. Several weeks later, I received a message prior to night shift stating that I needed to sign a death certificate for Marianne. I just sat and cried. I was in shock. I forced myself to finish working that night. The next day, I called her mother, who was listed as an emergency contact. She did not know the cause of death for Marianne but thanked me for calling. She said Marianne had commented about our office visit and how I helped her by listening.

Marianne is someone I will always remember. She taught me no matter how hard life hits you, it pays to be gracious to others. She gave me a different perspective on patients who are grumpy—who knows what difficulties they were experiencing before I walked into the room? I will never be a perfect person or doctor, but the only way we survive in medicine is to take the good and the bad and turn them into life lessons. The brief doctor-patient relationship I had with Marianne made a lasting impression on me. I only wish I could send her a thank-you note saying as much.

Kristin Willfond, a graduate of the Franciscan Health Family Medicine Residency program, currently practices in Indianapolis, Indiana. She is originally from Portage, Indiana, and completed her undergraduate education at Indiana University, Bloomington. Prior to attending the IU School of Medicine, she obtained her master's degree in public health through the IU School of Medicine's Department of Public Health. She enjoys reading, cooking, and spending time with her husband and two daughters.

The Night the Hospital Almost Burned Down

CHRISTINA PINKERTON, DO

The hospital emergency room was surreal at any time of the day or night but never so much as at 2:00 a.m. The dingy mint-green plaster, stark overhead lights, and ravaged bodies on gurneys lent an apocalyptic feel to the vast, sprawling emergency room. For a naïve farm girl, it was a fascinating look at lives gone wrong. The gynecology resident and I had been called down for a case of pelvic pain, possibly due to an ectopic pregnancy, a potentially life-threatening condition where the fertilized egg implants in the fallopian tube instead of the uterus. It was *the* condition that had to be ruled out in any female patient of child-bearing age with pelvic pain. Right after that was a woman with severe pelvic inflammatory disease, a sexually transmitted disease that could also be fatal, just not as quickly.

The resident, already in a foul mood because of the late hour, gestured at me to go in the room and do the exam on the woman with the possible ectopic. The results of the pelvic ultrasound and blood work had already come back normal, ruling out an ectopic, so the next undertaking was to do a pelvic exam for sexually transmitted diseases. The sheriff's deputy, a paunchy, middle-aged guy, moved away from the exam room door as I approached. "Come get me when you're done with her. I'm going for a smoke," he said. She had been brought in under escort from the Girl's School.

When I entered the room, she sat bunched up on the corner of the gurney, her almond-shaped eyes wide with fright and her complexion the color of nutmeg. Quite pretty. I explained the vaginal exam and her eyes got even wider and she violently shook her head no: "The last doctor who put one of those metal things in me ripped me, and I bled for a week. I'm not doin' that ever again!"

"Well shit," I thought. The resident will have my head if I do not get this exam done and quickly. "Don't you want the pain to stop?" I asked her. "I can't help you if I can't examine you and find out what's wrong. I'll be gentle. I know how it feels."

Her eyes look around, and then she leaned closer to me and whispers, "Can you get me a match?"

"What? Why do you need a match?" I ask.

"I need a smoke. The school won't let us smoke. I haven't had a smoke in so long. I have the cigarette; I just need a match. If you get me a match, I'll let you do the exam."

Well, I knew a couple of the emergency room nurses that smoked, and one of them was on duty over in the orthopedic section. I knew she would have a lighter or a match. "Fine," I said. "But I need to get this exam done first because the results will take a while to come back from the lab." At that, she brightened and scooted down to the edge of the table with alacrity and put her feet in the stirrups.

Nothing under the microscope. I looked in several areas of the slide. I would need to give her antibiotics prophylactically for gonorrhea and chlamydia as those tests would take several days to come back from the lab. But with nothing seen in the vaginal fluid and a normal white blood cell count on the CBC, pelvic inflammatory disease was very unlikely. We could wrap this up and maybe all get back to bed.

I head straight to her room when I realize I forgot her match. I'm stopped in front of her door when the bleary-eyed sheriff's deputy comes up and asks if we are done.

"Ya know what she's in for, don't you? Arson. Burned down her family home with her mother and siblings inside. Started the fire in a wastebasket and walked out the door. By the way, is she ready to go?"

"Yes she is," I said, and turned abruptly to disappear down a back hallway. I can hear her as they drag her out, cussing and spitting and screaming. I shiver at the near disaster and decide I should better wise up in a hurry!

Christina Pinkerton grew up in Thorntown, Indiana. She spent her childhood riding a tractor and helping her grandfather, who was a farmer and was first in her family to continue her education past high school. Pinkerton graduated from the Indiana University School of Allied Health in Medical Technology. She attended the IU School of Medicine and the Saint Vincent Family Medicine Residency in Indianapolis. She was one of fifteen cofounders of American Health Network, where she has practiced family medicine in Indianapolis for more than twenty-eight years. She likes to garden, scrapbook, and enjoys visits from her adult children.

Regalos

CHRISTINA PINKERTON, DO

She was a little abuelita, but that is redundant. It was 1995 and there was not much of a Hispanic population in Indianapolis yet. It was my third year in practice, and I was discovering the joy of reoccurring patients. She never missed an office visit, and one of her granddaughters always came to translate. But not today.

How was I going to communicate? At that point, my high school Spanish was twenty years in the past, and I had not used it except for my fourth year of college with my roommate, Isabella, a doctor from Spain who lived with me part of the year when she was not in Venezuela with the Indiana University Medical Genetics Department helping with research on Huntington's disease. Either way, neither experience had prepared me for the needs of a medical conversation in the language.

There she sat with a smile on her face even though she had to be more intimidated than I. "Buenos días" she said. Well, I could handle that.

"Buenos días," I said back. "Me llamo Doctor Pinkerton." Well damn, why did I say that? She already knew who I was. After all, it was not her first visit. Okay, think. "Dolor" means pain. How is it conjugated? It is one of those weird stem-changing verbs where "o" goes to "ue." "Donde le duele usted?" (Where do you hurt?) At that, her smile got broader and she pointed to her left knee. It did look swollen, although not hot. "Por cuento tiempo?" (How long?)

"Seis meses" she said. I remembered my numbers. Six months. "Me duele mi rodilla mas fuerte de la tarde cuando trabajo muchas horas en la cocina." Okay, I got most of that. It hurts when she has been cooking all day. I wrote her a script of piroxicam, instructed her to take it once a day with "una comida" (a meal), but what was the word for pill?

I went home that day and looked it up. I also looked up and refreshed my knowledge of all the body parts. Later I bought a medical Spanish dictionary and learned "mareo," "picasón," and "hinchazón" (dizzy, itchy, swelling.) After a while, her granddaughters stopped coming.

Our ten-doctor practice was located near Lafayette Square Shopping Center in Indianapolis, and over the next decade the Hispanic population exploded in that area. Word of mouth and my partners referring Hispanic patients grew my practice and my proficiency.

It was very satisfying to be able to dismiss the children (who were there to translate) and let them be kids while I had the satisfaction of talking directly to their parents. I am sure I butchered the grammar at times, but one mother was particularly grateful that I released her twelve-year-old daughter from the room before telling her that her husband had given her a sexually transmitted disease. And there was the elderly senora from the Dominican Republic who left my office crowing, "Mi Doctora me entiende!" (My doctor understands me.)

I was also able to help her elderly husband, who had been in the United States for ten years with healthcare for the first time. I asked him "Diez anos vive in los Estados Unidos; porque no aprende la idioma?" (For ten years you live in the United States; why haven't you learned the language?)

"Ah, Doctora," he said. He explained in Spanish that he worked three jobs to provide for his family here and in the Dominican Republic. There was no time or money for classes.

As for my original abuelita, we conversed over the years and when she noticed I was embarazada (pregnant) with my daughter, she knitted the most beautiful peach-colored sweater and pantaloons with a variety of complicated stitches. Both Jessica and Megan have outgrown them, but I am saving it for a grandchild.

She went back to Mexico; I have not seen her in years, but her gifts continue. Every time I meet a new Hispanic patient and greet them with "Me llamo Dr. Pinkerton" and see their faces light up, I remember her. She gave me the regalos (gifts) of communication, tolerance, and understanding of another people, another culture, and I am the richer for it.

Men of Faith

GEORGE KANE, MD

"The map is not the territory"
Alfred Korzybski

"See those nuclei? Those are not happy nuclei."

I am a second-year medical student sitting in a pathologist's office tucked away in a maze of crisscrossing hallways at Saint Mary Medical Center in Evansville, Indiana. I am only a few weeks into my summer externship, but I have already auscultated over two dozen chests, removed suture and staples from healing wounds, and worked a five-hour code with an intensivist in the Intensive Care Unit. This morning I am sitting at a microscope with two viewing stations over a single tray that the doctor rapidly loads with samples.

"This is an aggressive cancer. Pretty advanced. Not good news for this guy, what's his name . . . ah, Ivan Illych."

Next, we go to the path lab, where there is a walnut-sized adrenal gland tumor, freshly excised, sitting in a paper towel on the counter. Just like I had read about in first year of medical school! This sucker pumped out too much epinephrine for the body to handle and needed to be removed stat. It is just like I pictured while reading about it, only more firm, yellow, and evil-looking. It does not squish between my fingers and feels heavier than I had expect. Our job is to make frozen slides of the growth's peripheries to make sure the surgeon did not leave any tumor behind.

In the afternoon, I go up to the sixth floor to shadow oncology nurses. I learn all about different chemotherapy regimens, how it taxes the patients and the staff, and what comfort measures can go a long way to help the patients' quality of life. Toward the end of the day, I follow a nurse into a patient's room. The patient is about to get a consult with the oncologist who has some bad news. The patient's name is Ivan Illych.

"Pathology says it's an aggressive cancer," the nurse whispers to me. Those words did not bother me in the lab this morning, but now they do. This morning those words meant an interesting diagnosis, but this afternoon these same words mean an ashen-faced, scared father of three looking shriveled in his bed.

The oncologist comes in, shakes the patient's hand, and sits on a couch under the windowed overcast sky. The patient, doctor, and nurse decided on a plan for aggressive chemo. The doctor and nurse leave, and I am about to follow suit when I realize I never introduced myself to the patient. We started to chat, and when I asked him how he was handling this all he said, "Well, I believe in God, so I'm not too scared." I told him I believed in God, too, and asked if he wanted to pray together. He did.

I was able to visit with Mr. Illych several more times throughout his stay mostly talking about God and living as men of faith in a cynical world. At one point, I gave him my phone number. He was discharged for nursing home care, and I did not hear from him for nearly a month. Then, one Saturday I got a call from Ivan out of the blue! He wanted to let me know that he had finished his third round of chemo and was feeling much better. We cheered together over the phone, caught up on each other's lives, and wrapped up by tentatively planning a time to hang out and catch up again.

While Ivan did eventually succumb to his cancer, I remain grateful to have accompanied him in both the dark and light moments of his initial diagnosis. None of the patients I take care of during my career will escape our mortal nature, but as a physician my honor will be to accompany them as a steadfast guide and faithful companion to the end.

George Kane wrote this story as a senior medical student at the Indiana University School of Medicine. He plans to train to become a family physician. As an undergraduate, he majored in medical humanities at Indiana University–Purdue University, Indianapolis, and enjoys finding higher meaning in medicine. He lives on the Old Northside in Indianapolis with his wife, Anne, and their young son Lazarus.

Touching

JOHN NAGEL, MD

It is December. I suppose it is the time of year that reminds me of an experience with one of my patients more than forty years ago.

In July 1974 I was in the third year of my psychiatric residency when I was assigned to work in an outpatient clinic dedicated to the care of patients who were considered over utilizers (commonly referred to in the medical field as "frequent fliers") of the emergency room. It was there that I met Katarina, who was a forty-four-year-old Yugoslavian Jewish Holocaust survivor who was living in an apartment alone provided by a nearby Temple.

According to her medical record, she was coming into the Colorado General emergency room two to three times a week with vague abdominal complaints, joint pains, and headaches. In our first meeting she presented as a quiet, rather plain (without makeup) woman who appeared to be much older than her stated age. I listened to her recite a list of physical complaints, and then I asked her to tell me about her background, starting with her growing up.

Katarina told me that she had grown up the youngest of five children in Yugoslavia with her father supporting the family as a tailor. She said that her childhood had been happy until the Nazi occupation of her town when she was fourteen years old. It was there in about February or March 1944 that she and her family were taken into custody and put on "a train full of other families." They were transported to Munich and on to the Dachau Concentration Camp. As they got off the train, she, her mother, three sisters, and her oldest sister's baby were separated from her father and older brother, who she never saw again. Meanwhile, all the female members of the family were housed in a barracks with other women.

She described the terrible austerity and deprivations of the situation; they never knew what was going to happen next. At least they had each other's support and comfort. Then on a late September day, camp guards had them line up, and as the line moved, they could see that women with babies were being separated out with their babies. Her older sister gave her baby to Katarina, and she was separated from her mother and sisters. Later she learned that her sisters and mother along with the other women were gassed. Katarina struggled with taking care of the baby until November, when lack of food and bitter cold took the baby's life. She talked about how she had struggled to survive then as now. Gradually, she started to reach out to her Jewish community asking for more support. I saw Katarina on a weekly basis, and as we developed good rapport, her visits to the emergency room diminished.

I continued to see her. It happened on a bitter cold mid-December morning clinic appointment. She had brought me a tie as a Christmas present. As we talked, she said, "You know, sometimes I miss the Camp." I was overcome with surprise and disbelief and asked her how that could possibly be true. She responded, "I live alone, I have no friends, and no one ever touches me. It's like I'm radioactive. When I was in the Camp on bitter cold nights, we would stand together and sing and sway to keep from freezing, and I'd be touched all around." As the session ended that morning, I offered to give her a hug, which she seemed glad to receive.

Katarina went on to talk about how she had managed to survive with the care and support of older women until, finally, on April 29, 1945, American GIs arrived and liberated the survivors. Months later she was taken to Holland for refeeding. She showed me a picture of her taken at the time at sixty-eight pounds. As a displaced person without family, she remained in Holland until the Jewish community in Denver "adopted" her and arranged her housing and subsistence.

I found it interesting that Katarina insisted that I must be Dutch with my blond hair and blue eyes. She ignored the fact that she must have known that my last name is German (I knew that she spoke several languages, including German and English). I realized that sometimes patients though transference make you into whomever they need you to be. I was so deeply impressed by that experience that I remember it as though it happened yesterday. I still cannot tell her story without being overcome with tears.

Some years back, I came across Abraham Verghese's TED talk "A Doctor's Touch." The reader should search for it and take the time to watch it. He has a longer talk on YouTube that one might also want to find. Watching those, one may better understand why I have never been able to adjust very well to telemedicine. Touch is a part of the sensory encounter with each other, and it is healing. In this time of COVID, we are all touch deprived and need to seek out that comfort when and where it is safe and comfortable.

John Nagel was raised in Littleton, Colorado. He graduated from the University of Colorado in 1966 and the University of Colorado School of Medicine in 1970. He also completed a psychiatric residency at the University of Colorado School of Medicine in 1975. Nagel practiced in several Colorado locations and in1990 became medi-

cal director of Mountain Crest Hospital in Fort Collins, Colorado. During his time in Colorado, he was an assistant clinical professor at the University of Colorado School of Medicine. In 2013 he moved to Flagstaff, Arizona, to continue inpatient practice. Nagel retired in October 2019, but he continues to teach nursing and medical students. Throughout his career he has maintained a special interest in cross-cultural medicine, with a focus on Hispanic and American Indian health.

"I cured with the power that came through me. Of course, it was not I who cured, it was the power from the Outer World; the visions and ceremonies only made me like a hole through which the power could come to the two-leggeds. If I thought that I was doing it myself, the hole would close up and no power could come through. Then everything I could do would be foolish."

Black Elk (left), medicine man of the Oglala Sioux

An Appreciation of Traditional Healing

JOHN NAGEL. MD

As I was working the Denver Veterans Administration Hospital's psychiatric consultation service in the spring of 1975, I was asked to consult on Frank Eagle Plume, who was identified in the request as "difficult and uncooperative with treatment." He was on a medical unit receiving peritoneal dialysis in treatment of both acute and chronic renal failure.

His chart identified him as a thirty-eight-year-old, single, unemployed, VA disability-dependent American Indian living in Denver with his sister. I saw that he had been followed in the VA outpatient clinic for chronic renal disease. It was noted that he would occasionally present alcohol intoxicated and had a history of multiple inpatient stays for acute renal failure. He had presented with fluid retention, weakness, fatigue, and shortness of breath, and his labs showed significant reduction in his kidney function. As his hospitalizations had become more frequent and his renal function had become progressively worse, the possibility of kidney transplant had come up. His sister was tested as a possible donor; she proved to be a good match and was supportive of donating a kidney. When Frank's attending physician approached him, Frank became angry and resistant, threatening to leave the hospital, which prompted the psychiatric consultation request.

When I met with Frank, he was lying in bed undergoing peritoneal dialysis and appeared weak and tired. I asked him about his kidney problems and when they had started. He told me that he had been born and raised on the Red Lake Chippewa (Ojibwe) Reservation in Red Lake, Minnesota. He gave account of a "rough childhood," indicating that both parents were alcoholic and that "Dad took off when I was young." He talked about having a younger brother and two older sisters. After his father left his mother continued to drink and became abusive. Most of his care fell to his sisters; predominantly the sister he was currently living with. He had been raised "traditional," attending ceremonies. He started drinking alcohol young, "when I could sneak it." He said that he dropped out of high school in the spring of 1954 and joined the U.S. Army. Then as he was visiting back home in the summer of 1955, he "got sick" saying, "a lot of people were sick" with something similar.

When he returned to his army post "sick," he ended up being hospitalized "on account of having blood in my pee." Apparently, he had contracted a strain of streptococcus that was documented at the time in a July 1955 article in the *Journal of Pediatrics* titled, "Epidemic Nephritis at Red Lake." His acute glomerulonephritis was treated. However, his convalescence was long, and he noted, "I never got back to active duty, so I was medically discharged and came to Denver to live with my sister." He initiated medical follow up in the VA outpatient clinic and was awarded a VA disability. Even so, he described making frequent visits "back home in the summer and fall" to visit family. He said that a lot of his social life in Denver was through the DNAU Indian Center.

In my second interview with Frank the next day, I brought up the fact that his doctors were recommending a renal transplant. This upset and angered him as he made it clear that he did not want that. When I told him that his sister had been tested and was a match, he declared that he did not want any part of having his sister inside him. He voiced spiritual concerns about having "any part of any women inside me, controlling me." I suspected that, in part, his spiritual concerns were related to his abusive mother and "bossy" older sister. He ended the interview, saying the he would not talk about it anymore. The next day, he insisted on leaving the hospital "Against Medical Advice." As he was signing out, the chief medical resident speculated, "He'll be dead in a few weeks, but there's nothing more we can do."

Weeks went by and I wondered what had happened to him, thinking I would probably never know. Then about three months later, his sister brought him in for an outpatient clinic visit, and I was contacted. Lab tests done at that time of the visit showed his kidney function was improved, having only moderate dysfunction. His sister asked to speak with me and she told me that when he left the hospital she had taken him "back up home" to Red Lake, where he was treated traditionally with almost daily "sweats" in a sweat lodge. She explained to me that if he "gets really sick again, we should have Wallace Black Elk (a local Medicine Man whose sweat "inipi" he had attended) and some of his "guy friends" talk to Frank about a transplant." She said that Wallace honored traditional and Western practices, seeing them as complementary rather than competitive. Wallace had encouraged Frank to essentially "Let them do their thing over there, and we'll take care of this end."

Talking with Frank's sister, I realized my failure in not talking with her and others important in Frank's social and emotional life when I had seen him in the hospital. Later, I reflected on the fact that Western Medicine is "egocentric," focused on the identified patient apart from that individual's social matrix. Indigenous medical practice is "sociocentric," which meets the patient in their social environment and allows for input and support from family and friends in a ceremonial context.

I learned to respect certain aspects of indigenous "traditional" healing practice. A medical search in the library rewarded me with an April 1966 article from the Scandinavian literature titled, "Sauna Baths in the Treatment of Chronic Renal Failure." My experience with Frank made me curious to learn more about indigenous American Indian medical practices. I was reminded of a presentation that I had attended where a medical historian asserted that the Lewis and Clark expedition had relied more on indigenous Indian practitioners than they had on instruction they had received from the eminent Doctor Benjamin Rush prior to their departure from Washington, DC, in 1803. After that, I found it important to meet with family and concerned friends. At the same time, I always found it interesting to ask about what "traditional" treatments patients may have had.

Respecting the spiritual aspects of traditional healing is also critical, and something I have come to greatly appreciate. I remember a conversation with Southern Ute medicine man Eddie Box. We were talking about Western medicine versus traditional Indian medicine. He started unbraiding one of his braids. As he did that, he told me that white man's medicine just addresses physical and mental, while leaving out the spiritual. He made his point that without addressing the spiritual, nothing hangs together and treatments fall apart. I have always been interested to know about a patient's early religious instruction and the progression of their spiritual development since. When I asked Frank about his personal spirituality, he described offering his personal prayers by performing the pipe ceremony with both the pipe and ceremony given to him by Wallace Black Elk.

It has been a great privilege to be a psychiatrist and have the time to explore those aspects of patients' lives.

Editor's note: "Inipi" is a purification rite and is necessary to help a person enter a state of humility and to undergo a kind of spiritual rebirth. The sweat lodge is central to Inipi. Prayers offered there draw on all the powers of the universe—Earth, Water, Fire and Air. Inipi is done before any major undertaking to purify the body and gain strength and power. It is one of the Seven Sacred Rites of the Lakota Sioux that has been passed down through the generations.

Wallace Black Elk, a Lakota elder and spiritual interpreter, was likely a relative of Nicholas Black Elk, the great Holy Man of the Oglala Sioux and the subject of John Neihardt's Black Elk Speaks, *mentioned in chapter 67.*

My Patient Phil

MERCY OBEIME, MD

I first met my patient Phil in 2014. It was a time when there was a great amount of public discussion regarding the opioid crisis and finding solutions to this epidemic. State legislators got involved and enacted laws they thought would help, but these measures made it more difficult and time consuming to prescribe opioids. Physicians felt threatened and under scrutiny. These laws sent a panic across the medical-provider community, and many doctors opted to stop writing any opioid medication.

I got a call from a recently graduated physical medicine and rehabilitation specialist to see a patient needing hospice care but who was not really dying. I sensed the desperation in her voice as she told me about this patient who she thought was on lethal doses of opioids. I did not think the patient could be taking this much medicine, and I immediately thought that this patient could be illegally diverting! I accepted the patient and was faxed his medical records. Reading through his record made me very sad. This young physician was very disturbed by the number of opioids this patient was receiving without much supervision, and she had no intention of taking on the responsibility of prescribing these high doses of opioids to a patient who was not imminently dying.

The patient was described in the records as a forty-five-year-old male with a very unusual familial neurologic disease that compromises circulation along with immune-deficiency disorders. He had one leg amputated and amputations of multiple fingers of the left hand. He had been in this practice for more than ten years and on the same dose of opioids with some functional improvement. He used a wheelchair for mobility and was incontinent. But for the past six months he had been on extremely high doses of multiple opioid preparations but without any significant adverse effects. His quality of life revolved around his dependence on the computer and his mother. I found it interesting that this doctor felt that because he has signed a Do Not Resuscitate form, he had to see a hospice and palliative medicine doctor since he was dying! She contacted several hospice and palliative medicine providers who declined to assume his care before finally making the call to me.

I was also impressed by an x-ray report that showed striking abnormalities involving the hands, feet, and left arm with a multitude of missing bones and marked deformities. One partial finger remained.

When Phil came to see me, he was in a wheelchair he maneuvered effortlessly with his one finger. His mother walked beside him. He was unique to say the least. My background in genetics told me he had a syndrome of some kind. His speech was understandable, though it was clear that he had to compensate and work hard to move his tongue around to get the words out. And he had a lot to say.

He had also Googled me, researched my work, and found that I was originally from Nigeria; he wanted me to recognize that he liked to know his providers. He told me having a good relationship with his care team was a very important lesson he learned as a Riley Children's Hospital kid. Finally, he told me about himself.

His timeline started before his parents got married. He talked about his birth and diagnosis of Riley Day syndrome and meeting the Riley (no relationship to James Whitcomb Riley, the poet, the hospital was named in honor of) in the Riley Day syndrome who told him he did not really meet the syndrome's criteria. He also told me about his social problems, dealing with peers, bullying by other children, and landlords. How he learned to fight for himself, his college days and inability to finish school, and the pain of his parent's divorce. He willingly signed a DNR order, telling me he signed it so many times and was not afraid of dying.

I was very impressed, but nervous about treating him with such high opioid doses. I had written very large doses of opioids for patients dying in hospice, but Phil was clearly not in hospice and dying. I knew I had to treat him because I had nowhere to send him. So, I told him I would take him on as a patient. I talked to him about our protocol for opioid-medication management at our clinic. He acknowledged reading about the new state requirements and very gladly signed all the paperwork. He promised me he would be the best patient I had ever had.

As I took the papers from him, he asked for a hug. Getting a hug was not an easy task because this too was unique since he essentially had no arms. He told me he had to tell me about one more thing: his surplus! I was not prepared for what I heard next. Could he have a few hundred pills at home? He explained that sometimes his previous physician could not get him in a timely manner, so over the years he saved medications so he would not run out. I told him I must see this surplus.

The next visit, he brought in the bottles. My medical assistant counted them, and the count was more than 600 pills of oxycontin and hydromorphone! We made a pact. He would use up the surplus, and I promised him I would always make sure he received his needed medications. For four years I saw him monthly. We reduced the dose of his medication a little bit, but he has strongly resisted any more reduction. Now, I see him every two to three months, he has no surplus, he has never run out of medications, and he has no problems with taking too many pills or diverting any pills to the best of my knowledge. He continues to update me on current government and political affairs, health policy, and the addiction crisis.

When he turned fifty, he told me he had done everything on his wish list except publish a book about his life struggles. He shared disappointment at being turned down several times. So, when this opportunity came to write about a patient, I chose my dear patient, Phil.

Phil taught me that palliative medicine may mean prescribing what some consider lethal doses of opioids. Caring for him showed me that opioid medications, known today as the cause of death for so many, can improve the quality of life for some who have no other means of dealing with the hand fate dealt them. The level of confidence I developed from taking care of Phil allowed me to accept more patients like him. The unintended consequence of this was that I found myself in a new field of practice in addition to hospice and palliative care: addiction medicine.

Treating patients severely addicted to opioid pain medications or heroin has been challenging but an opportunity to help with a public-health crisis. I would never have taken this path if I had not crossed paths with Phil. My one word to describe this relationship is gratitude. Phil has a lot to teach, and my career certainly benefited from the opportunity to care for him.

Mercy Obeime is a family physician with two areas of added qualifications: bariatric medicine and hospice and palliative medicine. She practices at Franciscan Health Indianapolis and was the founding director of the Franciscan Health Neighborhood Health Center. Currently, her position is the director of Community and Global Health, and her patient care is focused on chronic pain management and substance-abuse disorders. Obeime graduated from the University of Benin Medical School in Nigeria and completed the Indiana University School of Medicine Family Medicine Residency.

"It is the human touch after all that counts for most in our relation with our patients."

Robert Tuttle Morris, MD, 1915

Answered Prayers

RICHARD E. SPENCER BSN, RN, CMSRN

I would like to share with you a recent experience at the bedside that showed me how the power of a nurse's faith can provide healing for even the most broken of hearts. My story involves the power of a prayer, and a shared awareness of patient needs beyond the physical. For every patient at Franciscan Health Indianapolis, the hospital where I work, each nurse strives to uphold our mission to continue Christ's ministry in our Franciscan tradition. I hope you, the reader, will share in my experience as the following story is a reflection and a testament to that creed.

First, a little about myself. I am a male registered nurse with more than nine years of nursing practice at Franciscan on a thirty-four bed postsurgical unit. I practice here as a professional caregiver because the organization is first and foremost a place for spiritual as well as physical healing. From my earliest days as a foster child in a Christian orphanage farm in Kansas, God has touched my life and soul in countless ways. In my career, I have also seen how God's holy presence, exemplified through my healing hands, has transformed the lives and outcomes of our most vulnerable patients.

My story begins on a night shift. I was working on the floor as a patient-care assistant on an extra twelve-hour shift due to low staffing. Sometimes, RNs like myself are asked to step outside our traditional roles to fill staffing needs to provide safe and quality care. During this shift our unit was full, and many patients were designated at a high level of acuity, meaning their care required nursing interventions beyond the norm. So, like many nights on a busy nursing floor, it was a tough night to say the least. I spent most of the shift helping patients to the bathroom, helping my fellow colleagues do admission histories, assisting with giving medications, and providing comfort and safety to our patient population.

I particularly remember also feeling stressed that night because of the way my assignment was made. It consisted of a total of ten patients—five who were located at the very front of the unit and five located at the back of the unit. This is a very large unit with three long split hallways, so an assignment that was split like mine was difficult to carry out. I expected that I would be sleeping very well after I reported off at the end of the shift in the morning.

Around midnight, we had a middle-aged female who came in from the emergency room who was having uncontrolled pain and nausea from a bad gallbladder. Our charge nurse took over primary care for this patient as our staffing was still short. I saw the patient come in on the gurney and offered my assistance to the charge nurse to take vitals and help process her admission to the unit. As we helped the patient to her bed, I could immediately see that she was very anxious and fatigued. Her eyes were red and watery from the pain and the experience of waiting in the ER for a long time to be admitted. Her husband, who accompanied her, was supportive, but the patient still seemed miserable and on the verge of fresh tears as we helped her into bed.

After I introduced myself and my role in her care, I could sense from observing and talking to this patient that she was having a difficult time adjusting to fact that she might be in the hospital for an undetermined length of time, feeling miserable, and anticipating an unexpected surgery. She was not only in abdominal pain, but also suffering from something that seemingly was more personal. I asked her if there was anything I could do to help, but she said that she did not want to discuss what was bothering her. I decided then to not push the issue, but I also let her know that I or a counselor would be here at any time to help or listen to her. I let her know that we would address her pain promptly and address any other needs she or her husband may have. I then wrapped up my work with her admission and let the charge nurse know if she needed my help that I was available at any time. Throughout the wee hours of the morning that followed, I made sure to peek my head in the door to see how she was doing, but it appeared that her fatigue had finally caught up to her; I could see her sleeping soundly.

As morning came, I was extremely tired from running all over the unit performing baths, helping administer medications, helping my fellow nurses admit patients, and charting my care. In the mornings the routine is for all the patient-care assistants do what we call "zone vitals" for the primary-care nurse and canvas each patient room for their vital signs. I was assigned to the room with this patient who I had helped earlier. As I approached her room, I could hear her crying. The charge nurse had recently attended to her pain and offered additional comfort measures, but the patient's crying was inconsolable, and it seemed that all the comforting words or pain medicine would not help this patient find relief from her unspoken sorrow.

At first, I stood at her bedside with the charge nurse. We tried unsuccessfully to comfort this inconsolable patient with comforting words, but then in a moment of power and love, I felt Jesus speak into my heart and mind and say, "Let me help." I then allowed myself to listen intently to not only the words she was saying but her body language as well. This permitted me to fully open my heart to the suffering of this patient. I realized that the care she needed would not consist of pain medicines or encouraging phrases, but a healing silence and an offering of the heart to let her know that she was not alone in her pain, and she did not have to carry her burden alone.

So, I offered to pray with and for her. I did not say it was going to be okay or any of the usual condolences nurses give to patients during a hospital stay. I simply offered to sit with her and pray for her with the charge nurse and her husband in the room. I told her that I could see she was hurting more than just physically. I said that I felt that giving whatever she was going through to God would help her get through this trial. I sat down next her and held her hands, and I prayed for her emotional and physical healing. In my prayer, I gave thanks to God for meeting this patient and gave recognition to Christ as the healer of all ills. I also prayed for a successful potential surgery and expedient recovery. I fervently asked God and Jesus to give this suffering person the strength and peace she needed to withstand her pain and anxiety. I used her full name in my prayer and made sure our full nursing love and presence was there for her and her husband.

After I prayed, she seemed to take a long sigh, and her crying seemed to soften. She said she appreciated the prayer and that she was going through some difficult times at home, and she did not expect for this to happen. She said she had been in pain most of the night and nothing seemed to have helped. I gave her a hug and told her that God is in control and all the nursing and medical staff on the unit were there for her for whatever she needed to make it through to her discharge and beyond. All she had to do was ask and we would try to move heaven and earth to make her stay with us a little more pleasant. I thanked her for sharing with me, and I told her I would come back later to do her vitals so she could rest. Her primary-care nurse would again attend to her pain at that time.

She eventually had her gallbladder surgery the next day and was released a couple of days later to go home with her husband after being treated for a perforated gallbladder. While I did not get to say good-bye to her since she was discharged on the off shift, I knew that she had touched my heart, and I had answered her prayers with the power of Jesus and the love of each nurse caring for her.

Reflecting on that night, even though I was really fatigued physically, I remember being refreshed emotionally. I was able to offer her the spiritual comfort, which so many patients in the hospital need to heal. I received written thanks afterward from the charge nurse for my attentiveness and unexpected prayer for the patient in her time of anguish. But the real satisfaction and reward I received was the feeling of Jesus working through me to give healing care. I rested comfortably that morning knowing that I exemplified the best of our nursing profession and the mission and values of our Franciscan care.

I chose to share this story with you, the reader, because at the core of our Franciscan practice, either as a doctor, nurse, or therapist, is the recognition of Jesus Christ as the ultimate healer and that all our patients have unspoken needs beyond physical pain. The ability to not only embrace and recognize that belief, but also to be confident enough to act upon it, takes the form of answered prayers. Caring with an open heart and sharing the love of Jesus truly reflects the mission of service in the Franciscan tradition. This experience with this brave woman reinforced my belief that compassionate care is the essence of what professional nurses, like myself, are pledged and called to do.

Richard E. Spencer is a certified postsurgical bedside nurse with more than nine years' experience at Franciscan Health Indianapolis. In addition to his baccalaureate degree in history from Ball State University, he received his associates in nursing degree with honors from Ivy Tech Community College and his baccalaureate in nursing with honors from the University of Indianapolis. Spencer is formally recognized by Franciscan Health as a clinical nurse expert, received the Transformational Leadership Award for Staff in 2013, and the nationally recognized Daisy Award for Nursing Excellence in 2015. He is also a local public relations officer with Sigma Theta Tau International Nursing Honor Society.

Turning Complexity into Simplicity

SARAH ASTORGA, MD

Early in my third year of residency, I had my first appointment with a patient with whom I would have one of my most meaningful patient-doctor relationships. It was with a middle-aged woman who seemed no different than many of my other patients. As I prepared for her first visit by looking at her past records, I started to dread the appointment. I only had thirty minutes with her, and not only did she have uncontrolled Type 2 diabetes, but also high blood pressure, depression, and fibromyalgia. She was also on both long-term opiates and long-term benzodiazepines, which I would have to take over the risk of prescribing.

When I walked in the room, she looked ten years older than her age. It was obvious that she had not taken care of herself with a proper haircut or new clothes in years, and she did not smile at all. I struggled through our first few appointments trying to get her blood sugar under control by finding a medication she could tolerate and afford. And I started checking off all the important boxes on the checklist of diabetes care.

Each visit I eked out a little more of her history. I learned that she had been severely abused and sexually assaulted by her ex-husband, who had given her syphilis. I learned that her son struggled with addiction, and that she now had full custody of her grandchildren with no support and limited income. She told me that she had no idea what foods to eat or what she could do to improve her health and pain. Instead of listening to what she was telling me, I shortsightedly focused on continuing to increase the doses of her diabetes, blood pressure, and mood-stabilizing medications. I unwisely assumed that she was just looking for more medicines to control her diabetes and other conditions, since it appeared that she could not afford healthy foods and had little knowledge of how to prepare it.

Because I only had fifteen minutes at follow-up visits to spend with her, and because she had so many concerns, I did not think lifestyle discussions were worthy of much of that precious time. I referred her for diabetes education and to a therapist. I updated her Pap smear. I ordered a pneumococcal and flu vaccines for her, again checking off all the boxes for chronic disease management. But I was not listening. I failed to look at her more simply as a person. I failed to look past the ever-changing complexity of her diagnoses.

About six months after we met, she unfortunately had to have a gyneco-logical procedure that was extremely painful and difficult for her, especially with her history of sexual abuse. Of course, that day the exam table that would move her into proper position with all the other procedural equipment was not working. With grace and dignity and wearing nothing but a hospital gown, she voluntarily helped us shuttle all the equipment across the entire space of the clinic to another room, smiling and laughing with us.

Once we finally got her settled and ready, I was just focused on trying to figure out how to do the procedure properly and keep her from passing out due to discomfort. But after the procedure and this little episode in the office, I came to the realization of how much she was invested in her care and her health. Very invested. I realized that she was doing her best and was mostly just asking for advice on everyday living to feel a little better. She was not asking for miracles like I had imagined. She could not think about preventing heart disease or neuropathy in the future because she could only think about how she was going to buy food and clothes for her grandchildren. She was not even bitter about her chronic pain and trauma. Rather, she was willing to do the hard things that could improve her health.

I eventually allowed myself to simply sit with her. I permitted myself to tell her that what she was going through is not only hard but more stressful than any human being could expect to handle or should ever have to try to handle. And then I tried to give her what she had been telling me she needed this whole time. We talked about how to start with breakfast and move from only simple carbohydrates to a more balanced meal. We discussed how she could get her grandkids involved in the process of preparing food and to try more vegetables.

I asked her about hobbies that she used to enjoy that she could start again. We talked about small self-care choices she could make. None of these took away all her symptoms or cured her diabetes or took away the daily pain. But when I saw her after those meetings, she was smiling. She was more forth-coming. Her diabetes numbers did get a little better, and together we settled for "better" instead of perfectly at goal. Like 99 percent of my patients, I did not completely cure her or even accomplish all the things that are supposed to equate with optimal health. But turning complexity into simplicity made leaps-and-bounds-more headway into improving her everyday life than I could have foreseen.

Like many residents going through training, my patient interactions varied wildly. I went through times of just trying to address my patient's main complaint and then through times of really digging into charts to make sure any number of recommendations were completed based on preventative-health guidelines. There were other days I was simply "putting out fires" and getting laboring mothers to the hospital or doing an unexpected procedure. These unknowns certainly made training unpredictable, exciting, exhausting, draining, and sometimes fun, but for me, at least, unnecessarily, overwhelmingly complex. My patient helped teach me not only the power of lifestyle changes but also the importance of empathic listening and really putting myself in my patients' everyday shoes. I can find myself coming down out of the clouds of complexity and down to earth in the simplicity of "what can we do today." That simple space can be a lovely and healing place.

Today I work in the lifestyle and integrative medicine field, and my experience with her certainly shaped the conversations I have with my patients today. I start the relationship with each patient by asking them to tell me their story and what they think is important, instead of trying to decide for them.

Sarah Astorga grew up in Fort Wayne, Indiana, and completed her training at the Indiana University School of Medicine and Franciscan Health Indianapolis Family Medicine Residency. She then completed a fellowship in Integrative Medicine at Kansas University. She currently practices Integrative Medicine at Essentia Health in Duluth, Minnesota. She and her husband, Juan, enjoy winter camping, mountain biking, their two cats, and generous pours of Don Julio with good company.

Phone Calls

GERALD C. WALTHALL, MD

For the first decade or so of my private practice of Otolaryngology-Head and Neck Surgery at Saint Francis Hospital in Indianapolis, my partner and I covered the emergency head and neck trauma cases as part of our services. One late night, about 2:00 a.m., I was awakened by an urgent phone call from the emergency room. The ER physician requested that I come urgently to attend the victim of an explosion who had suffered severe facial injuries and was in acute airway distress. Upon my arrival in the emergency room, I beheld a man named Jason whose face was so shredded and swollen that human features were barely recognizable. His airway was so severely compromised from oral and pharyngeal swelling that it was necessary for me to perform an emergent tracheotomy under local anesthesia. His wounds were then cleansed and bandaged with moist dressings.

Jason was admitted to the intensive-care unit to stabilize his condition and assess him for possible intracranial or vascular injuries. Fortunately, no additional organ systems were damaged, and the next morning he was taken to the operating room, where I spent several hours repairing lacerations and reconstructing his nose and oral cavity.

Jason steadily improved from his physical injuries, but as the days progressed, I became aware of the deep emotional trauma he also suffered. The authorities determined that a jealous rival of the lady Jason had been seeing had placed dynamite outside the bedroom of his home. The subsequent explosion not only destroyed the house and injured Jason but also killed his young son, who was sleeping in the same room. His other son was fortunately not injured.

Over the following several years, Jason required several revision surgeries to his face to repair the perforations to both eardrums and to fit hearing aids for his noise-induced hearing loss.

As the years progressed while I treated Jason, I was privileged to have received the gift of his trust and friendship. He shared his deep emotional scars as we worked to reduce the physical scars from the terrible trauma that had brought us together. During this time, he came to consider me and my office staff as extended family and would often come by to bring the staff candy, tell a few jokes, and visit with us. Gradually his visits became less frequent, and I assumed he was getting on with his life, but we all missed his impromptu appearances.

As Paul Harvey was wont to say: "And now for the rest of the story."

It had been a long while since I had heard from or about Jason. One evening a few years after I retired from practice, I unexpectedly received a phone call. The voice on the phone inquired if I was the Doctor Walthall who practiced head and neck surgery at Saint Francis several years ago. Hearing me say "yes," the man identified himself as Jason's son. He explained that Jason had passed away a few weeks before and had not wanted any memorial or obituary. His son, however, did want me to know how often Jason had spoken kindly about me and the office staff.

He shared that Jason struggled with depression and alcohol over the years after his traumatic experience and how deeply he appreciated the times he received a lift when he would come and visit with us. I suspect Jason suffered from what we now know as Post Traumatic Stress Disorder. His son indicated that a while before Jason died, he had developed dementia but would usually respond alertly when someone would speak of his relationship with our practice.

I must confess that as I listened to his son express the gratitude that he and Jason felt for the care and friendship they received, I was deeply touched and moved to tears. A phone call brought us together during a tragedy, but a special relationship prompted a phone call with different tidings. The latter call recalled the gifts that I received from my shared experience with Jason.

Jason and I were blessed to have more than a doctor-patient relationship. We had shared a bond more akin to brotherly love and were both enriched by the journey we traveled together. That phone call reminded me that being a physician is not just a job, but a calling that allows us to touch others and in return be deeply touched ourselves.

Gerald C. Walthall was born and raised in Evansville, Indiana. He received a bachelor of arts degree from the University of Evansville and his medical degree from Indiana University School of Medicine. In 1974 he completed an otolaryngology head and neck surgery residency also at the IU Medical Center. Walthall engaged in private practice Otolaryngology in Indianapolis until 2005, when he became medical director of Palliative Medicine at Franciscan Health Indianapolis. Retired since 2017, he enjoys spending time with his wife Linda, three children, and six grandchildren.

Editor's note: Doctor Walthall died on September 28, 2022.

Stressed Out

RICHARD D. FELDMAN, MD

Ray Chamberlin was a longtime patient who was a carpenter. He had his own business specializing in custom-made cabinets. He was an honest contractor and just an overall nice gentleman. I had Ray make and install some cherry cabinetry for an office in our home. We accepted his bid for the work, and he did a beautiful job. An unusual thing occurred when I looked at the final bill. It was for an amount less than the submitted bid. That had never happened before to me and as you might expect, it has not occurred since! Ray said, "Well, the job didn't quite take the time I had anticipated, and I got a great price on the cherry, so I passed the savings on to you." And it should be of no surprise, we chose him to do additional work when we remodeled the space over the garage into a family room.

Ray was generally healthy for a middle-aged man. He was always pleasant with a smile on his face when I saw him in the office. He appeared to be an easygoing fellow, but something was boiling inside him. He had a single medical issue I was addressing: He had hypertension that was resistant to all my efforts to control. We tried multiple medication trials with no success, and I did some blood work and imaging to rule out treatable causes of his elevated blood pressure. I maintained him on several blood- pressure medications that gave him better control, but just not optimal.

This went on for a few years. Finally, Ray came in one day and announced that he had gone off all his medications. He was feeling great and told me he no longer needed blood-pressure medications.

Worried, I said, "Why did you do that? You need them to control your blood pressure!" Ray just looked at me with a big smile.

I reviewed the nurse's vital signs she had taken and recorded in the chart. The blood pressure was stone-cold normal! I took his pressure myself with the same result.

"Ray, what happened?" I inquired in disbelief.

"I got rid of my problem!" he replied with a satisfied smile.

"What was the problem?"

"I got rid of my accountant who was embezzling money from my business for years. I was under constant stress keeping the business open. I worked harder and harder, and my business became increasingly successful attracting more and more jobs. But I was barely making a profit. It was the financial stress, doc!"

I guess it was. Although I knew from my medical training that stress is certainly a factor in some disease processes, I always seemed to discount that factor. For example, many people treated for hypertension come in with suboptimal readings in the office and say they are just having a miserable day and then rushed to get to the appointment. I am still prone to respond with the fact that many patients have a horrible stressful day and come in with a normal blood pressure. I suggest taking some additional pressures at home to make sure the pressure is truly under control. Other patients only have elevated pressures in the doctor's office—the well-known "White Coat Syndrome." And, indeed, many do have normal pressures taken at home and at work and document them for me.

So, since the experience with Ray Chamberlin, I am much less apt to discount stress affecting medical conditions. Undoubtedly, it's a major factor with some patients. And certainly, in hypertension!

Life Goes On

WARRICK L. BARRETT, MD

I am most grateful to have been privileged to serve as a physician during this lifetime, and I am most grateful for circumstances under which I have lived.

There have been many educated people in my family. I have a maternal great-grandfather who was responsible for the operations of the principal building of a small college in Ohio. I have a maternal grandfather who became a college professor. I have a maternal grandmother who became an elementary school teacher. I have a father who became a military officer, a high-school teacher, and a high-school administrator. I have a mother who was an elementary and middle-school teacher and who became a member of a college faculty.

As a young man, I learned to appreciate the importance of education. I became interested in the sciences and grew up enjoying several television programs about physicians including *Ben Casey* and *Dr. Kildare*. Ultimately, I felt that I wanted to become a physician and enjoyed sufficient family support and encouragement to do so. As a physician, I felt that it was important and my responsibility to heal every patient I cared for. I felt deeply defeated when there was a circumstance in which a patient of mine could not be healed and passed away.

Eventually, I had a patient who was diagnosed with a terminal malignant illness and who was not at all discouraged by his circumstances. He, however, perceptively recognized that I was very discouraged. He sensed my defeat.

He encouraged me through our conversations to come to understand that all of us must experience a physical death at some point. We indeed then make a transition to a realm in which we are alive but without the bodies that accompany us during our earthly lifetimes.

I am now very confident that "life goes on" in a spiritual realm that transcends the lives that we have experienced in the physical realm. I am most grateful to this patient who first brought this remarkable realization to me.

Born as a military dependent at Fort Dix, New Jersey, Warrick L. Barrett grew up in Springfield, Ohio. He is a graduate of Saint Louis University and the Cornell University Medical College. He completed postgraduate medical training at the

University of Pittsburgh Medical Center and the Wright-Patterson Air Force Medical Center. He resides in Indianapolis, Indiana, where he provides occupational and urgent medical care.

"The One"

STEPHANIE MARSHALL CASE, PsyD

There is a concept identified as "The One." It relates to mitigating factors to life's adversities, particularly during one's formative years. Repeated research backs the notion that having at least one supportive person can promote resilience. An important element of this relationship is the individual's ability to challenge the other's point of view. The idea is that challenging patterns of thinking or behaving result in novel and more adaptive ways of coping with what may come.

Laura and her family were well known to the clinic. In fact, she had also made quite the reputation in the school and juvenile court systems. Clinically, she had been given nearly every psychiatric diagnosis from A to Z. She had also managed to drop out of school by the eighth grade and matriculate to the juvenile justice system throughout her years. Her family life was difficult, and she made a point to find ways to be anywhere but home. Her guardian was beyond frustrated and nearing the end of her legal say in any system—Laura's eighteenth birthday was in three months.

Laura's guardian hoped to have a definite diagnosis for Laura. She believed nailing down the correct diagnosis and treatment would help Laura go back to school, start a career, or just "do something." Laura, however, was not so motivated. She often failed to appear at appointments, and when she did show up, regardless of the chief complaint, physical or psychological, was nasty to providers. She would swear at staff members, refuse to do check-in procedures, insult providers, and respond sarcastically to questions relevant to treatment. She was extremely difficult.

My unique journey as a provider was a move from molecular biology to the more person-focused social science of psychology. I quickly had to acknowledge that as a practicing psychologist, there was not the certainty of serological tests, imaging, and flowcharts for best practice in treatment. Psychological assessment data often comes in the form of self-report from the patient, family, teachers, and others, which is routinely skewed based on each individual's perception and personal bias. Early in any provider's career, there are several factors that might interfere with our ability to adequately assess and treat patients. Among these are the pressure to perform, a pull to "fix" a patient, and the gap between academic knowledge and clinical application. Enter Laura and her guardian with the plea, "This is my last chance, please help."

As a person who acknowledges that I like a challenge, I met with Laura expecting we would sort out whatever was happening through psychological testing. I believed this would be an easier route than long-term therapy because testing is often time limited, highly structured, and less invasive. Three no-show appointments later, I was surprised to see that Laura checked in to an intake appointment. Although she was in the office, she still displayed all the qualities of defiance and difficulty. The interview went as expected; no real information was reported, but her general demeanor conveyed anger and sadness. I recommended testing and explained the course of action over two to three more sessions as per the usual routine. However, I am not sure why, but I ended the interview differently. I told Laura, "You know, it's hard to fall off the bed when you are lying on the floor."

She said something along the lines of "What the hell is that supposed to mean," got up, and slammed the door. After that encounter, I did not expect her to come back, but to my surprise she did.

Over the next few months, with the anticipated failed appointments in between, I built rapport with her and came to enjoy her sarcasm. I challenged her when she was being difficult and set boundaries by ending sessions when she was obviously displaying frustration in herself. Over time, Laura's presentation transformed into a person who was fragile and self-doubting and becoming guarded when she was overwhelmed. We eventually completed the necessary testing.

After assessments are complete, psychologists often write comprehensive reports to explain scores, findings, diagnoses, and treatment recommendations. During a feedback session, the content of the report is explained to the patient and when a minor is involved to the guardian(s). Laura and her guardian no showed the feedback appointment. A few months later, a now eighteen-year-old Laura called to make an appointment to hear the feedback. At this appointment just she and I discussed the results and recommendations. My hopes were that hearing her correct diagnosis would validate that everyone else had been wrong about her and that Laura would realize that she was wrong about herself as well.

I suggested she make a follow-up appointment for therapy. Instead, she sat in silence throughout my explanations and at the end mumbled some sarcastic self-deprecating insult to herself, then toward me, and left the office. After she left, I was not surprised, I was not hurt, I was relieved. Not that she was gone, but because I told her something she needed to hear.

But then came the silence. Two weeks before I was set to move on from this clinic assignment, I received a voicemail from Laura telling me she was "ready to get up off the floor" and make an appointment for therapy. She no showed that appointment, and I moved on to my next clinic. To be honest, I selfishly hoped at the time she would come back so I could hear how I changed the trajectory of her life, and because just one person cared enough, everything was different. I am hopeful for her, but I will probably never really know.

I consider myself fortunate not only to have had her early in my career, but also because I took the chance to listen to the advice of many seasoned veteran psychologist colleagues. It is so easy to get caught up in solving the problem or giving expert advice. How common it is to feel reinforced when we fix something or solve the problem. Rather, Laura was the one patient who illustrated to me that solving the problem is not the greatest challenge. At times, it can be selfish and even get in the way of the purpose of a psychologist. What I learned was what is most gratifying is to be part of the journey with another person and finding a way to be okay with not completely seeing that journey to the end.

As much as I would like to think I was "The One" for Laura, I am confident she was my "One." She helped me, early in my own professional development, to remind myself of why I wanted to shift my focus from lab tests and empirical data to forming relationships, being present, and sitting with the uncertainty of human nature.

Stephanie Marshall Case is originally from South Bend, Indiana. She received her undergraduate degrees in microbiology and psychology from Indiana University at Bloomington, Indiana, and a master's degree in molecular biology from Purdue University. She worked for Eli Lilly and the Indiana University of School of Medicine as a bench scientist before returning to graduate school to receive her doctorate in clinical health psychology from the University of Indianapolis. Case has a passion for integrated healthcare and the biopsychosocial factors that contribute to overall wellness.

What the Heck Just Happened?

PAUL DAY, MD

The reason for the office visit noted on the electronic chart stated, "Late prenatal care, establish." I read through the only previous note; it was from a triage visit to labor and delivery the week before.

"Oh man," I thought, "she's around thirty-two weeks. This is gonna be a hot mess."

I walked into the exam room and saw a young woman; her name was Kathryn. The first three things I noticed were the overwhelming smell of tobacco, her blue hair, and her lack of eye contact. I obtained her history of past pregnancies and past medical problems. The eye contact did not really improve that much. I asked her who she lived with and what type of support she had at home. I received vague and nonspecific answers. I then asked some screening questions for abuse. Not an issue. I asked what kept her from seeing us sooner in her pregnancy, and she said she was not sure. So, I went through the rest of the medical part of the visit and stressed the importance of getting her blood work done.

To be honest, I walked out of the room bewildered and a little frustrated. What the heck just happened in there? I was right, this was going to be a hot mess.

At her follow-up visit, after missing an appointment, her eye contact was better. I got to know her a little more. At the next visit she said, "Yea, so I haven't told my parents yet. I'm afraid they'll be really mad at me." Apparently, she was wearing loose and baggy clothing, and they had not noticed she was pregnant. Again, what the heck just happened in there? Oh, and I write for some azithromycin for chlamydia, a sexually transmitted disease.

Now she was around thirty-six to thirty-seven weeks. I walked in the exam room, and she said, "I think I want to give my baby up for adoption." As much I was prepared for surprises with this patient, she kept managing to surprise me. We talked for quite a while about this, and she had very good reasons for wanting to do so. So, we got the ball rolling on that. What the heck just happened in there?

At around thirty-seven to thirty-eight weeks, she finally told her dad who, to her surprise, was not angry with her and was very supportive of adoption. She also heard back from the adoption agency and things were looking promising. I got a test of cure for chlamydia, and the results that I received, after she had left the office, indicated that she was still infected. I was unable to get ahold of her to go to the pharmacy to pick up another antibiotic prescription or come in for an observed antibiotic dose. What the heck was happening here?

It was Easter weekend, and my in-laws were in town. We were out having dinner for my father-in-law's birthday. The pager went off. Kathryn was in labor. Her boyfriend, being a bit of a doofus, was probably not going to come after all, and she was pretty upset about it. I was pretty upset that her child was probably going to get a chlamydial infection. So, one of my colleagues, Doctor McDaniel, was on labor and delivery, thank goodness, and gave her IV azithromycin. She also had a good long chat with her about her doofus boyfriend. We decided to allow labor to progress slowly to allow time for the antibiotic treatment. What. The. Heck?

I showed up and thanked Doctor McDaniel for all her help. Kathryn received her epidural and looked comfortable. Her dad got off work at 2:00 a.m. and was going to come in to be her support. So, at this point, to be honest, I was a little stressed out about this baby due to the smoking and chlamydia history, not thrilled about the timing with my in-laws being in town and knowing it may not be a very restful night. What the heck?

Labor progressed, not perfectly but pretty well, and now it was time to push. I walked into the room and her dad was there. He asked me if it would be okay if they prayed before she started pushing. I will never forget that moment. The sun was shining in the window on Easter Sunday morning, I am with this patient who has been driving me nuts for two months, and this father was praying for strength for his daughter and saying how proud he was of her. Kathryn pushed like a pro and the baby was delivered without any problems. She asked for the baby to be taken out of the room, worried that she couldn't emotionally handle hearing the baby cry. The baby was whisked away a few rooms down where the adoptive parents were waiting. Kathryn was crying tears mixed with joy and sadness, and her dad was right there beside her. What the heck just happened?

This is what happened: I saw a chief complaint in the medical record and decided my patient was going to be a disaster. After our first visit, I felt this was truer than I had anticipated, and our subsequent visits seemed to constantly reinforce my opinion. By the time we got to the delivery, I was just hoping things would medically go smoothly. I almost missed the fact that

Kathryn had something to teach me. Her courageous and selfless act, despite everything she was going through on a personal level, truly inspired me.

I still see Kathryn in clinic. She has continued to have struggles but has come a long way since our first visit. I see her daughter for well-child checks, and the adoptive parents are some of the sweetest people you will ever meet. I am in awe at what a privilege it is to be a physician and serve all these amazing people. More specifically, I am blessed to be a family physician and be a part of their lives.

What the heck just happened?

Paul Day was born in Owensboro, Kentucky, the fifth of seven children. He obtained his undergraduate and medical degrees from the University of Louisville and trained at the Franciscan Health Indianapolis Family Medicine Residency, where he served as chief resident. Day currently practices in Cincinnati, Ohio, where he lives with his wife and children. He serves as guild president for the Cincinnati Catholic Medical Association and pursues his interests in how medicine and health are influenced by spirituality, exercise, relationships, and storytelling.

From Here to Eternity

DAVID EARL SCHULTZ II, MD

From Here to Eternity is an epic war movie where love, separation, hope, and, finally, death are explored. Interestingly, we live in societies around the world that are built basically on perceptions of eternity. Furthermore, we commonly allocate resources and efforts trying to prepare for that eternity, such as establishing trusts, funeral preplanning, and so on. But we as people spend little time discussing what will happen at that moment.

In my career, there are several examples when my beliefs regarding eternity played a significant role in patient care. There was an older lady, Helen, who was a pastor's wife. She was an obese individual who had chronic respiratory failure due to her excessive weight. Every time she fell asleep, she would experience profound shortness of breath, provoking one to speculate if she would even survive the night. There was one such time in the hospital when I had her in for a urinary tract infection with metabolic encephalopathy from which she did not awaken. I rounded on her early in the morning and asked the nurse how she was doing. The nurse replied, "Oh, absolutely fabulous!" To my utter surprise, I walked into her room and found Helen unconscious, unresponsive, and near death. She was not breathing.

I immediately called a "code blue" and started chest compressions and even had to give her epinephrine and two shocks to bring her back. As the monitor resumed bleeping, she opened her eyes and her first words to me were amazing and haunting. She asked, "Why did you rob me of eternity, Doctor Schultz?" I was stunned. Normally when people are resuscitated, the usual questions of "What happened?" or "Where am I?" occur, but not this day. It was "Why did you rob me?" I apparently neglected the fact she had a "Do Not Resuscitate" order on her chart. Unfortunately, I am not alone in making that mistake from time to time.

This pastor's wife regarded salvation in Jesus Christ as the principal foundation of her life, and yet, I slowed that up. She was ready to go to her eternal home. She lived for several years after that and then died in a nursing home all alone. She is now in eternity and united with her family, friends, loved ones, and her Savior.

About that time in my career, there was another patient named Ralph. One could tell Ralph was the remnants of a hardened U.S. Marine Corps veteran who stormed the beaches of Iwo Jima facing Japanese bullets and shrapnel. He even took particles of war home embedded within him. He had severe COPD, and in the last two or three years of his life, he required oxygen to sustain him. He was still reminded of those war years, but he never talked about them—not to anyone. Over the years, he confided in me regarding some of his actions during the war, but he always held his story short and never elaborated further than he thought he could.

Ralph had several admissions to the hospital in the last several months of his life. One winter day, when we had more snow than is usual in our part of Indiana, Ralph made it to the office to get a COPD assessment, while some of my more-healthy, able-bodied individuals canceled. This provided me more time to do my job and to give that man a quality visit.

Jack requested to talk about end-of-life issues with me, and in doing so, he asked these questions: "Why am I still here? Why have I not died? What is left for me to do? I've been a good man; I go to church; I've been a good husband, and I've worked hard. What does God want from me?"

Without knowing how to respond to his questions, I asked him, "Are you right with God?" He replied that he still had a lot of guilt from Iwo Jima, and the guilt was only buried by the years of patriotism he exhibited toward our country. After all, he was just doing his duty. He said that he felt something missing in his faith. After much discussion, he finally admitted that he never had a relationship with Christ, and this is what was holding him back. That day, he decided rather than just knowing about God, to make his faith personal.

Ironically, it was about a week later that I got the call from his wife, Cora, saying that Ralph had gone home. He had closed his eyes in his chair, folded up his paper neatly as he always had done, and gone to sleep, never to awaken. His body and soul finally remained quiet after all those years.

Thus, we see two stories that involve faith, some of which is mine but more so from my two patients. Whether a physician has religious beliefs or not, as physicians, we inadvertently deal with what may come after this life because when end of life arrives, *every* person is faced with eternity. Do physicians have, or should we have, a role with patients as their life concludes? The answer is obvious. Family physicians need to be involved as much at the end of life with dignity as we are at birth with celebration.

David Earl Schultz II, a family physician, is a lifelong Hoosier. He lives in Newburgh, Indiana, with his wife, Kendra, and children and practices in Evansville, Indiana.

He is a graduate of the University of Evansville and the Indiana University School of Medicine. Schultz completed residency training at Saint Mary Medical Center in Evansville. He is past president and chairman of the board of the Indiana Academy of Family Physicians.

The Haircut

DAVID EARL SCHULTZ II, MD

Early in my medical career, we often had to do emergency room coverage in my community at undesirable times of the day. This included the overnight hours. Back then, my hair was rather longer than it is now. That was partly because of a terrible haircut experience that I had in Carmel, Indiana, while in medical school and because of which I decided to "rebel." That prompted me to let my hair grow out a little longer, and in fact, it was quite long.

In the wee hours of the morning, we provided service calls for one of the local hospitals. This entailed seeing the family-medicine patients who made their way into the emergency department at night. One emergency-room physician did not have a fondness for my long hair. In fact, he informed me that, "If I wanted to work in his emergency department, I would have to get a haircut because he did not allow liberals in his department." And so, I did what any other young doctor would do, I got my hair cut.

There was one night that I had seen my fair share of people in the emergency department with opioid-induced problems as well as those having mild episodes of rhinorrhea, diarrhea, the doldrums, and even war wounds for which there is no cure.

The message I was given was very simple. It indicated that there was a sixteen-year-old African American male who was in the emergency department because of testicular pain. At 3:00 in the morning, my immediate assumption was that this was some type of sexually transmittable disease or an individual seeking out pain medication. I took my time in running down to the emergency department, stopping by the hospital cafeteria to get a cup of coffee. As I reluctantly made it into the emergency department, I found Room 26. There was a well-dressed, well-kept family. I saw the mother who had a look of concern, the father, and that young patient, approximately fifteen years old, laying on a hospital bed appearing frightened and in some pain.

I asked him what his problem was, and his mother immediately explained that he developed sudden onset of testicular pain. She was concerned that he had testicular torsion because he had two older brothers who had similar circumstances in their teenage years and had become infertile. She asserted that he was a very good young man with hopes of becoming a minister in a Baptist

Church. She poignantly explained that he was the last hope to carry on their family genes, their inheritance, and their legacy.

I immediately was rife with guilt and conscience for I had judged this individual incorrectly. It was never about his skin color as I had attended an inner-city high school where diversity needed no explanation. My prejudice developed over his age, his medical complaint, and the time of the early morning. I learned a very hard lesson that night—not to judge a patient. Preconceived notions can lead to a misdiagnosis and personal bias, which makes me less effective as a physician.

I ordered a testicular ultrasound and within five minutes was told by the ultrasound tech that he truly had testicular torsion. I requested a urologist to consult who was able to save this individual's testicles. This boy did eventually go on to college and is a hardworking family man even today.

I learned from this event that in the practice of medicine, I need to look at the entire situation, all the data, and consider all the facts before I let personal emotion affect my decision-making process. However, I also discovered that sometimes the medical environment in which we work can be influenced by biased perceptions toward fellow physicians and other coworkers. This is certainly exemplified by an arrogant and judgmental emergency physician informing me to get a haircut.

"*My patients brought me so close to the reality of human life that I could not help learning essential things from them. . . . The finest and most significant conversations of my life were anonymous.*"

Carl Gustav Jung, MD, 1961

Blind People Do See

NICK F. HRISOMALOS, MD

*"You never know how strong you are until being strong is your
only choice."*
Bob Marley
"The only thing worse than being blind is having sight but no vision."
Helen Keller

My mission in life—all I trained for; all the hours in medical school, residency, and fellowship; and all the hours in the library, cadaver lab, and the wards—is to save eyes. But ironically, I removed the eyes of my most appreciative patient.

This is a tale about a girl who cannot read this book. A young girl whose travels and travails through life are an amazing inspiration to us all. A tale of obstacles overcome, and a life lived to the fullest despite the severest of impediments.

Dena Polston was born a beautiful baby on September 29, 1962, in Shirley, Indiana, to loving and caring parents. But she was born blind.

She was born three months premature at one pound, thirteen ounces. Oxygen and an incubator, required to prevent cerebral palsy and brain damage, had the side effect of taking her sight due to the ravages of retinopathy of prematurity. Her retinas detached and her eyes filled with blood. Back then, there was no treatment for this condition—babies went blind, but we were thankful to have avoided cerebral palsy. Now we can save the sight in many of these preemies with injections of drugs in their pea-sized eyes.

Dena's mother says she was the "smallest baby to survive in these parts in 1962." Dena says she might have had some bare light perception early on, but "has never seen colors and does not know what colors look like." In fact, she does not know what black or white looks like, just light or dark.

Dena spent most of her early years at the School for the Blind in Indianapolis, and she struggled for a while because she did not understand why she could not be home with her family. Dena never needed to cope with losing her sight—she never had any to lose. She still developed friendships and learned at the school ways to cope and adapt. She learned Braille in kindergarten and became fluent by the fourth grade. Dena says this was a most wonderful tool;

Dena Polston

she feels that Braille leads to literacy and that "it is very helpful to be able to read and not just listen."

Louis Braille, the French educator who invented the system of reading and writing for the blind in 1824—at age fifteen—was an idol of Dena's. Louis coincidentally was blind himself. His blindness was caused by an injury with an awl, which by happenstance later was the same tool he used to create the dimples in paper, the "tactile code" that is now called Braille. This system has remained unchanged to this day and has been adapted for use in different languages as well as on computer keyboards; it bridges the communication gap between the sighted and the blind.

To most of us, the patterns of dots look like a labyrinthine mess, but to Dena they convey ideas and meaning. Dena persevered and despite all the obstacles, including transportation and so many others, incredibly achieved a bachelor's degree in criminal justice and a masters in adult and community education, both from Ball State University.

She has gone through four different service dogs in her lifetime—canines that helped her navigate and gave her friendship. She marvels at the new ways of coping we have today, including phones that talk back and forth with the user, Alexa devices from which she can get all the information she needs, and transportation, including Uber and Lyft that she can summon through her voice-activated cell phone. It was not as easy in the past. Dena worked in several different jobs, including her parents' restaurant and the Muncie Eye Center switchboard, where they printed the patient schedule in Braille, and she would make patient appointment reminder calls and do outreach marketing.

Dena's mother was always trying to find a cure for Dena's blindness. She would ask anyone she knew and search any inkling of a clue down so many paths. She would do anything to help her little girl. I started my retina surgery practice in 1987, and my new practice sent out brochures introducing me to the community. One of these brochures was sent to Dena's grandmother who had recently passed. Dena's mother found the mailing and immediately called for an appointment for Dena to see the new retina specialist in town. That is serendipitously how I first met Dena.

Dena was happy and doing so well. Then came the pain.

A boring, deep, unrelenting pain in the eye made it impossible to sleep or concentrate. Dena's eyes did not perform the function for which they were intended. There was nothing—not blackness, just nothing. But now there was excruciating pain. But Dena was positive; she knew something could be done to help her.

It has been said that "The pain you feel today will be the strength you feel tomorrow." And Maxime Lagase said, "Every pain is a gift. Every pain is an opportunity." Dena knew that there were two types of pain—pain that hurts you and pain that changes you. She wanted to make a positive change and needed to relieve the pain. Dena came to the office with her mom with hopes somehow her sight could be restored. That was not to be.

Dena's pain was the result of severe eye pressure elevation, a form of glaucoma called "neovascular glaucoma" caused by her retinopathy of prematurity. There were no hopes of restoring sight but there was of eliminating the pain. This would require "enucleation," removal of the eyes.

Helen Keller wrote, "Self-pity is our worst enemy, and if we yield to it, we can never do anything wise in this World." She also once remarked, "Although the World is full of suffering, it is also full of the overcoming of it." Dena had surgery, and her eyes were removed. The pain was gone.

Her eyes were so severely damaged they could not be used as donor eyes. Nobody would see through these eyes again. As few really know, when an eye is "donated" upon death, only the cornea is used (for corneal transplants) and the sclera is used for "patch-grafts" if some part of a living persons eye needs a patch over a thin spot or implanted device.

Dena was fitted with prosthetic eyes, inserted into the empty eyeball socket like contact lens. These remarkable prostheses are convex shells carved and shaped individually by an "ocularist" who not only is an artisan, but also an artist. The ocularist paints the iris and conjunctival vessels on the acrylic to look like a normal eye, but of course they do not see. They are valuable in keeping the eye socket comfortable, creating a "normal" facial appearance to others, and preventing contracture of the socket and eyelids. Dena had prostheses created and she wears them confidently.

Dena returned to work, unshackled from the pain, and with renewed energy. She wanted to do something to reciprocate and express gratitude for those at the Eye Center and hospital that helped her. Without sight, many blind individuals will develop an appreciation and even a talent for music. There is Braille music that can be read, and the music sense might be heightened with lack of a visual stimulus. There have been many amazing blind vocalists, including Stevie Wonder, Ray Charles, Ronnie Milsap, George Shearing, and Andrea Bocelli. Dena developed a beautiful voice and could sing heavenly. We were to be the beneficiaries of her musical aptitude.

For months, Dena came to the eye clinic and would sing in the middle of the waiting room for the patients waiting for their examinations. This was one way she could repay the vanquishing of her pain. She did this out of heartfelt generosity and her love for people. It was a remarkable thing, and she was an inspiration to all that heard her elegant voice.

Dena has taught many so much through her adversity. In the past when I was in a comical mood in the office or in surgery, I'd often tell a patient, "You know, your eyes are very important for your vision, and your vision is very important for your sight." Then I would watch the blank expression on their face.

It is funny, but now I have a totally new insight (sorry for the pun) and appreciation of my joking around. "Sight," "Vision," and "Seeing" are all metaphors and are not interchangeable. Although Dena does not have eyes, she has the most acute vision of anyone I've ever known. She has sight and insight and can see what others cannot. Myles Monrow once said, "Sight is a function of the eyes, but vision is a function of the heart."

Dena has all of these—sight, vision, and seeing, even though she is blind. She is now married and her husband Lehy is also blind from a severe car accident in which he almost also lost his life. His car plunged off the side of a cliff, and his optic nerves connecting his eyes to his brain were severed. Lehy says he lost his sight that day, "but blindness opened my eyes. It opened up my life." As reported in the *Cape Cod Times*, at their wedding party the reverend performing the ceremony summed it all up: "There are people with 20/20 vision who are blind to what life is about."

Dena and Lehy are not really blind. In English, we use the word "see" to mean understanding. Dena and Lehy could not physically "see," but they *could* see. Few realize that Helen Keller had eyesight and hearing until she was nineteen months old, when some sort of viral infection took them both from her. Keller said, "Just because a person lacks use of his eyes, doesn't mean they don't have vision. . . . Blindness is an unfortunate handicap, but true vision does not require the eyes."

Maybe Dena was born premature for a reason; maybe she needed to get out into the world as soon as possible to have all these positive effects on others and to release the stigma and preconceived notions on blindness.

It seems so. We are taught by Dena's example to be thankful for what we have. One of my most favorite quotes is from Oprah Winfrey: "Be Thankful for what you have; you'll end up having more. If you concentrate on what you don't have, you will never have enough."

These are lessons I've learned from Dena.

We see not only with our eyes. Blind people do see, and they can see without eyes.

Dena Polston requested that her name be used in this essay.

Nick F. Hrisomalos is from Bloomington, Indiana, where his father was a family physician, working until he died at age eighty-six. He attended Indiana University in Bloomington and then the IU School of Medicine in Indianapolis, where he also completed his ophthalmology residency before attending the Northwestern University Retina Surgery Fellowship. Hrisomalos started a solo retina surgery practice in 1987 and has for the last few decades been a member of Midwest Eye Institute in Indianapolis. His brother Tom and two of his children, Frank and Emily, are also physicians.

Thank You for Believing in Me

TIMOTHY MUSICK, MD

As I walked into the exam room a woman sat in the hard, plastic chair in the sterile white room. She looked disheveled; her long hair was a mess, nails blackened and dirty, and her clothes had obviously not been washed for many days. She was wearing a long sleeve shirt that did not match the ninety-degree weather outside, especially in the humid Indiana weather. Entering the room, she did not make eye contact, instead choosing to stare at the floor and purposefully choosing to look anywhere except at me. Her name was Allison, and she was here for her first Suboxone appointment. The first appointment for medical-assisted treatment for heroin or opioid abuse is always difficult; not only will she be discussing some of her most shameful and closely guarded secrets, but she also will be in withdrawal from heroin. She needed to begin this medication to get off heroin.

I lowered my voice, and I dimmed the light, a trick I had learned from my psychiatrist mentor, to help with her horrible headache that she was no doubt experiencing as a side effect of the withdrawal. At this kind gesture, she looked up at me, almost quizzingly, like this small action was the first act of kindness that she had experienced in months. After introducing myself, we started the interview. I always liked to start with a simple, open-ended question that invited patients to share without forcing them to reveal too much to a stranger. "Tell me about how you ended up seeing me today?" And this is where Allison's story begins.

Allison unfortunately had an all-too-familiar story. It started with an abusive father, who unfortunately, she was forced to continue to live with. This abuse led to her seeking escape, and one fateful day when she was a teenager, someone offered her some hydrocodone "to help with the pain." That was the start of her fall.

One hydrocodone a day led to two, which led to five. Eventually she was taking twenty a day. She would steal for them, barter, do anything she could. Finally, she developed a dependency on them, and she knew she was in trouble. Her heartbreaking words of "when I would get sick without them, I knew I had crossed a line that I would never be able to uncross."

The cost of twenty hydrocodone was too much for her, and she found herself introduced to heroin. She told me that when she first started using it, she would snort it. "I promised myself I would never inject it," she said. However, as her dose of snorting increased, and the high was ever fleeting, she eventually crossed the "no injection line" and began injecting heroin intravenously. Her voice lowered as she told me that at her highest use, she was paying $200 a day to support her heroin addiction.

During this downward spiral she lost her job and alienated her family by stealing and lying to them to cover her addition. Her voice cracked slightly when she told me that her family thought she had a general lack of character and should be able to "kick the habit." She discovered one day that she was pregnant while using, which she would later admit was due to prostitution to pay for her habit. She continued to use throughout her pregnancy and delivered a baby girl who was immediately removed from her custody by Child Protective Services. It was at this point that her eyes began to tear up. She told me that she was only allowed to see her daughter with a chaperone watching and had never had her daughter spend the night with her at her home. Her daughter was six by the time Allison came to my clinic for help. She had done multiple stints in rehab, as well as on methadone, but she was never able to keep clean.

"Why get clean now?" I asked. It was a question that I knew she had thought long and hard about. Medication assisted treatment is not easy; it is an extensive time commitment and an uncomfortable experience with dose reductions causing mild withdrawal. She looked up at me with a light in her eyes that was not previously there, a fire in her eyes that really showed that she was ready.

She told me about how her probation officer and the Child Protective Service workers had told her that she had the potential to get her child back if she could "get her life together," and that was exactly what she planned to do. She told me about being in her daughter's life and being there for her was what motivated her. She told me about how she wanted to be a better parent for her daughter than her parents were to her so that she could break the cycle. The appointment continued, and she was given a small script of Suboxone and told to follow up in one week to monitor her progress. We also discussed Narcotics Anonymous and the need to get counseling to help deal with the emotional aspects of addiction.

Allison showed up exactly on time for her follow up appointment. Although she still appeared unkept, she appeared to be feeling better. She told me that the medication was helping to keep her out of withdrawal, and that she was no longer craving medications. She also brought in her "to-do" note-book, which was chronologically listed with what she thought she needed to do to "be an adult" and get her child back.

She came to her appointments monthly, excited to tell me about her progress and what she was learning. Together we worked to get through crav-ings, she met with my psychologist mentor at the residency clinic who helped her deal with stress in a healthy way as she had only dealt with it previously through using. And she helped her address the psychological side of addiction while weaning her medication. At the end of every session, she would tell me what her goals for the month ahead would be, and I would ask about them on the follow-up appointment.

The goals started with small things like "save up enough money to get nice clothes for a job," which once accomplished allowed her to get employment. After the first job, and when she had money coming in, she got a better-paying job. This allowed her to move out of her abusive father's house into her first apartment. The joy in her eyes as she told me about all she was doing and what her life was like now compared to when she was using was infectious. She continued to work hard for over one year, slowly making progress, step by step getting better financially and emotionally. Slowly, Allison began to heal and get better.

It was July, close to a year since our first appointment. This would be our final appointment together as I was graduating residency. As I walked into the room, I saw her warm smiling face, her smile lighting up the room. There was an indescribable difference between the first time I saw her and the last time. The first time her face was sunken in, her eyes looked dull and hopeless. This time she was dressed nicely, smiling, eyes full of life and excitement about the future. In her lap was her daughter, now eight years old. It was during this appointment that I discovered that she had completed her to-do list; she had completed everything she wanted for her recovery. She had finally received custody of her daughter.

As the appointment concluded and I got up to leave, tears filled Allison's eyes, and she asked if she could hug me. She gave me a warm hug, and I will never forget what she said. "Thank you for believing in me. Thank you for not seeing a junky but for seeing the potential inside of me. You have helped me achieve a life I had only dreamed about while using, and I am truly grateful."

Allison's kind words emphasized to me that no patient is a "lost cause" and the inner strength of people can far outweigh the challenges they face.

Sometimes patients need some things as simple as a smile and for someone to believe in them. They can gain the ability to change their lives forever.

Timothy Musick is a graduate of the University of Nevada School of Medicine. He completed the Franciscan Health Indianapolis Family Medicine Residency and now practices as a hospitalist in critical access hospitals in Nevada, Arizona, and California.

Indiana Grandma

TIMOTHY MUSICK, MD

In our family medicine residency, we were "forced" to do home visits. I use the word forced because at that time I believed that everyone was able to leave the house, at least for an hour to come to the doctor's office. My home visit was with a pleasant lady named Sheri, who lived with her daughter in a nice house in a classic Indiana suburban community. Unknown to the community was that once you got inside her house, the secrets started.

Sherri lived with her daughter who was a hoarder. Sherri had two daughters, the one with a problem with hoarding and another daughter who was a nurse. There was significant tension between the two daughters and poor Sherri was stuck in the middle. Unfortunately for Sherri, she was mostly bed bound secondary to her terrible osteoarthritis and congestive heart failure, and if she was to leave the house, she had to use a wheelchair. This complicated caring for her because if Emergency Medical Services needed to be called, they were unable to get the stretcher into the house due to the hoarding. Her family was thrilled that I was willing to do home visits as none of her specialists would come to her home, making managing Sherri's multiple medical conditions difficult. She was also on chronic narcotics and according to Indiana law, I was required to see her every three months. As you might expect, Sherri and I became close during these visits.

The home visits started out as a convenient way to leave work early. I would swing by Sherri's house to say hello, check on her, prescribe her medications, and then move on with my day. Her two daughters were always present, and the tension was palpable. They would argue over the best course of treatment for their mother, and inevitably the discussion would come down to the daughter who was the nurse wanting Sherri to move in with her and move out of her current home with her hoarder daughter.

After a year of multiple visits, I had established a good relationship with both daughters in addition to Sherri. It was during this time that she became interested in my life. She was a sweet lady, her room filled with pictures of family and friends. Her daughter told me she would always light up on the day of my visit and would ensure that her daughter helped her get ready for my visit. I told her about my life, growing up in Nevada and moving to Indiana, where I knew no one. That I had no family in Indiana greatly distressed her, and she insisted that I consider her my "Indiana Grandma."

She listened to stories about my family, about medical school, how residency was going and so on. She was genuinely interested, wanting to know everything that I was willing to share. We laughed and joked around, and slowly the time that I would spend at her home began to increase as our friendship deepened. Eventually, I would spend the entire two hours at her home—one hour caring for her medical problems and managing medications, and then second hour talking and catching up as only family can do.

Slowly her health began to fade. It started gradually with increased lower extremity swelling and worsening lower leg pain; this led to increased falls. She began falling multiple times a month and eventually was unable to get out of bed without falling. During this time, I saw her more frequently, not out of obligation, but because I wanted to make sure that my Indiana grandma was taken care of and had everything she needed. Her nurse daughter would greet me at the door with a hug, and we would check on Sherri together.

Finally, Sherri was completely bed bound, and she was nearing the end of her life. During a visit, both daughters knew that this was probably the last time that I would see her, and so they excused themselves from the room so that I could talk with her one last time and say good-bye.

I got on my knees, close to her head, and held her hand. She began telling me about her life; she talked about her best friend who died eight years ago, who she missed dearly. Sherri's eyes sparkled with life and laughter as she told me about the adventures they went on and the good times they shared. It was just like countless times before when she told me stories of her past.

Finally, she began to tire. As I told her I would leave to let her rest, she grabbed my hand and pulled me toward her. She asked me to lean closer, and then she kissed me on the cheek as a grandmother would kiss a child. She told me how proud she was of me, what a great doctor I would be, and how honored she was to have come to know me.

Tears welled up in both our eyes as I thanked her for giving me a home in Indiana and for being my Indiana Grandma. She asked if she could ask me one final favor. She asked me to discuss with her daughters her final wish. Sherri told me that for her final days, all she wanted was "peace in the family." She wanted nothing more than to have her two daughters stop fighting and be a family. I think she feared that when she was gone that her family would drift apart, and this saddened her. She wanted her daughters to have each other and have the relationship that only sisters can have. I hugged her tightly and told her I would do my best.

Her daughters and I did have that discussion, and they insisted that they would not fight in their mother's presence. Sherri passed away two weeks later, "old and filled with years, surrounded by family" as written in her daughter's note to me. In that note, they thanked me for everything and told me that as she passed, she held both daughter's hands. Sherri finally had the peace that she always wanted.

Sherri taught me that we are more than a physician for one patient. We take care of an entire family. She also taught me that deeply connecting with our patients in a personal way is therapeutic for them as well as for ourselves. In the age of physician burnout, connecting with our patients on a personal level is one of the best ways to get a sense of personal accomplishment and achievement. We give, but we also receive.

How Can You Make Me Leave?

TAMMY WILLIAMS, RN

This story addresses an ethical dilemma I encountered during the CO-VID-19 crisis.

I am a primary-care nurse coordinator in the Emergency Department. One night, around 8:00 p.m., one of my staff nurses came to me and said she had a sick COVID patient who was going to be admitted. The patient's daughter was upset that she was not allowed to go upstairs to the hospital ward with her dad. I told the nurse to kindly explain to the daughter that there is a "no visitor policy" and it was not just our hospital but all hospitals. The policy is in place for her and everyone's safety because we wanted to limit the spread of the coronavirus.

About thirty minutes later, the nurse returned. She said the daughter is really upset and she did not know what to do. I asked the nurse if the patient was very sick because patients thought to be dying are allowed a family member. The nurse replied yes. I called the floor nurse who was receiving the patient. She said the daughter could only come up if her father had "End of Life Orders." I told her the patient was a "Do Not Resuscitate" but they had not progressed to the decision of EOLO because he was on a mask for oxygen; EOLO required morphine orders and only a nasal canula for oxygen. The daughter was not ready to make that decision yet.

I went to the patient's room and again explained the policy. The patient was having a difficult time breathing but was still able to ask for ice chips. The daughter was crying and really upset. She told me her mother just passed away recently, and she did not make it to the nursing facility before she died. She expressed that she could not understand how quickly this happened to her father. She said she had just visited her dad the day before at the nursing home, and he was up walking around and harassing the staff. He always teased all the staff and continually joked with everyone there.

I could see the patient was really having respiratory distress. I left the room and called the floor nurse again. I told her I was going to tell the daughter you will call her if there are any changes with her dad. The nurse said she would. Right after we hung up, she called back and asked me to find out if they had cell phones because she could FaceTime them. I felt very good about her promise to call the daughter since she took the time to call me back and ask me about the cell phones.

Approximately three hours had passed since the emergency department nurse came to me the first time. I went back to the patient's emergency department room to tell her about the cell phones and that the nurse would FaceTime them. I will never forget her face as she sat at her dad's bedside holding his hand looking up at me with huge tears running down her face. She asked me: "How can you make me leave? I promise I won't be in the way." Her dad was barely able to talk now but mumbled out to her that it was okay.

I was crying and thinking, what if that was my family member? There was no way anyone would have made me leave. They would have to drag me out of the hospital. I called the nursing supervisor and explained the situation. She said, "Tammy, haven't you heard about these stories on the news? This is policy. Do you want me to come down and talk to her?" I told her that was not necessary. I just wanted her to tell me what she would do if this was her father.

Still crying, I went to the ED physician and explained the situation to him. I told him the patient would probably pass before 3:00 a.m. (it was around 11:00 p.m. at the time), so I was going to keep him in our department. If he had not passed by then I would talk to the daughter about having to move the patient upstairs to the floor. The physician said, "That's fine. I'll do whatever you want. Do you need me to write and order?" I told him no. I just wanted him to be aware and that if anyone got in trouble it was my decision and I would take responsibility.

As I was heading back to the patient's room, I saw the daughter walking down the hall. She was crying and said she was going home. I told her that I talked to the doctor, and we were going to keep her dad in our department so she could stay with him. I explained the EOLO policy and said it would be a decision she would probably need to make in a few hours. He was really struggling, and she would not want to see him suffering. She said her dad told her to go home because he did not want to get the nurses in trouble. Here this man is dying and in his final time he is worried about the nurses. I told the daughter no one is going to be in trouble and encouraged her to stay. She said she did not want to upset her dad and that she was going to go home. I told her the floor nurse would call if there were any changes, and we moved the patient upstairs.

I was so upset. I planned to check on the patient the next day, but I just could not bear to do it. I knew he would not make it through the night. I called my manager and told her this story. I related to her how unethical I felt the situation was and that it needed to be taken to the ethics committee. She asked me if I checked on the patient and how he was doing. I told her I just could not.

She called me later that day to tell me the patient had passed away in the night around 2:30 a.m. She said the daughter and the chaplain were at the bedside. That did give me comfort, but how sad the patient had to worry about the nurses getting in trouble and the daughter not being able to be at his bedside during the last four hours of his life. That was about three months ago, and I can still see her face sitting at her dad's bedside holding his hand looking up at me with huge tears running down her face asking me, "How can you make me leave?"

I understand the reason for the no-visitor policy. It's not just the policy of our hospital but is a best-practice coronavirus policy for all hospitals. But how can that ethically be the right thing to do? The COVID-19 crisis has created situations that we never thought were possible. I know this is a COVID story that will haunt me for the rest of my life.

Tammy Williams grew up in Indianapolis and attended Indiana University. She has been an emergency department nurse for more than twenty years and loves what she does. She remarks that she has had so many experiences, good and bad. Her husband is a police officer, so they both have high-stress jobs. They work hard but play harder. Tammy and her husband love being outdoors and enjoy riding motorcycles and spending time on their boat.

Remembering Kindness

ADAM M. PAARLBERG, MD

"I am so sorry, it looks like cancer." These are the words I so painfully remember uttering to Suzanne and her husband one summer morning after receiving the results of her abdominal CT scan. I distinctly recall the tears and pain that we all felt in that dark moment; the throngs of family and friends that arrived to provide love, prayers, and comfort; and the dreadful feeling that I had just delivered a death sentence to this poor woman and her family.

Suzanne was a sixty-year-old patient of mine as well as a dear friend and wife of a close colleague. As an associate director of a family-medicine program, I happened to be staffing the residency inpatient medicine service during that momentous week; our wonderful team included an upper-level resident, intern, and medical students. Suzanne was hospitalized following four days of crampy abdominal pain associated with a complete loss of appetite and debilitating nausea. She had recently been treated for a urinary tract infection and kidney stone resulting in placement of a stent. On this occasion an extensive initial workup, including an abdominal CT scan, labs, and endoscopic ultrasound, yielded a diagnosis of pancreatitis of unknown cause, the treatment for which is largely supportive.

However, Suzanne did not improve clinically. Her pain and nausea persisted despite our best treatments. Our consulting gastrointestinal specialist seemed to be at a loss. Maybe we just needed a little tincture of time? But this was not a satisfactory course, as the diagnosis did not seem to explain what we were seeing clinically. Perhaps instead we needed to broaden our differential diagnosis.

So, we did. We addressed her anxiety and recognized that she had not had a bowel movement in days. We continued to collaborate with our specialists, provided supportive care, and repeated many of our initial evaluations to see if anything had changed. Nonetheless, days passed without improvement; in fact, her pain worsened. Was this just pancreatitis? We continued to have serious doubts. I knew Suzanne not just as a patient but as a close friend; she was not known to be a complainer and possessed a high tolerance for pain. Something was seriously wrong with this clinical picture. So, despite the growing pressures to reduce healthcare costs and not expose patients to unnecessary radiation, we repeated her CT scan, this time with IV contrast that would provide more detail.

The result sank my heart: a soft tissue mass in the pancreas suspicious for pancreatic cancer completely encasing a large artery that supplies a significant portion of the intestines; and in addition, there was an associated clot in this vessel. An MRI that followed confirmed these sinister findings. We braced for the worst.

A cancer specialist was consulted, and more labs and tests were completed. Heparin, a blood thinner, was started. The pain continued to worsen, so we brought in a palliative-care specialist to help with pain control who suggested an IV pain pump. A chaplain was called to provide spiritual care. All in all, this was an absolute worst-case scenario: If you were to reach into a bag of various cancers, pancreatic cancer is among the last you would want to pull. For most, especially for one completely encasing a vital artery, it is a death sentence.

Nonetheless, despite the ominous prognosis, we vowed to take things one step at a time. After taking time to provide comfort, support, and spiritual care, we regathered our team of specialists and got to work. And then, something very strange happened: Everything came back negative. CA 19-9, a pancreatic cancer tumor marker, was negative. A biopsy of the pancreas revealed no malignant cells and was, in fact, more consistent with infection or inflammation. We again broadened our ever-evolving differential diagnosis. We started broad-spectrum antibiotics. We obtained additional imaging and consulted our vascular surgeon and infectious disease specialist for additional guidance.

Other possibilities emerged: Perhaps a blood clot of this important vessel ultimately led to inflammation and infection of the pancreas, accounting for the appearance of something as ominous as cancer on the CT and MRI. We covered both possibilities with blood thinners and antibiotics and performed a nerve block to help with the pain. Other studies were completed to help determine the reason for the blood clot. And finally, Suzanne started to feel better.

In a complete reversal of fortunes, pancreatic cancer went from near certainty to very unlikely. Suzanne recovered well enough to be able to go home. In a matter of a few short moments, Suzanne's life had changed forever: In one instance, she stared certain death in the face, and in the next, hope of life was returned. How can one even begin to describe such an experience?

Fortunately, her follow-up scans showed interval improvement and eventual resolution of this inflammatory process that was once mistaken for a deadly cancer. It was since discovered that she has an autoimmune clotting disorder; she will likely have to take a blood thinner for the rest of her life, but that pales in comparison to what we originally feared.

Suzanne's story is nothing short of incredible, and the lessons learned as it unfolded will continue to shape the young physicians who were fortunate to be part of it. They learned to know their patients, to trust what their patients are saying irrespective of labs or scans. They learned to be patient, to allow a clinical course to unfold over time, and to continue to expand their differential diagnoses. They learned to be flexible and willing to abandon one course when convincing evidence suggests another is more compelling. They learned to take ownership of their patients and realized the benefit of investing time, energy, and heart to this end. They learned that specialists are invaluable members of a multidisciplinary health team but not necessarily the final word. We surely would not have achieved success without specialist guidance, but family physicians have the benefit of knowing patients over time, establishing relationships informed by mutual understanding and trust, and possessing a holistic view of healthcare.

Most important, our young physicians learned the value of instilling kindness and compassion into their care. To this day, Suzanne remembers very little of her story and the events that forever changed her life. But she does remember the kindness that was shown to her by the many doctors, nurses, and hospital staff who were committed to helping diagnose and cure her illness. Most of all, she remembers the kindness shown by the team of young family physicians thrown into the case of their life only a year or two removed from medical school. She remembers that we believed in her and advocated for her during the most vulnerable time in her life.

On the final day of Suzanne's hospitalization, two of our residents closed their long day with a casual walk on the fitness trail around the hospital. Sure enough, Suzanne and her husband passed them on the road on their way home, honking, waving, and overflowing with gratitude. At that moment, they experienced the joy that comes from helping patients through the hardest times of their lives. It is surely a joy that will stay with them for a lifetime, and in this they experienced the ultimate reward of doctoring. It is an absolute honor that we are allowed every day to be part of our patients' life stories, and as family doctors, we find value and lessons in the tragic stories as much as the uplifting ones.

It is always nice when the story ends happily ever after.

Adam M. Paarlberg is a family physician from Crown Point, Indiana. He obtained his bachelor's degree in religion at Wabash College, his medical degree at the Indiana University School of Medicine and completed his postgraduate medical training at Franciscan Health Indianapolis Family Medicine Residency. He has been practicing medicine for more than ten years, initially in private practice and more recently as an associate director of the Franciscan Health Indianapolis Family Medicine Residency. His clinical interests include geriatrics, emergency medicine, and global health.

Epilogue

Relationships

RICHARD D. FELDMAN, MD

Most every story contained on the pages of this book is about how physicians and healthcare professionals have been touched in some way by their patients. In the final analysis, I really believe it is about the development of close meaningful relationships between doctor and patient. How can it be otherwise?

One will note that many of the stories in this book involve life-and-death situations or the death of a patient. This is what I naturally anticipated as nothing is more poignant for a physician or other healthcare professional than the loss of a patient. Experiencing a death may be an entryway to a better understanding of life.

Over the years, I have gone to the callings or the funerals of patients with whom I developed especially close relationships. This is certainly not unique to me as a physician. Nothing underscores the significance and the personal aspects of these relationships more than a physician's desire to attend these final events.

For me, these patients were all very different people with diverse personalities, backgrounds, beliefs, values, and life experiences. A unique relationship developed with each, and for reasons that I find difficult to articulate, I felt compelled to attend their final tributes to say good-bye and to let the family know he or she was a remarkable person who I admired.

I remember the funeral I attended for an elderly patient of many years. As I greeted the family, also my patients, to my surprise my voice cracked as I expressed my condolences and that he was a good man. I had lost something along with his family, and I shared some measure of grief with them. When other special patients died, I felt like I had lost a grandparent or close friend. It was that distressing.

I recall the time that one of my long-term patients was admitted to the hospital. I was out of town, and the residents on the inpatient service under the guidance of faculty cared for her. Her condition was failing quickly. The two residents, despite the short time they treated her in the hospital, became very close to her. When she died, they decided to attend the funeral, certainly

Richard D. Feldman, MD

because of the feelings they developed for her, but also to represent me. They understood she was one of my special patients. How kind and big-hearted.

Sometime later, I saw my patient's husband in the office. He told me how much he appreciated the resident physicians attending the funeral. He looked at me reflectively and said, "I don't know who cried more, me or your residents?"

Hearts touched by sweet relationships.

Index